ANNALS OF THE NEW YORK ACADEMY OF SCIENCES

Volume 907
April 2000

EVOLUTIONARY PERSPECTIVES ON HUMAN REPRODUCTIVE BEHAVIOR[a]

Editors
DORI LECROY AND PETER MOLLER

CONTENTS

[a]This volume is the result of a colloquium and seminar series entitled **Evolutionary Perspectives on Human Reproductive Behavior** held during Spring 1999 as part of the Ph.D. Subprogram in Biopsychology at Hunter College of the City University of New York, New York, New York.

Financial assistance was received from:

- PH.D. PROGRAMS IN ANTHROPOLOGY, BIOLOGY, AND PSYCHOLOGY OF THE CITY UNIVERSITY OF NEW YORK
- UNIVERSITY FACULTY AND DEVELOPMENT PROGRAM OFFICE OF RESEARCH AND UNIVERSITY PROGRAMS (CUNY GRADUATE CENTER)
- DORI AND WALTER LECROY

EVOLUTIONARY PERSPECTIVES ON HUMAN REPRODUCTIVE BEHAVIOR

ANNALS OF THE NEW YORK ACADEMY OF SCIENCES
Volume 907

EVOLUTIONARY PERSPECTIVES ON HUMAN REPRODUCTIVE BEHAVIOR

Edited by Dori LeCroy and Peter Moller

The New York Academy of Sciences
New York, New York
2000

Library of Congress Cataloging-in-Publication Data

Evolutionary perspectives on human reproductive behavior/ editors, Dori LeCroy, Peter Moller.
p. cm. — (Annals of the New York Academy of Sciences ; v. 907)
Includes bibliographical references and indexes.
ISBN 1-57331-253-3 (cloth : alk. paper) . — ISBN 1-57331-254-1(pbk. : alk. paper)
1. Genetic psychology—Congresses. 2. Human evolution—Congresses. I. LeCroy, Dori. II. Moller, Peter. III. Series.

Q11.N5 vol. 907
[BF701]
500 s—dc21
[155.7] 00-026920

GYAT / BMP
Printed in the United States of America
ISBN 1-57331-253-3 (cloth)
ISBN 1-57331-254-1 (paper)
ISSN 0077-8923

In Memoriam

(Photo courtesy of Jeffrey Joy.)

W.D. Hamilton, 1936–2000

We dedicate this volume with love and respect to the memory of W.D. Hamilton, who died March 7, 2000, after a short, severe illness contracted during field work in the Congo two months earlier. Bill was perhaps the greatest evolutionary thinker of the twentieth century, and his work influenced all of us in profound and positive ways. He was a teacher of great originality and power who unerringly chose the most important topics on which to make fundamental advances: kinship and inclusive fitness, sex ratio, age, spite, sex, sexual selection, and cooperation, among others. He was also a person of unusual warmth and character. He was only 63, was very active, and had many new projects in his sights. He will be sorely missed.

Introduction

DORI LECROY AND PETER MOLLER
Hunter College and the Ph.D. Subprogram in Biopsychology of the Graduate School of the City University of New York, New York, New York 10016, USA

For more than 25 years, each spring semester, the Biopsychology Ph.D. Subprogram of the City University of New York organizes a combined topical seminar and public colloquium. We have chosen *Evolutionary Perspectives on Human Reproductive Behavior* as the topic for the Spring 1999 series. An evolutionary view of human behavior is, of course, an interdisciplinary concern. And so, over the course of the term, 11 speakers—among them eminent psychologists, anthropologists, biologists, and primatologists—discussed, debated, argued, and speculated about evolved psychological mechanisms, our evolutionarily adapted environment, and the evolutionary links between non-human and human primates. A growing number of social psychologists have turned to evolutionary biology and applied its principles of adaptation and natural selection to all aspects of human behavior. Evolutionary psychologists in the 1990s have taken on the task of asking questions about the phylogeny of complex human social behaviors, and thus carry on and expand the scope of human ethology and sociobiology.

Charles Crawford (p. 21) comes straight to the point in stating that all theories about human behavior must be compatible with evolutionary theory. David Buss (p. 39) goes even further and suggests that different branches of psychology (cognitive, developmental, and social) currently consist of unconnected mini-theories in need of a unifying metatheory that evolutionary theory could provide. David Haig's work (p. 149) on competition within the genome might not just reflect, but even provide such a unifying theoretical framework. He describes how inclusive fitness, the fundamental principle of evolutionary theory, normally applied to individual-level selection thinking, operates at all levels within the organism. This suggests that unification under evolutionary principles can apply beyond the social sciences to all the natural sciences, true consilience indeed.[1] Jerome Barkow's thought experiment (p. 164) about extraterrestrials extends this principle even beyond life on earth.

This is an exciting time for those of us interested in evolution, but not one without controversy. Just as when Darwin published his *Origins of Species* in 1856 (a theory of evolution by natural selection), there was an uproar *(what? my grandmother was a monkey!* you ask) and much more recently when sociobiology emerged,[2] there was the uproar again (*women do the dishes and men go to the moon because it's in our genes?*). Today, the ever-growing field of evolutionary psychology is also meeting with ambivalence and resistance from both academia and the public. Misleading caricatures of the ideas and of the theorists presenting them are inciting the public and activists of various sorts while filling media pockets. Innuendoes and accusations of racism and sexism are hinted at or blatantly hurled. Fortunately, the protests are less vigorous this time around. No one was physically hurt at our public lectures, although on a few rare occasions it appeared as if the *ad hominem* attacks were intended to do exactly that. Some of our speakers told of the vicissitudes of support and the antipathy they encountered within their own institutions as well as from outside. They spoke of the wisdom of graduate students specializing in disciplines that consider human behavior from an evolutionary perspective, and noted that this choice might turn out to become a most marketable specialization.

At the conclusion of the series, we invited several faculty and students who had attended the seminar or the colloquium or both to provide us with commentaries, constructive critiques, and observations. These contributions reflect the gamut of current acceptance of evolutionary psychology as an academic discipline by addressing strengths and weaknesses in linking evolutionary biology with social psychology, in linking highly complex human behaviors such as mate attraction and courtship with an evolved genetic substrate. We chose the paper by Glen Hass and his students as the introduction to these proceedings.

Here are some of the fundamental assumptions of the evolutionary perspective: (1) Behavior is a function of coordinated, complex mechanisms involving perceptual input, processing and integration of information, and motor output. (2) The only source of such complexity is natural selection. (3) Differences in individuals' responses to identical input are due to differences in internal psychological mechanisms due to species, age, or sex, and because evolved psychological mechanisms are sensitive to context and developmental stage, to differences in immediate conditions and prior experience. (4) Since the Pleistocene constitutes the period of human evolution, including that of evolved psychological mechanisms, behavioral adaptation is relative to conditions (physical and social) that recurred at that time. Theorists disagree on how relevant to present conditions evolved psychological adaptations might be in light of the dramatically different Pleistocene environment.

In our first essay, Charles Crawford addresses this disagreement. Counting babies during the Pleistocene might have established the legitimacy of certain behaviors as evolved adaptations, but can it today? In reading his paper we will see how the contrast between conditions, then and now, plays havoc with our evolved mechanisms. The following three papers focus on different aspects of human mate preferences. David Buss explores similarities and differences in human mate selection and mate-retention behavior that are predicted from sex differences in the minimal investment necessary to raise reproductively successful offspring. Steven Gangestad describes his work on the influence of the male's scent on female choice. He suggests that in their quest for genetically advantageous matings, women exercise a sensitivity to and preference for indicators of male fitness that is expressed in a condition-dependent manner. The specificity, efficiency, and economy of this feature, he will argue, reveal a special design that is evidence for a mechanism achieved through evolution. Geoffrey Miller similarly discusses criteria used to identify psychological adaptations. By comparing the nature of adaptations that were shaped by natural and sexual selection, he will dispute the use of the same defining criteria for both. He will argue that when criteria for identifying evolved survival and social functions are applied to sexually selected characteristics that function as fitness indicators and are expressed through high individual differences, we may underestimate the evolutionary origins of human creativity. The next two papers, the first by Sarah Blaffer Hrdy and the second, jointly authored by Amy Parish and Frans de Waal, take a comparative approach. Dr. Hrdy not only makes cross-cultural comparisons of human mating and social systems, but also addresses those of our primate cousins. One of her aims is to explode the myth of the "coy" female as she discusses monogamy and polyandry in human females in the interest of exploring the extent and limits of the impact of evolved mechanisms. In comparing the sexual and social behavior of our two closest cousins, the chimpanzee and the bonobo, primatologists Drs. Parish and de Waal have similar interests. One hope is that such comparative and cross-cultural studies will reveal something about the behavior of the common ancestor of humans, chimps, and bonobos, and about the likely subsequent course of psychological evolution in our own species.

What about our daily routines, our subjective experience, and the decisions we make? And what about all the indecision, confusion, mixed motives, doubt and internal conflict we all are so intimately acquainted with? A little introspection and a critical reading of Shakespeare or other great literature attests to the fact that we spend considerable time bewildered by these. It is clear the mind is not all of a piece. How do we make sense of all this in the light of inclusive fitness theory? The next two papers, by Robert Trivers and Dennis Krebs, point the way.

Writers and philosophers, pre- and post-Freud, have described what he called defense mechanisms. Concepts like repression, projection, denial, reaction formation, and so on are common parlance in the psychodynamic set and are used more commonly as well. The essential function of defense mechanisms is to deceive the self and motivate behavior within a distorted reality. First described as pathologies, the defense mechanisms are now accepted as coping strategies we all use daily. So, in the belief that such a complex and pervasive feature must arise by natural selection we are obliged to ask: how can delusion serve survival and reproduction? Dr. Trivers' chapter on self-deception addresses this question. Similarly, as believers in natural selection as the generator of complex social behavior, how are we to think of moral systems as emerging from the inclusive fitness principle? How, for example, are we to reconcile Kohlberg's stages of moral development with genetic self-interest. Dr. Krebs undertakes this exploration in his examination of Kohlberg's stages and finds that the later stages differ from the early stages in their biological justifications, and that biology supports judicious cheating as well as moral behavior.

Our final two papers move from the minute (in size only) to the immense. David Haig's focus is intragenomic, about conflict at the genetic level. He addresses conflicts that can occur in physiological systems because the "self-interest" of alleles derived from one parent might not match that of other aspects of the genome coming from the other parent. The phenomenon of genomic imprinting has given rise to fascinating ramifications. Not the least of these comes from the fact that imprinting occurs differently in different tissues within the same individual, even within different areas of the brain. Hence, all sorts of possibilities for intra-individual conflict on all levels including the behavioral present themselves.

Although most of our speakers did speak directly about reproductive behavior, some strayed afield a bit. But no one went as far as Jerome Barkow did when he went intergalactic with his intriguing thought experiment about the extension of the universal human traits of ethnocentrism and xenophobia to extraterrestrials. Life forms complex enough to have the intelligence to contact intelligent life forms of other galaxies, he suggests, would have evolved by principles well known to us with certain inevitable results. In other words, by analogy, if we were to rewind the reel of life on our planet and let it roll forward again we would recognize the results.

As organizers of this 1999 seminar/colloquium series we thoroughly enjoyed all aspects of this project. We are grateful to our speakers for their participation and good will. We particularly appreciated their candor with our students during the morning seminar discussions. These exchanges have left a lasting impact on them as attested by the contributions to this volume from Diana Praschnik-Buchman (commenting on Dr. Hrdy's paper), Cynthia Schupak (on Dr. Buss), and Tom Terleph (on Dr. Haig). Our colleagues, who so eagerly came out in support or voiced reservations with the approach taken by evolutionary psychologists, deserve ample credit for enhancing this document in scope, content, and breadth of treatment. We thank Glen Hass, Vita Rabinowitz and Virginia Valian, and Jason Young and Roger Persell.

Let it be known that important issues and differences were amicably resolved over delectable dinners at select restaurants on New York's Upper West Side, along the avenues of Columbus and Amsterdam. The only downside to it all was that it ended.

ACKNOWLEDGMENTS

We would like to thank the Ph.D. Programs in Anthropology, Biology, and Psychology of the City University of New York for financial support. A substantial grant from the University Faculty and Development Program Office of Research and University Programs helped defray some of the costs. Herbert Krauss and Dean Ann Cohen (both of Hunter College) found us an auditorium at the Hunter College School of Social Work, and we are grateful to Dean Bogart Leashore for his hospitality. I extend my thanks to my (P.M.'s) assistant, Ellen Breheny, for helping with logistics, to biopsychology students Rebecca Smart, Tom Terleph, and William Wisotsky for expertly staffing the audiovisual booth, and to Sarah Kuniholm for assembling and formatting all manuscripts for submission to the Academy. We thank Sheila Kane of the Editorial Department of the Academy. We are also indebted to Justine Cullinan, Managing Editor of the *Annals*, for her help and suggestions, particularly during the final stages of production, and we acknowledge the superb technical assistance of Stephanie J. Bludau. Finally, we are also thankful to the several persons who responded to a call to get a picture of W.D. Hamilton and in particular to David Haig and Michael Worobey.

As program head of the Biopsychology Ph.D. program and on behalf of the faculty and students, I (P.M) wish to conclude this introduction by expressing my sincerest thanks to Dori and Walter LeCroy for the generous support that made this seminar and colloquium series possible.

REFERENCES

1. Wilson, E.O. 1998. Consilience: The Unity of Knowledge. Alfred A. Knopf. New York.
2. Wilson, E.O. 1975. Sociobiology: The New Synthesis. Harvard University Press. Cambridge, MA.

The Relationship Between the Theory of Evolution and the Social Sciences, Particularly Psychology

R. GLEN HASS, NEIL CHAUDHARY, EMILY KLEYMAN, ALEXANDER NUSSBAUM, ALLISON PULIZZI, AND JULIE TISON

Department of Psychology, Brooklyn College, Brooklyn, New York 11210, USA
The Graduate School, City University of New York, New York, New York 10016, USA

ABSTRACT: The application of the theory of evolution to human social behavior has, along with some illumination, produced friction that occasionally bursts into flame. In this paper we will examine the relationship between the theory of evolution and the social sciences, psychology in particular. We will identify some of the sources of friction between proponents and opponents of applying evolutionary theory to the social sciences, and we will suggest that listening carefully to both sides in the debate points the way to an enriched understanding of human social behavior.

The impact of the theory of evolution[1,2] on psychology and other social sciences has grown dramatically in recent years. In the process, long-standing conceptual orientations are being challenged. Though often misunderstood as disputing existing theoretical models, the challenge posed by the application of the theory of evolution to psychology and other social sciences more typically comes in the form of a provocation to broaden our conceptual analyses into domains usually viewed as separate, or even incompatible. These challenges can be expected to have (and indeed already have had) reciprocal influences on psychology, other social sciences, and the biological sciences, as well as on our understanding of evolutionary theory itself.

CONCEPTUAL INTEGRATION AND PSYCHOLOGY

The principle of conceptual integration is taken for granted in the natural sciences.[3] There is a long tradition of recognizing the importance of a hierarchical, nonreductionist relationship among the sciences. Theories in biology, chemistry, and physics are evaluated in part on the grounds of multidisciplinary and multilevel compatibility. It is understood that conceptual analysis in each area must be compatible with neighboring fields. While biological conceptualizations are coherent, stand on their own, and are irreducible to chemistry, theories in biology and chemistry must be compatible. Similarly, chemistry, while irreducible to physics, must be consistent with physics. Each level of analysis adds principles special to that level that cannot be reduced to, nor are they derivable from, principles of other disciplines. Nonetheless, conceptualizations at each level must be compatible with those at other levels of analysis. They cannot contradict one another and both be correct. If a chemist proposed a theory that contradicted accepted principles in physics, both chemists and physicists would agree that they couldn't both be right. Exactly this situation occurred a few years ago when a group of chemists proposed "cold fusion." In this case the principles of physics prevailed, but that needn't always be the case. For example, Lord Kelvin's criticism of Darwin's theory of evolution was based on mistaken assumptions about planetary cooling, which led to erroneous calculations of the age of the earth.[3,4]

Carried forward, this principle calls for consideration of consistency between biological, psychological, and cultural levels of analysis—consistency, but not reductionism. Each level of analysis adds emergent properties that are irreducible. Biological theories do not and cannot constitute psychological theories. And psychological theories do not and cannot constitute explanations of culture. They each only provide the foundation for the next level in the hierarchy.[4]

Unfortunately the historical relationship among the social sciences has been to neglect or even vigorously reject the principle that scientific knowledge should be mutually consistent across disciplinary boundaries (e.g., Durkheim[5] and Murdoch[6]). As a result, scholars in the social sciences typically have maintained an institutionalized neglect, even a prideful ignorance of the concepts and literature in fields neighboring their own, and social sciences in the 20th century have grown ever more fragmented and insular.

Consistent with, and perhaps encouraged by, the tradition of compartmentalization between the social sciences, similar isolation of conceptual domains from one another exists within psychology. Psychology is an extremely broad discipline, containing topics ranging from the functioning of single neurons to complex social behaviors between individuals and groups. The breadth of its domain combined with the social science tradition of compartmentalized conceptualizations has led the field of psychology to become a maze of empirical generalizations and isolated mini-theories, each with its own specialized area of application. The conceptual fragmentation within the field shows itself in most psychology departments by the tension that frequently exists between faculty in different subdisciplines, especially the basic process/complex processes division (referred to more pejoratively as hard and soft psychology).

The absence of conceptual ties between the biological and social sciences, and the seeming conflict between biologically based explanations with an orientation toward innate processes and socially based explanations that emphasize cultural/learned mechanisms, together have increased the scientific separation between the biological and social sciences. This conceptual isolation also has led to an exaggerated separation in people's minds regarding the contributions of the two fields to understanding human behavior. This mental division is a poor reflection of reality. The debate has been framed as nature versus nurture, a turf war between the worldview of different disciplines battling over a boundary line conceived as the percentage to which the cause of a behavior could be attributed to biological or social processes.

THE INTERPLAY BETWEEN NATURE AND NURTURE

Fragmenting the individual into isolated "biological" versus "learned/cultural" parts (nature versus nurture), although sometimes a useful heuristic approach, has been carried too far. It has led to a fundamentally flawed perspective of human psychology, typified by attempts to separate nature from nurture, and quarrels about how much of the cause of a behavior is due to one and how much to the other. This conceptual isolation and fragmentation inhibits a full and exciting appreciation of the rich complexity of human psychology and its mixture of cognitive and emotional mechanisms, embedded in a strongly social/cultural world, and embodied in a physiological system. Psychologists are increasingly coming to recognize that the nature/ nurture distinction is largely false, and that the impact of neither one is fully understandable without consideration of the other.[7–9]

The traditional nature/nurture debate holds that the biological and social/ experiential processes that underlie behavior are separable components that have an additive relationship to one another. Just as the disciplines are considered independent, the understandings they provide are cognitively isolated from one another. A portion of the cause of a behavior is viewed as biologically induced and a separate, independent portion is attributable to social or learned input. Interestingly, researchers in both domains are discovering that the rigid boundaries of our academic disciplines do not exist in reality. In most cases there is a rich interplay in both directions between processes thought of as "nature" and those considered "nurture." Rather than being separable and additive, they are typically intertwined, inseparable, and richly interactive (multiplicative).

Take the development of myopia (nearsightedness) for example, a condition in which the eyeball is too large, causing the lens to focus the image of the outside world in front of the retina rather than on it. Myopia is a condition that results from the biological structure of the eye. It is common. About 25% of the U.S. population is nearsighted, and it has a strong genetic or heritable component. If an individual is nearsighted, it is probable that one or both of his/her parents are nearsighted. If one identical twin is myopic it is almost certain that the other will be.

Why does such a debilitating heritable condition still exist? Since good corrective lenses became generally available only within the last century or so, one would think the burden myopia presents to survival and reproduction would have insured its elimination from the human genome long ago. Someone with even moderate nearsightedness on the savanna is likely to be lion lunch, to say nothing of vulnerable in battle, accident-prone, a poor hunter or gatherer, and socially awkward at anything but close distances. Indeed, myopia is virtually unknown among current hunter/ gatherer societies. So, why is it so common in modern cultures? As with other hunter/gatherer societies, myopia was virtually unknown among the native peoples of the Arctic prior to contact with Europeans. But once their children began going to school, myopia emerged at a rate similar to that of other modern societies.

For the eye to grow during childhood (resulting in an increased distance between the lens and the retina) and simultaneously maintain a properly focused image on the retina requires a complicated feedback system between the growth mechanism and image quality. (Imagine moving a projector back while simultaneously maintaining a precisely focused image on the screen.) The shift toward a higher percentage of close visual work required of children learning to read disrupts the feedback mechanism among those genetically predisposed, resulting in permanent nearsightedness. The gene has no similar effect in the environment in which humans evolved and in which we have lived through most of our history, so there has been no reason for it to have been selected against. (This and other gene–environment interactions affecting medical conditions are discussed in more detail in Nesse and Williams[10]).

To try to divide the explanation for myopia into separate biological/genetic and experiential/cultural percentage components is meaningless. If one does not have the gene, one does not develop myopia regardless of the environment, so the effect is 100% genetic. But if one does not have the typical childhood school experience of a modern culture, one doesn't develop myopia regardless of the genes one possesses, so it is also 100% determined by experience/culture. Put another way: myopia is the result of a complex interaction between biological and social factors. Like all interaction effects, it is not divisible into separate percentage components. Such a question has no meaning. When variables interact they form a new variable that is different from the sum of the components, just as water cannot be described as any sum of the characteristics of its component elements, hydrogen and oxygen.

We chose the example of myopia in order to illustrate an interaction between social and biological factors on what might normally be thought of as a biologically determined outcome—eyesight. Interactions between social and biological variables are common and affect behavioral outcomes as well. For example, consider the following thought experiment involving two individuals—Mike and Mozart. Mike and Mozart differ in their innate musical aptitudes, Mike having little and Mozart being a potential musical genius. In an environment with little exposure to music and devoid of musical training, Mozart will probably exhibit little of his musical potential. He will show somewhat greater musical talent than Mike to be sure, but probably not much greater. Now imagine instead that Mike and Mozart grow up in an environment where a rich variety of music is frequently heard and musical training is readily available. Both Mike and Mozart will benefit from the enriched environment, but the increase in Mike's musical capability will be dwarfed by the emergence of Mozart's genius. Aptitude and the environment will interact. Indeed, that is what is meant by saying someone has a high aptitude for a skill – he/she possesses an innate potential that will benefit from experience (training) more than others will benefit from the same experience. The innate potential and experience interact in the development of a behavioral skill. Rather than being a simple additive effect, the effect of the environment will vary depending on the level of a person's innate aptitude. Once again, trying to explain behavior in terms of percentages attributable to nature and nurture will prove fruitless and misleading.[a]

Rather than producing separable effects, nature and nurture act together, each influencing and being influenced by the other, both at the level of individual development over a lifetime, and at the level of multi-generational selection processes. Across generations humans' biological nature influenced the species' social nature. But in many ways humans' social environment has influenced our biological nature as well.

[a]Statisticians and behavioral geneticists distinguish between two types of interplay between biological/genetic and environmental/social influences on behavior: (1) The role of genetic factors on people's susceptibility to different environments (gene–environment interactions) and (2) the role of genetic factors in the likelihood of a person's exposure to different environments—gene–environment correlations or covariance (e.g., parental mental disorder may create both genetic and environmental risks for their offspring). Both forms of gene–environment interplay are important processes in the non-independence of nature and nurture. See Rutter[8] for further elaboration of the distinction between the two.

THE INTERPLAY BETWEEN CULTURE, PSYCHOLOGY AND BIOLOGY

Humans as animals have a social nature that is built on (adapts to) their psychological and biological natures. Culture is not a random process. All cultures are heavily influenced by, bound to, limited by, and incorporate our animal nature. Any cultural characteristic takes as a given, as a starting point, our biological characteristics. For example, imagine how different all human societies would be if our biological nature was different in any of the following ways that are common in the world of mammals:

(*a*) Suppose all human females had an annual estrus cycle leading both males and females to be interested in sexual relations only during several weeks in June. Social relations between the sexes would be very different and society would reflect those differences. It might result in a period each year during which all other activities are set aside while fevered sexual interaction and intense competition between males to secure mates dominate all interactions—like Mardi Gras, but even more so. At other times of the year male–female flirtation and sexual interest, as well as male–male competition might wane and not intrude on other activities. Then imagine that, as a result of this limited period of sexual activity, all human infants are born nine months later in March. Such a change in our biological nature would have an enormous impact on economic, educational, and social practices in all cultures.

(*b*) Or imagine the impact on family structure, as well as marriage partnerships and their duration if human infants could care for themselves and live independently after their first year of life.

(*c*) Or suppose that humans typically gave birth to litters of six to ten infants at a time.

(*d*) Or consider the consequences if human males sought a solitary existence, apart from other males as well as females, except during the mating season.

(*e*) Or suppose both males and females could reproduce at any age in their lifespan. In fact, advances in reproductive science now make it possible for women to overcome the reproductive limitations of menopause. Even the reproductive barrier of death has been surmounted through fertilization with previously frozen semen. As minor in scope and infrequent as these "alterations to our biological nature" are at this point in time, nonetheless they are already forcing society to wrestle with their ethical, legal, and social implications.

If any of the preceding hypothetical situations were true, human psychology and social interaction in all cultures would be profoundly different from any we know. Cultures still would be variable, and their exact descriptions are impossible to predict (just as the specifics of existing cultures are neither predictable from nor reducible to knowledge of human biology). Nonetheless, all cultures would share characteristics designed to "wrap around" and cope with these biological requirements. Cultural institutions would be unlike any known human society. There would be enormous differences in cultural institutions such as the family, educational systems, business, government, and relations between men and women. (Note that this is not a reductionist argument. The cultural differences are not derivable from hypothetical changes in human biological nature. They merely must be consistent with them.)

In most cases human biological, psychological and cultural natures are mutually responsive to similar design features and work together in concert. Take, for example, incest avoidance, which reduces the likelihood of biological inbreeding and its deleterious effects. There is a psychological tendency, known as the Westermarck effect, for adults to avoid selecting as sexual partners other individuals with whom they were raised from infancy. Normally, children raised together are biologically related, but not always. Studies find a reduced sexual desire in both males and females for individuals with whom they were raised as young children, including brothers and sisters raised together in the same family, but also including stepchildren and other biologically unrelated children raised together, or very close childhood friends. The diminution in sexual appeal between individuals raised together occurs even when sexual relations as adults between such individuals are not socially proscribed. For example, children reared in crèches of unrelated companions on Israeli *kibbutzim* form life-long friendships, but rarely marry. And some Taiwanese families practice "shimpua marriage," in which a daughter is brought up by the family of the man she will marry (in effect her stepbrother). Such marriages are often infertile, largely because the partners find each other sexually unappealing. By contrast, two biological siblings reared apart are surprisingly likely to find each other sexually attractive if they meet at the right age. (See Wolf[11] for a review of the substantial anthropological evidence on sexual attraction and childhood association.)

The Westermarck effect illustrates how psychological mechanisms are distinct from, but act in concert with biological processes. The psychological mechanism (of not finding childhood companions sexually appealing as an adult) does not specifically identify others based on their degree of biological relatedness. Instead, it utilizes a "quick and dirty" marker (childhood companions) that normally is a close approximation of the biological target. It also illustrates how a biological predisposition is calibrated by social experience (childhood companions) to produce a psychological mechanism (level of sexual interest) that is compatible with a biological adaptation (avoidance of inbreeding). Factors at each level of analysis operate together performing mutually compatible functions.

In other instances our cultural nature helps resolve strain between competing parts of our biological nature. For example, the social part of our biological nature is aided by human cultural inclinations designed to control other aspects of our biological nature that threaten group/social living. All cultures facilitate the social part of human biological nature by providing restraints against socially disruptive human tendencies such as aggression/murder, stealing, cheating, lying, and indiscriminant or uninhibited lust.[b]

Furthermore, the relationship between human social/cultural nature and biological nature can change over time. For example, evolutionists[12–14] and social structuralists[15] agree that the patriarchal relationship that has historically characterized the relationship between men and women across cultures has its origins in men's greater size, strength, status, wealth, power, desire for sexual control of women, and ability to control resources. Though adherents to each orientation differ regarding the nature of some of the underlying psychological mechanisms related to patriarchy, they are agreed that social and economic equality between men and wom-

[b]Note that it is social, not genetic, identity and definition of group membership that determines whether or not these human tendencies are restrained by other pertinent psychological mechanisms. Toward outgroup members, inclinations toward aggression, etc., may be less inhibited or even enhanced (e.g., war).

en will require culturally institutionalized economic, social, legal, and educational forces that oppose and minimize the impact of these gender differences, rather than sustain and amplify them, as has been the normal historical state of affairs.[16]

Just as the psychological and cultural nature of humans is built on our biological nature, humans' biological nature is influenced in many ways by our social environment. At a multi-generational level, any species' biological nature is selected for (adapts to) its environment. In the case of humans, social/group living has been a fundamental aspect of our environment for tens of thousands of years, and of our prehominid ancestors for millions of years before that. We have been selected for, and seek out, group living.

In addition, at an accelerating pace, research is demonstrating that our social nature profoundly affects our biological nature as individuals as well. For example, work from the neurosciences shows that neural plasticity plays a role in behavioral phenomena as diverse as perception, cognition, language and emotion.[17] Neural plasticity is the ability by which the brain's anatomy and neurochemical and metabolic processes are shaped by experience, including social experience. This plasticity includes the development of new neural connections, the pruning of old ones, and the ability of a synapse to transmit nerve impulses. During the first several years of life a profusion of neural connections occurs in an individual's brain. Through usage influenced by experience these connections are then pruned back into more permanent circuitry. For example, juvenile play that mimics the social relationships and behaviors of adults promotes the development of appropriate neural connections that influence the subsequent performance of adult social behavior.[18]

These anatomic, neurochemical, and metabolic changes in neural functioning can occur at virtually any point in the life cycle, although some are more confined to sensitive or critical periods, while others, such as learning and memory, occur throughout the lifespan.[17] Far from demonstrating a "hard wired" or deterministic nature, neuroscience research is increasingly showing that development of an individual's brain and his/her behavioral profile are *not* genetically hard wired. The impact of genes on biological and social development depends in turn on inputs from nutrition and hormones as well as from an appropriate physical, educational and psychological environment.[19] Social/cultural experience shapes our biological nature.

EVOLUTION AND PSYCHOLOGY

Applying a functional analysis and the principles of evolution to questions of human psychology encourages breaking down the barriers between the social and biological sciences, and helps cast aside the flawed and conceptually limiting nature-versus-nurture debate. The theory is a broad, overarching *meta*-theory that ties together isolated mini-theories within psychology, as well as conceptually connecting them to biological and anthropological analyses.[20,21] It is an integrating framework that encourages consideration of multi-level analyses and explanations of human behavior. And, like any good theory, it makes novel and testable research predictions.

Because the theory of evolution has come to the social and behavioral sciences from biology, where it has been firmly established for decades, it has led to a suspicion by some that it reflects an attempt to "biologize" psychology: to explain human psychology in terms of genes and biological "hard wiring." There is also a fear that an evolutionary approach to psychology will emphasize nature and minimize the role of social experience in affecting human behavior.

These fears are not without historic foundation. Attempts to biologize human behavior led earlier in the 20th century to the now discredited eugenics movement,[22] and to recurring attempts to explain differences between races in genetic terms.[23-25] Although space limitations prevent a thorough discussion and refutation here, these arguments fail largely because they consistently confuse a complex and interactive genetic role in social behavior with an oversimplified and nonexistent genetic control of these behaviors. They also confused the issue of *heritability* to mean biologically fixed and unmodifiable. Both notions are fallacious. Heritability estimates are limited to the particular time and sample from which the measures were collected. They have no implication for what could or would happen if circumstances change.[8,26] For example, height and phenylketonuria are highly heritable. Yet heights have risen steadily over several generations because of improved nutrition, and the mental retardation produced by phenylketonuria can be controlled or eliminated by removing phenylalanines from the diet of the afflicted child.[25] In these instances highly heritable tendencies are also highly modifiable by appropriate environmental changes. Far from condemning an outcome to be hopelessly unchangeable, identifying genetic inputs often suggests effective environmental interventions (e.g., the nature of environmental remedies, when in the life cycle to apply them, and so on).

Moreover, far from promoting arguments of racial differences, the application of evolutionary principles provides a scientific rather than political argument for the existence of a common "human nature" across racial groupings.[4]

Another source of the fear of biologizing explanations of social behavior comes from the political agenda of some regarding sex differences. The notions of genetic control are at the foundation of "biology is destiny" arguments of sex differences. Yet, if one accepts that a "woman's place is in the home" because, compared to men, women are equipped to feed and nurture children, then one must also accept that males' greater aggressiveness and propensity for violence means that a man's place is in prison. Biologically deterministic arguments are equally flawed in each case. Evolutionary analyses do not lead to conclusions about how things "have to be," nor to conclusions about how things "should be."

EVOLUTION IS A BEHAVIORAL THEORY

For some the fear of biologizing psychology arises from the mistaken equating of evolutionary theory with genetic explanations. To equate evolution with a genetic analysis represents a mistaken understanding of the evolutionary processes of selection. Genes are not the raw material of selection, behaviors are. Behaviors lead to survival and reproduction. Individuals who behaved in ways that led to greater survival and reproduction are our ancestors. Those who behaved in ways that led to an early death and/or who failed to reproduce left few descendants.

Behaviors select genes (not vice versa), which then help sustain the behavior across generations, so long as the environment does not change in such a way as to make the behavior no longer adaptive.[c] The psychological mechanism that produces a behavioral tendency must exist in at least some rudimentary form (so that the behavior recurs when circumstances call for it), in order for it to be selected at the biological level.[d]

For example, it is the psychological aversion we call *fear* that causes one to flee from danger. Our ancestors were individuals who felt distress in the presence of danger, rather than indifference to it. They also experienced psychological enjoyment of sweetness and were drawn to consume ripe fruit rather than eat twigs. Behaviors are the grist of selection. The proper focus of an evolutionary analysis is behavior, the psychological mechanisms that impel it, and the development, functioning, and modification of these mechanisms. Psychology, as the science of human behavior, should have much to add to evolutionary thinking.[e] And an evolutionary analysis of the mechanisms that produce human behavior should contribute to an understanding of human psychology as well.

EVOLUTION AND HUMAN ENVIRONMENTS

Modern humans emerged approximately 100,000 to 200,000 years ago. This period (and the one to two million years prior to it, the Pleistocene) that led to the emergence of modern humans has been termed the "Environment of Evolutionary Adaptedness" (EEA) by the psychologist John Bowlby.[27] For 99% of the time the genus *Homo* has lived on Earth, our ancestors lived as hunters and gatherers in environmental conditions much like those in which we first evolved. We are "living fossils" of adaptations that in some ways are more suited to those conditions than to modern society. For example, we tend to be more easily frightened by ancient threats such as snakes and spiders than by modern dangers such as cars and slippery bathtubs. And, as we have observed, our compulsions for rich and salty foods are a holdover from the less abundant times typical of all but the most recent human history.

In the last few thousand years, and especially during the last few hundred years, humans have been responsible for substantial changes in their own environment. In many ways we have shaped the environment to adapt to our needs rather than the other way around (e.g., heated homes, electric lights, high-rise buildings, highways,

[c]To ensure the enduring entrance into the human behavioral repertoire, the psychological mechanism requires a heritable component and a stable environment.

[d]Cultural transmission is another process by which behaviors are maintained across generations. Of course, it also requires appropriate psychological mechanisms of transmission (e.g., language or observational learning). More to the point, however, behavior is the mechanism of selection for cultural transmission as well: no behavior, no cross-generational cultural continuity.

[e]The biological study of other species might also benefit from consideration of the psychological mechanisms that underlie their behavior. For example, when a male cricket digs a hole from which it issues its call for a mate, how does the cricket come to dig a hole of the particular size and shape that is characteristic of others of his species? What psychological feedback mechanism does the cricket use? Some sort of pleasurable experience must occur and direct the cricket (akin to the pleasurable sensation that urges humans to seek out and consume ripe fruit). But is it the "feel" of the hole? The effect the hole has on the sound of the cricket's chirp? The view provided from the hole? One can imagine bringing the armory of laboratory techniques from experimental psychology to bear on the question (manipulating variables designed to affect the cricket's tactile, auditory or visual feedback, and examining the impact on the hole the cricket digs). The end result would yield a richer understanding of the behavior of the cricket than by merely describing the hole digging as a biologically programmed process and leaving it at that.

telephones, computers, antibiotics, agriculture). But in some ways, the fact that human psychology is better adapted to past environments shows through our reactions to modern environments (e.g., obesity, the stresses to living in densely populated cities, road rage).

When changes in the environment occur, the suitability of previously successful adaptations may diminish in the new circumstances. Selection pressure may then lead to the emergence of new adaptations. The key point here is that adaptations follow changes in the environment, and because natural selection acts slowly, adaptations lag behind environmental changes. Evolutionary processes continue, but they operate slowly over many generations. Our being better adapted in some ways to the Pleistocene does not mean that human evolution stopped, only that recent environmental changes have occurred. If those recent environmental changes remain stable and if they influence human survival and reproduction, then adaptations of relevant psychological mechanisms may result, but they should not be evident for very many generations. As a result, the study of current psychological mechanisms will gain from consideration of conditions that existed in the Pleistocene and continued for almost the entirety of human existence, our "environment of evolutionary adaptedness."

EVOLUTION IS A THEORY OF ENVIRONMENTAL INFLUENCES

Because evolutionary theory comes to psychology from biology it is mistakenly assumed that it is a theory that emphasizes biological controls of behavior. In fact, it is difficult to think of another perspective in psychology that more broadly emphasizes the importance of environmental influence on behavior.

An evolutionary analysis places importance on the role of an environmental analysis at three different levels in the causal sequence.[20] At the *historical* level, an evolutionary analysis considers the importance of aspects of the environment in the selection pressures that humans and their ancestors experienced over thousands of generations. For example, humans show an automatic orienting response toward sudden changes in noise level, brightness of light, and motion in their surroundings. Sudden changes in the environment are likely to be associated with potential hazards and opportunities. The flash, rustle, or motion caused by another animal could indicate a food opportunity or a source of danger. Alert individuals who attended quickly to them are our ancestors. Those who were slow to react or remained indifferent left few descendants. Alone among theories, an evolutionary analysis considers the importance of the environment in creating the psychology of humans as a species.

At the level of the psychological *development* of individuals during the life span, and evolutionary analysis emphasizes the importance of the environment in calibrating or adjusting the psychological mechanisms that control behavior. For example, we have discussed the importance of early childhood associations on the development of later sexual attraction, the development of musical talent by Mike and Mozart, and more generally the importance of an appropriate physical, educational, and psychological environment on an individual's biological and social development. We will have more to say regarding psychological mechanisms and their calibration through environmental inputs later in this chapter.

Finally, an evolutionary analysis stresses the importance of environment at the level of the *immediate situational inputs* in the operation of specific psychological mechanisms, as, for example, the role of the environment (including the people in it) in arousing sexual interest, jealousy, anger, curiosity, or a willingness to help others.

By considering the role of distinct developmental and situational inputs, an evolutionary analysis provides a detailed and complex treatment of environmental factors that influence behavior. Although it has perhaps not been sufficiently or explicitly stressed by those advocating an evolutionary perspective, social and cultural elements are important components of the influences that operate at each of the three levels of environmental input.

SOCIOBIOLOGY: WHERE IS THE PSYCHOLOGY?

The nonreductionist conceptual approach of evolutionary psychology needs to be distinguished from the unabashedly reductionist orientation of sociobiology.[28,29] As the name implies, sociobiology intends an explanatory leap directly from the level of biological mechanisms to the level of social behavior. In the process, psychological mechanisms that produce behavior are ignored. Evolutionary psychologists, by contrast, consider psychological mechanisms as central to understanding human behavior, not a level of analysis that can be passed over or omitted. From the perspective of evolutionary psychology, experience and biology play important, intertwined roles in the development and operation of the psychological mechanisms that govern behavior. Those behaviors may be consistent with biological functions, but they are neither identical nor reducible to them.[4] This distinction is important and leads to different predictions regarding human behavior.[20]

Sociobiologists view behavior as serving biological functions, typically "maximizing inclusive fitness," that is, increasing the likelihood of one's genes being represented in future generations. For example, a sociobiological orientation views sexual behavior in terms of a reproductive urge or a "compulsion to procreate." Indeed, the biological outcome is the production of offspring, but at a psychological level the urge is usually for sex itself, not to replicate our genes.[20] We do it because it feels good.

The importance of this conceptual distinction regarding the motive that drives the behavior becomes apparent if we consider the impact of contraception on sexual behavior. If the mechanism that leads to sexual behavior is the desire to reproduce, introducing contraception should eliminate sexual interest. Of course, it doesn't. By contrast, eliminating the pleasure derived from sexual behavior should dramatically reduce the likelihood of choosing to engage in sexual interaction even if reproduction occurs.

By the same token, if the urge that led to sexual behavior was reproduction, men would willingly pay to make a donation to a sperm bank, and insist on getting paid to see a stripper, rather than the other way around. And because it does not lead to reproduction, masturbation would be unknown.

Another example of the distinction between a psychological analysis of behavior and an "inclusive fitness-monitoring" sociobiological analysis are the mechanisms that lead to food intake. We eat when we have the psychological experience of hunger, and we prefer to consume foods that provide pleasurable taste experiences: things that are sweet, salty, or fatty. Such foods were often scarce in the past and being strongly drawn to them when they were available (e.g., when fruit was ripe) served our ancestors' nutritional needs very well. In the abundance of modern society, however, these psychological urges lead to overconsumption, obesity, and reduced inclusive fitness.[20] In fact, many of us now consume large amounts of substances designed to produce these pleasurable taste sensations while at the same time being nutritionally vacant: artificial sweeteners and fats.

THE NATURE OF PSYCHOLOGICAL MECHANISMS

A common misconception of evolutionary psychology is that it postulates genetically determined, fixed behavior patterns that are immune to environmental influence. In fact, modern evolutionary psychology rejects such a position as vigorously as would any staunch social constructionist.[30] Evolutionary psychologists, like those who do not adopt an evolutionary framework for their conceptualizations, seek to discover, describe, and understand the nature of the psychological mechanisms that produce behaviors of interest. Psychological mechanisms are processes inside an organism that take as input some form of information that is either external or internal to the individual and transform that information into output that either regulates physiological activity, provides information for other psychological mechanisms, or produces overt behavior.[30] An evolutionary approach adds that the mechanisms must have contributed to the solution of a specific problem related to survival or reproduction recurrently over human evolutionary history. It is a functional and adaptive analysis. Enjoyment of sexual activity and the pleasurable taste of ripe fruit are examples of psychological mechanisms. (Note that, although we usually think of the quality "tastes good" as residing in the food we eat, it more properly belongs to our internal mechanism: an experience of pleasure that draws us to consume foods high in sugar, salt, and fat. A momentary consideration of the pleasure a dung beetle apparently experiences from the diet to which it is drawn makes clear that the pleasure of consumption is in the organism, not the food.)

Far from arguing that psychological mechanisms are "hard wired," fixed, unmodifiable, or invariably produce a particular behavioral outcome, an evolutionary approach seeks to understand their nature. The nature of psychological mechanisms will include consideration of issues of environmental inputs that activate them, including social inputs, as well as inputs that affect their plasticity, their modifiability, and the resolution of conflict between them. In order to illustrate some of the issues related to understanding psychological mechanisms, including the importance of environmental inputs to their development, operation and change, we turn our attention in the remainder of this paper to the topic of sex differences in human mate preferences.

EVOLUTION AND SEX DIFFERENCES IN HUMAN MATE PREFERENCES

At a conceptual level an evolutionary analysis suggests that differences between males and females are most likely in areas in which the two sexes have faced different adaptive problems over evolutionary time. They should not differ in areas in which they have confronted similar problems. By far the most significant areas in which men and women have confronted different problems are associated with reproduction, such as the acquisition of sex partners: males obtaining female partners, and females selecting male partners. Consistent with this prediction, meta-analyses of research on sex differences have shown small and declining differences between males and females in many areas, while gender differences in many sexual attitudes (particularly attitudes toward casual sex) and certain sexual behaviors are large and robust.[31]

More specifically, an evolutionary analysis suggests that because the *minimum* investment necessary to reproduce is so much greater for females (internal fertilization, placentation, gestation, lactation) than for males (sexual intercourse), females should be choosier in selecting sexual partners than males and should focus on somewhat different characteristics in their prospective partner.[32,f] Consistent with this analysis, researchers have reported considerable evidence corresponding with the theoretical view that men are strongly attracted to aspects of female appearance that communicate sexuality (e.g., reproductive capacity and availability), whereas women are relatively more attracted to male characteristics that communicate successfulness (e.g., status, dominance, earning capacity, and willingness to commit).[33–35]

These preferences have been demonstrated in an impressive variety of research including, for example: Buss's[33] cross-cultural study involving 10,000 participants in 37 countries (but see also Eagly and Wood's[15] reanalysis and social-structuralist commentary); Sprecher, Sullivan and Hatfield's[36] replication of Buss's findings using a U.S. national probability sample; Kenrick's[37] research on age and marriage patterns in the U.S. and elsewhere, and his research on the minimum standards acceptable by men and women for long- and short-term partners, and research by Deaux and Hanna[38] and others who have analyzed the content of personals advertisements. The results of these varied research approaches consistently show that males desire relative youth, beauty, and sexuality in females, while females seek signs of ambition, successfulness, and resources in males.

Although consistent with an evolutionary analysis, data from marriage patterns, personals ads, demographic information, and stated preferences are not direct evidence of psychological mechanisms. For example, stated preference data can be affected by participants' saying what they think they are supposed to say. The validity of self-report data is also dependent on the participants' having conscious access to the process being studied and the ability to accurately articulate it if they do.

In an effort to avoid the potential weaknesses of self-report data, and to more directly study the psychological mechanisms involved in opposite-sex attraction, we have conducted a series of experiments that have investigated cognitive processing of opposite-sex physical attractiveness by men and women.

COGNITIVE PROCESSING OF OPPOSITE-SEX PHYSICAL ATTRACTIVENESS

If men and women mentally represent opposite-sex physical attractiveness information differently as predicted by an evolutionary analysis, it should be possible to

[f] Human males can, and typically do, invest heavily in their offspring in terms of time, teaching, nurturing, and provisioning. The point here is that the *minimum* investment necessary to reproduce for males is less than for females. In fact, part of a female's choosiness often is to discern and gain assurance that her partner will indeed invest along with her in their offspring.

find evidence for the hypothesized differences in cognitive associations by using standard techniques for investigating cognitive processes. For example, when individuals perform a sequence of two cognitive tasks, if the two tasks are mentally related, then performing the first task should facilitate performance of the second. That is, some of the work necessary to perform the second task has already been done by having completed the first task. Therefore, if the tasks are cognitively related the second task can be accomplished more quickly. If they are not related, the first task will provide no benefit in performing the second. For example, if I am given two math problems to solve and the strategy required to solve the second problem is similar to the strategy required solving the first, then I should solve the second problem more quickly than I would if I had not already worked through the solution to the first.

Adopting the logic of this methodology to the topic of cognitive associations of physical attractiveness for men and women, we performed a series of experiments to test whether males mentally process physical attractiveness of women more in terms of sexuality, and whether females process physical attractiveness of men more in terms of successfulness. In each of the experiments participants twice rated "on-the-street" photos of opposite-sex strangers. We were not interested in the ratings themselves. Instead, we were interested in the time it took the participants to perform the second rating task, and whether the speed with which the second task was performed was influenced by the nature of the first rating task.

Consistent with predictions made from an evolutionary analysis, our results have shown that for men the task of rating the women's physical attractiveness was easier (could be completed more quickly) if they had already done the cognitive work associated with considering their sexual availability, than if they had first viewed the photos and processed the question of the women's apparent successfulness. For female subjects viewing photos of males, however, the reverse was true. They were able to perform the task of rating the physical attractiveness of the men in the photographs more quickly if they had already processed them in terms of successfulness than if they had processed them in terms of sexual availability. Presumably, in each case it was the overlap in the cognitive work required that made opposite-sex physical attractiveness easier to rate when doing so followed processing of sexuality issues for male subjects and successfulness for female subjects.

The results of subsequent experiments demonstrated that: (*a*) evaluation of an opposite-sex stranger's attractiveness spontaneously evoked thoughts of sexuality when males were rating females, and thoughts of successfulness among females who were evaluating males; (*b*) the observed effects only occurred when participants made opposite-sex judgments (for heterosexual subjects, at least); and (*c*) not only are there differences between males and females in the cognitive processing of opposite-sex attractiveness, but also there are within-sex differences that are consistent with predictions made by an evolutionary analysis that attractiveness for a short-term relationship is cognitively processed differently than attractiveness for a long-term relationship.[35] How males cognitively process a woman's attractiveness for a long-term relationship is different from how males think about the same woman's attractiveness for a short-term relationship (the women's sexual availability playing a larger role in men's thoughts regarding a prospective short-term relationship). Furthermore, there is still another set of differences that distinguish how females cognitively process the attractiveness of males for a long-term relationship (ambition and future earning prospects) and short-term relationships (immediate extraction of resources/extravagant life style).

All these observed differences in the cognitive processing of opposite-sex physical attractiveness are consistent with an evolutionary model. However, the theory also predicts areas in which the cognitive processing of opposite-sex attractiveness should be similar for males and females. These similarities should emerge where the reproductive interests of males and females converge. One example is the mutual need by males and females for a kind and cooperative long-term mate. Consistent with this prediction, we found that both males and females who had processed the opposite-sex photos for the person's attractiveness for a long-term relationship/marriage could make subsequent judgments of how "kind and understanding" the pictured person was more rapidly than participants (both male and female) who had first looked at the photos and evaluated the person's attractiveness for a short-term relationship/brief affair. In fact, the effect size was by far the largest of any of the experiments in the series. Not only does an evolutionary approach successfully predict psychological mechanisms that differ between men and women, but it also identifies areas in which sex differences should disappear as reproductive interests converge.

THE ROLE OF SOCIAL EXPERIENCE IN PSYCHOLOGICAL MECHANISMS OF MATE PREFERENCE

It is important to reiterate that psychological mechanisms, including those related to human mate preferences are not "hard wired," fixed, or unmodifiable. Many psychological mechanisms exist initially in a rudimentary, incomplete form. For example, humans are born "language-ready," but experience is necessary in order to acquire a specific language. Similarly, we are born "culture ready," but require socialization to learn the rules and expectations of our specific social domain.

Other psychological mechanisms, including some related to mate preferences are *calibrated* or *modified* by experience. We have already discussed the Westermarck Effect that leads to a reduced sexual appeal of opposite-sex individuals with whom one is raised during childhood. There is also increasing evidence that family experience during the first few years of life determines whether females later develop a reproductive strategy characterized by early onset of sexual activity and frequent, brief sexual relationships without careful choice of mates, or a strategy that employs stable, enduring relationships with carefully chosen partners. Girls are sensitive to features of their childhood environment that provide cues to the quality of male-female relationships and whether males can be counted on to invest in their offspring. When compared to girls whose fathers are active, supportive, and affectionate caregivers, girls whose early family experiences are characterized by discordant male–female adult relationships and relatively low or unreliable paternal investment (e.g., father absence or harsh, rejecting, inconsistent parenting and caregiving, especially from their father) develop more precocious sexual interest in boys and promiscuous sexual behavior, as well as an earlier onset of puberty.[39,40] Consistent with an evolutionary model, both physiological and psychological mechanisms associated with female sexuality are shaped by early social experience. (And, of course, the mechanism being calibrated probably was itself calibrated or shaped by still earlier environmental influences that might include hormonal, nutritional, or social inputs.)

Returning to the question of differences between male and female mate preferences, these psychological mechanisms must be influenced by social experience as well. After all, what constitutes male status in modern society is very different from the cues to status when humans lived in caves.[g] Presumably females (for reasons discussed earlier) are predisposed to learn and be drawn to the dimensions and cues that symbolize status and social dominance in their world. Their psychological mechanisms of perceiving male attractiveness become calibrated accordingly.[8,h] Males' mate-preference mechanisms, by contrast, should be more attuned to social cues of sexual availability and physical cues of fertility. When viewed this way, the question of the possible range in the plasticity of these mechanisms becomes very interesting. For females, any characteristic that leads to male social status and resource-acquisition should be appealing, and those characteristics could vary widely across time and cultures (e.g., from prowess as a hunter or warrior, to business, professional, or financial success). Since the physical cues of female fertility are more specific, an evolutionary model predicts a narrower range of cues that should appeal to males. Indeed, though there is cultural variation in cues to female attractiveness, the differences are much smaller than commonly thought.[41,42,i]

The misconception of considering evolved mechanisms as "hard wired" and reflex-like leads to another misunderstanding regarding the effect of social inputs on (in this case) mating preferences and behavior: thinking the behavioral *outputs* of the mechanisms will be inevitable or uncontrollable. While mating-preference mechanisms may produce powerful impulses to evaluate members of the opposite sex along specific dimensions, and strong behavioral urges, other psychological mechanisms may simultaneously *conflict* with them and attenuate their behavioral implications. As a result, the social inputs that affect one psychological mechanism may indirectly influence the output of another mechanism. For example, an aroused short-term sexual interest toward an individual may be restrained and remain unacted upon because of competing mechanisms such as fear of physical harm by a jealous partner or spouse, fear of disease or pregnancy, anticipated rejection by the desired person, social disapproval by others, or feelings of commitment to one's long-term partner. More than just the parental investment inspired mate-preference mechanisms may be aroused in a real-world situation involving opposite-sex attraction.

Finally, because mechanisms that control sexual behavior are, like other psychological mechanisms, attuned to environmental cues, one can expect historical, cultural, and other environmental changes to affect the calibration as well as the nature of conflict between psychological mechanisms. We have already mentioned the ef-

[g] Even what constitutes "resources" can vary culturally and historically, so long as they represent or can be translated into the ability to provide sustenance.

[h] Males are probably also predisposed to learn the dimensions associated with status and social dominance. However, for them this ability is not related to attractiveness, but to intra-sexual competition.

[i] Our discussion here is limited and does not include the full breadth of mate-preference characteristics (e.g., physical characteristics of males or qualities such as cooperativeness or parenting skills).

fect of historical changes on the factors that create male status. Some other examples of historical effect on the psychological mechanisms that control sexual behavior include:

(1) Sex Ratios. The relative scarcity or abundance of availability of opposite-sex partners is an environmental characteristic that can lead to powerful changes in mating behavior. Historically, during periods of time when women are scarce relative to men, men are willing to make and keep long-term commitments in order to retain a mate, women are choosier in selecting partners and gain social and economic mobility through marriage (often "marrying up" socially and "trading up" when possible), and men are alert to other males' attention to their partner, often resulting in women's being severely constrained, guarded, controlled, or secluded.[43]

By contrast, historically during periods of time when there is an oversupply of females relative to men, men are less likely to marry or, if married, are more apt to get divorced, women find it more difficult to achieve economic mobility through marriage, brief liaisons and adultery are more common, men have opportunities to move from woman to woman or to maintain multiple relationships with different women, and men are less likely to remain committed to the same woman throughout her childbearing years.[43] When males are unpredictable providers and cannot be counted on for protection, mothers are likely to rely on relationships with multiple male partners.[13]

These historic outcomes at the cultural level parallel the effects of father-presence or -absence on the calibration of individual young girls' sexual strategies described earlier.[40,44]

(2) Prosperity. As we have noted, nutritional prosperity has led to overconsumption of sweet, fatty, and salty foods because our evolved taste mechanisms still draw us to these now abundant foods. What effects should modern economic prosperity have on mating mechanisms? There is considerable evidence that females are attracted to males that possess resources and are willing to share them with their partner and offspring.[33,35,37] But there is some disagreement as to whether these are evolved preferences in their own right,[30,34] or whether they are an indirect result of patriarchal dominance and control of resources by males that stem from evolved desires of males to control female sexuality in order to ensure themselves of certainty of paternity of the offspring in which they invest.[12–14]

Consistent with the first hypothesis, there is evidence that women who achieve high professional status and financial prosperity (e.g., doctors and lawyers) continue to seek men whose status and resources are at their level or above. These preferences continue even though potential partners with still higher resources and social status become increasingly fewer in number as the woman's position increases.[45–47]

On the other hand, consistent with an explanation based on a patriarchal control of resources, Eagly and Wood[15] argue that across cultures an increase in gender equality is related to a decrease in men's interest in a woman's housekeeping capabilities as mate-selection criteria.

Even if qualities consciously associated with economic prosperity, such as men's earning capacity and the value of women's housekeeping skills, decline in importance, we speculate that other qualities less consciously connected to prosperity and gender equality will remain important mate-selection criteria. Indeed, Eagly and Wood[15] found that increased cultural gender equality was not associated with a change in sex differences in valuing a potential mate's physical attractiveness. In addition to men's continuing to value physical attractiveness, we suspect qualities such as women's perception of a man's reliability,[13] status, and dominance (in the form of competence and self-assurance), as well as kindness and cooperativeness in both males and female will remain important determinants of opposite-sex attraction mechanisms, affected little if at all by cultural prosperity.

(3) Contraception. Sought for several thousand years, the historically recent advent of safe, effective and reliable contraception techniques has, especially for females, affected the balance in conflict between psychological mechanisms that control sexual behavior. By reducing sexual inhibition resulting from fear of pregnancy, women are able to engage in and enjoy sexual relations more freely. As a result, during the 20th century, for the first time in human history, constraints against short-term relationships are reduced and women in long-term relationships can limit the number of children they have. The timing of births also can be planned so as to cause minimum disruption to other aspects of women's lives, such as careers. Women are no longer confined solely to bearing and rearing children.

The nature of the psychological mechanisms that produce behavior, their development, the inputs that calibrate and modify them, the consequences of conflict between mechanisms, along with the impact of culture and history upon them are important topics of study.

CONCLUSION

Our social nature and our biological nature are inseparable and indivisible. To argue that one or the other is predominant is a turf battle whose premise is scientifically inaccurate and an impediment to a thorough understanding of the nature of being human. Bringing the theory of evolution into psychology does not lessen the importance of social, cultural, or learned inputs to human psychology and behavior. It enhances the importance of these inputs by putting them in context, just as it puts human biology in the context of social and other experiences (e.g., the development of myopia). In so doing, an evolutionary approach provides a richer, more thorough and more interesting understanding of the interplay between nature and nurture. To our way of thinking, placing social experience and other environmental inputs in a larger context and coming to understand how they interact with our biology makes social processes more interesting, not less.

Just as social science cannot hope to understand human behavior without taking evolution into account, evolutionary psychology cannot hope to understand human behavior without taking into account history and culture.[13] Perspectives on human behavior that are either exclusively biological or exclusively social seem to us to be restricted and incomplete and to represent conceptual extremes. Just as the story of human behavior (and sex differences in particular) is not *merely* a story of biology at one extreme, it is equally not *merely* a story of culture or learning at the other. To fully understand the psychological mechanisms that control human behavior will require an appreciation of the rich and complicated interplay between our biological nature and all aspects of our environment, especially its social/cultural qualities. In our view, evolutionary psychology provides a broad theoretical middle ground where both social and biological conceptual orientations meet and interact, each contributing an indispensable part of the picture of human psychology. The result is an exciting synergy that is more than the sum of its parts.

REFERENCES

1. DARWIN, C. 1859. On the Origin of Species by Natural Selection, or the Presentation of Favored Races in the Struggle for Life. Murray. London.
2. DARWIN, C. 1871. The Descent of Man and Selection in Relation to Sex. Murray. London.
3. COSMIDES, L., J. TOOBY & J.H. BARKOW. 1992. Introduction: evolutionary psychology and conceptual integration. *In* The Adapted Mind: Evolutionary Psychology and the Generation of Culture. J.H. Barkow, L. Cosmides & J. Tooby, Eds.: 3–15. Oxford. New York.
4. TOOBY, J. & L. COSMIDES. 1992. The psychological foundation of culture. *In* The Adapted Mind: Evolutionary Psychology and the Generation of Culture. J. H. Barkow, L. Cosmides & J. Tooby, Eds.: 19–136. Oxford. New York
5. DURKHEIM, E. 1895/1962. The Rules of the Sociological Method. Free Press. Glencoe, IL.
6. MURDOCK, G.P. 1932. The science of culture. Am. Anthropol. **34:** 200–215.
7. GOTTLIEB, G. 1992. Individual Development and Evolution. The Genesis of Novel Behavior. Oxford University Press. New York.
8. RUTTER, M.L. 1997. Nature-nurture integration: the example of anti-social behavior. Am. Psychol. **52:** 390–398.
9. DE WAAL, F.B.M. 1999. The end of nature versus nurture. Sci. Am. **281:** 94–99.
10. NESSE, R.M. & G.C. WILLIAMS. 1994. Why We Get Sick: The New Science of Darwinian Medicine. Random House. New York Times Books. New York.
11. WOLF, A.P. 1995. Sexual Attraction and Childhood Association. Stanford University Press. Stanford, CA.
12. HRDY, S.B. 1997. Raising Darwin's consciousness: female sexuality and the prehominid origins of patriarchy. Hum. Nature **8:** 1–49.
13. HRDY, S.B. 2000. The optimal number of fathers: Evolution, demography and history in the shaping of female mate preferences. Ann. N.Y. Acad. Sci. **907:** 75 [this volume].
14. SMUTS, B.B. 1995. The evolutionary origins of patriarchy. Hum. Nature **6:** 1–32.
15. EAGLY, A.H. & W. WOOD. 1999. The origins of sex differences in human behavior: evolved dispositions versus social roles. Am. Psychol. **54:** 408–423.
16. CRAWFORD, C. 2000. The future of evolutionary psychology: counting babies or studying cognitive mechanisms. Ann. N.Y. Acad. Sci. **907:** 21 [this volume].
17. NELSON, C.A. 1999. Neural plasticity and human development. Curr. Dir. Psychol. Res. **8:** 42–45.
18. BYERS, J.A. 1999. Play's the thing. Natural History **108:** 40–45.
19. BROWN, B. 1999. Optimizing expression of the common human genome for child development. Cur. Direct. Psychol. Res. **XX:** 37–41.
20. BUSS, D.M. 1995. Evolutionary psychology: a new paradigm for psychological science. Psychol. Inquiry **6:** 1-30.
21. BUSS, D.M. 2000. Desires in human mating. Ann. N.Y. Acad. Sci. **907:** 39 [this volume].
22. SHIPMAN, P. 1994. The Evolution of Racism. Simon & Schuster. New York.
23. FRASER, S. 1995. The Bell Curve Wars. Basic Books. New York, NY.
24. HERRNSTEIN, R.J. & C. MURRAY. 1994. The Bell Curve: Intelligence and Class Structure in American Life. Free Press. New York.
25. STERNBERG, R.J. 1995. For whom the bell curve tolls: a review of "The Bell Curve." Psychol. Sci. **6:** 257–261.
26. DENNETT, D.C. 1995. Darwin's Dangerous Idea: Evolution and the Meanings of Life. Simon and Schuster. New York.
27. BOWLBY, J. 1982. Attachment. Attachment and Loss. Vol.1, 2nd ed. Basic Books. New York.
28. WILSON, E.O. 1975. Sociobiology: The New Synthesis. Harvard University Press. Cambridge, MA.

29. WILSON, E.O. 1998. Consilience: The Unity of Knowledge. Knopf. New York.
30. BUSS, D.M. 1996. The evolutionary psychology of human social strategies. *In* Handbook of Social Psychology: Basic Principles. E.T. Higgins & A.W. Kruglanski, Eds.: 3–38. Guilford. New York.
31. OLIVER, M.B. & J.S. HYDE. 1993. Gender differences in sexuality: a meta-analysis. Psychol. Bull. **114:** 29–51.
32. TRIVERS, R. 1972. Parental investment and sexual selection. *In* Sexual Selection and the Descent of Man: 1871–1971. B. Campbell, Ed.: 136–179. Aldine. Chicago, IL.
33. BUSS, D.M. 1989. Sex differences in human mate preferences: evolutionary hypotheses tested in 37 cultures. Behav. Brain Sci. **12:** 1–49.
34. BUSS, D.M. & D.T. KENRICK. 1998. Evolutionary social psychology. *In* The Handbook of Social Psychology, Vol. 2, 4th ed. D.T. Gilbert, S.T. Fiske & G. Lindzey, Eds.: 982–1026. McGraw-Hill. Boston, MA.
35. BUSS, D.M. & D.P. SCHMITT. 1993. Sexual strategies theory: an evolutionary perspective on human mating. Psychol. Rev. **100:** 204–232.
36. SPRECHER, S., Q. SULLIVAN & E. HATFIELD. 1994. Mate selection preferences: gender differences examined in a national sample. J. Pers. Soc. Psychol. **66:** 1074–1080.
37. KENRICK, D.T. 1994. Evolutionary social psychology: From sexual selection to social cognition. Advan. Exp. Soc. Psychol. L. Berkowitz, Ed. **26:** 75–121.
38. DEAUX, K. & R. HANNA. 1984. Courtship in the personals column: the influence of gender and sexual orientation. Sex Roles **11:** 363–375.
39. BELSKY, J., L. STEINBERG & P. DRAPER. 1991. Childhood experience, interpersonal development, and reproductive strategy: an evolutionary theory of socialization. Child Dev. **62:** 647–670.
40. ELLIS, B.J., S. MCFADYEN-KETCHUM, K. DODGE, G.S. PETTIT & J.E. BATES. 1999. Quality of early family relationships and individual differences in the timing of pubertal maturation in girls: a longitudinal test of an evolutionary model. J. Pers. Soc. Psychol. **77:** 387–401.
41. CUNNINGHAM, M.R., A.R. ROBERTS, A.P. BARBEE, P.B. DRUEN & C. WU. 1995. "Their ideas of beauty are, on the whole, the same as ours": consistency and variability in the cross-cultural perception of female attractiveness. J. Pers. Soc. Psychol. **68:** 261–279.
42. SINGH, D. 1993. Adaptive significance of female physical attractiveness: role of waist-to-hip ratio. J. Pers. Soc. Psychol. **65:** 293–307.
43. GUTTENTAG, M. & P.F. SECORD. 1983. Too Many Women? The Sex Ratio Question. Sage. Beverly Hills, CA.
44. DRAPER, P. & H. HARPENDING. 1982. Father absence and reproductive strategy: an evolutionary perspective. J. Anthropol. Res. **38:** 255–273.
45. KENRICK, D.T. & R.C. KEEFE. 1992. Age preferences in mates reflect sex differences in reproductive strategies. Behav. Brain Sci. **15:** 75–133.
46. TOWNSEND, J.M. 1989. Mate selection criteria: a pilot study. Ethol. Sociobiol. **10:** 241–253.
47. WIEDERMAN, M.W. & E.R. ALLGEIER. 1993. Gender differences in sexual jealousy: adaptationist or social learning explanations? Ethol. Sociobiol. **14:** 115–140.

Evolutionary Psychology: Counting Babies or Studying Information-Processing Mechanisms

CHARLES CRAWFORD

Department of Psychology, Simon Fraser University, Burnaby, BC V5A 1S6, Canada

ABSTRACT: Evolutionary psychology focuses on the study of adaptations. Its practitioners put little credence in the study of reproductive success in recent and current environments, and argue for an information-processing, cost-benefit conception of adaptation. Because ancestral and current environments differ, it is necessary to distinguish between innate and operational adaptations and between concurrently contingent and developmentally contingent behaviors. These distinctions lead to an evolutionary classification of behaviors into true pathologies, pseudopathologies, quasinormal behaviors, and adaptive-culturally-variable behaviors. I argue that a complete study of the functioning of a behavioral adaptation involves modeling ancestral selection pressures, cross-cultural research, experimental studies of mental processes, and studies of the proximate biological correlates of information-processing adaptations. Finally, I claim that evolutionary psychology can help us avoid making both naturalistic and moralistic fallacies.

INTRODUCTION

The world we live in is not what it was when our anatomy, physiology, and behavior-producing mental processes took their present form. For several million years, our *hominoid* and *hominid ancestors* lived a hunter-gatherer-like existence. About 10,000 years ago our most recent ancestors developed agriculture and settled down in permanent communities. If we compare our environments to those of our preagricultural ancestors we find that population densities are greater; social, economic, and political structures are more complex; group sizes are larger; the range of altitudes and latitudes inhabited is greater; multinational corporations now dominate the production of goods and services; and international conflicts seem a normal part of our lives. These, and a profusion of other differences, interact to produce a world that our Pleistocene ancestors would likely find strange and unnerving. Yet we survive and prosper in our new world.

If the world where natural selection shaped our adaptations has vanished, how can we use the theory of evolution by natural selection to help us understand why we think what we think and why we do what we do today? I claim the answers can be found in the study of adaptations. I begin with Edward O. Wilson's definition of an adaptation. I then distinguish Darwinian anthropology and evolutionary psychology and briefly summarize why evolutionary psychologists put little credence in the study of reproductive success in recent and current environments. I then argue for an information-processing, cost-benefit conception of adaptation, and distinguish between innate and operational adaptations and between concurrently contingent and developmentally contingent strategies. These distinctions lead to an evolutionary classification of behaviors into true pathologies, pseudopathologies, quasinormal behaviors, and adaptive-culturally-variable behaviors. I conclude the essay with the claim that a complete study of the functioning of a behavioral adaptation involves modeling ancestral selection pressures, cross-cultural research, experimental studies of mental processes, and studies of the proximate biological correlates of information-processing adaptations. However, before presenting my arguments, I wish to briefly discuss the social value of the explanations developed by evolutionary psychologists.

ON NATURALISTIC AND MORALISTIC FALLACIES

A central question for all societies is: How can we set up a society that is founded on moral principles, and yet is pliable and comfortable enough for people to live in so that it will persist? This question has perplexed thinkers in Western civilization since Plato wrote the *Republic*. Those who attempt to use evolutionary thinking to help resolve it are often accused of committing the *naturalistic fallacy*: the fallacy of assuming that what is, is what ought to be, in other words, what tends to be the case ought to be the case. Some examples are: "Women are more caring than men, therefore they ought to be more caring," "Men are more aggressive than women, therefore they ought to be more aggressive," and "Men are taller than women, therefore they ought to be taller." Clearly, these statements are fallacious. One cannot go from what is to what ought to be. Although men's average height in all known cultures is greater than women's average height, we cannot conclude that men ought to be taller than women.

However, the identification of a naturalistic fallacy can lead us astray if we then conclude that the state of nature leading to it ought to be changed, or can easily be changed. Identifying the claim that "Men are taller than women, therefore, they ought to be taller" as fallacious does not imply that men ought not to be taller than women, or that the world would be a better place if men were not taller than women. Moreover, identifying the fallacy does not imply that it would be easy to change the state of nature so that men are not taller than women. Similarly, identifying the fallacies concerned with gender differences in caring and aggression does not imply that it is either advisable or easy to change the state of nature so that the gender differences in caring and aggression no longer exist. It is as fallacious to go from *is* to *ought not* as it is to go from *is* to *ought*.

Although the naturalistic fallacy can be pernicious, another fallacy is equally noxious. It is the *moralistic fallacy:* the fallacy of assuming that what ought to be is, or that what ought to be can be. A prominent example of such thinking is "Racial differences in intelligence ought not to exist, therefore, they do not exist; and if anyone finds such differences he must be using poor research methods or be politically motivated in his research." There are many other examples in contemporary thought. Some that come to mind are "sexuality ought not to be a motivation for rape, therefore we assume it is not," "day-care ought to be as good as mother care, therefore we assume it is," and "abortion ought to have no negative consequences, therefore, we assume it does not." Anyone putting forth either arguments or data that challenge moralistic fallacies can expect a rough ride.

TABLE 1. Homicide and reproductive success in Yanomamo men[a]

	Committed a Homicide					
	Yes			No		
Age	*N*	Number of offspring	Avg. no. of offspring	*N*	Number of offspring	Avg. no. of offspring
20–24	5	5	1.00	78	14	0.18
25–30	14	22	1.57	58	50	0.86
31–40	43	122	2.83	61	123	2.02
>41	75	524	6.99	46	193	4.19
Total	137	673	4.91	46	193	1.59

[a]Data from Chagnon.[43] Adapted with permission from the American Association for the Advancement of Sciences.

Yet, I believe that some of the greatest tragedies of history have been the result of moralistic fallacies. The history of Russia in the 20th century provides one of many examples. Forty million people died under Joseph Stalin's rule.[1] Although many Russian communists were good people who worked for what they believed, the belief "that what ought to be can be" can have evil consequences when applied to a whole society.

Therefore, I believe that the study of evolutionary psychology is not only an exciting experience, but also has great practical value. Understanding how we can set up a society that is founded on moral principles, but is pliable and comfortable enough for people to live in so that it will persist, requires knowledge of human nature that needs a major contribution from evolutionary psychology. As Darwin[2] said in the closing paragraph of *The Descent of Man,* "Man, with all his noble qualities, ...still bears in his bodily frame the indelible stamp of his lowly origin." We cannot hope to understand ourselves unless we use knowledge of our "lowly origin." Evolutionary psychology is one of the sources of that knowledge.

ADAPTATIONS

If we are to develop an evolutionary science of human behavior, it must be based on the concept of adaptation. In *Sociobiology: The New Synthesis,* Edward O. Wilson defined an adaptation as "...any structure, physiological process, or behavior pattern that 'makes' an organism more fit to survive and reproduce in comparison with other members of its species."[3] The beaks of Darwin's finches provide the classic example.

Note that the word "reproduction" has an important place in Wilson's definition. There is evidence that many traits in nature are associated with survival and reproduction. Beak depth in Darwin's finches, for example, is associated with survival.[4] Since reproduction is related to survival, beak depth is also associated with reproductive success. This association has led some researchers to focus their attention on reproductive success in the study of adaptation in humans.

TABLE 1 provides information on the reproductive success of Yanomamo men who have committed a homicide.[5] Clearly, men who have killed another man have greater reproductive success than those who have not. But how should data on current and recent reproductive rates be interpreted? Some researchers focus on how behaviors are involved in maximizing reproductive success. Alexander writes,

> The theory of lifetimes most widely accepted among biologists is that individuals have evolved to maximize the likelihood of survival not of themselves, but of their genes, and that they do this by reproducing and tending in various ways offspring and other carriers of their own genes—descendent and non descendent relatives.[6] (p. 38)

and

> Quite different sets of such proximate mechanisms may lead to what appears to be the same goal in different individuals, or to different goals in the same individual at different times and in different circumstances.[6] (p. 18)

and Irons claims that

> [t]he discussion of culture in this essay is phrased in terms of behavior, rather than ideas, beliefs and sentiments because it is actual behavior that influences reproductive success directly. Ideas, beliefs, and sentiments, from the point of view of behavioral biology, are important to the extent that they affect behavior.[5] (p. 9)

These quotations put the emphasis on behaviors that help individuals to behave in such a way that they project the maximum number of genes into subsequent generations. From this perspective, Yanomamo men are behaving in ways that contribute to the goal of maximizing their inclusive fitness. They can somehow choose behaviors that enable them to purse their fitness goals. Presumably, if the situation changed so that homicide was no longer associated with reproductive success, they would adopt behaviors that did contribute to their fitness goals. Because the emphasis is on behaviors for maximizing reproductive success, and because individuals in all times and places have similar goals, the difference between ancestral and current environments is not crucial. Finally, because a variety of different mechanisms may contribute to fitness maximization, the emphasis is on general purpose, rather than on special purpose, psychological mechanisms. This perspective on using evolutionary theory in the study of human behavior has come to be known as *Darwinian anthropology* or *Darwinian social science*[7] and has been criticized by those who refer to themselves as *evolutionary* or *Darwinian psychologists*.[8,9]

First, they argue that although adaptations were selected because they maximized ancestral reproductive success, this does not mean they act to maximize it today. Although seeking foodstuffs containing sugar may have contributed to ancestral reproductive success, it is incorrect to say that individuals like the taste of sweet substances because it helps them contribute to their current reproductive success. Second, they claim that behavior itself does not contribute to fitness. Their claim is that the psychological mechanisms that produce behavior should be the focus of scientific interest. It is not sugar-seeking behavior that should be the focus of scientific interest, but the naturally selected design of the physiological mechanisms making sugar taste sweet. Third, they claim that the focus of evolutionary psychology should be on specialized psychological mechanisms. Natural selection cannot produce general-purpose mental mechanisms since there were no *general* problems in our ancestral environment. Finally, given these three arguments, the difference between ancestral and current environments becomes very important because the specialized psychological mechanisms that make up the human psyche were selected to function in particular ancestral environmental conditions. If these conditions change, psychological mechanisms may not function as they were designed to function. Humans evolved to find sugar sweet because the sweet taste motivated individuals to do the work necessary to obtain it. Nowadays, sugar may be obtained with little work, and therefore, its sweet taste may motivate us to eat more of it than is good for our health, and thereby decrease our reproductive success.

The approach of evolutionary psychologists is becoming the dominant paradigm for the evolutionary study of human behavior. I claim its implementation requires developing a more adequate conception of psychological adaptations and how they functioned in ancestral and current environments, as well as feasible methods for studying psychological adaptations. Let us consider several instructive examples of adaptations. The first is a physiological rather than a behavioral example, but one that illustrates the vital principles of responsiveness to environmental contingencies and the cost-benefit balance of coping strategies.

Because many parasites have evolved to live at the normal body temperature of their hosts,[10] an effective way to fight them is to raise body temperature to create an inhospitable ecology. But this adaptation has costs as well as benefits. Energy is required to raise body temperature to the appropriate level and to maintain it at that level until the invaders are overwhelmed. Moreover, if body temperature becomes too high or is maintained at a high level too long, the body may be damaged. Hence, the fever adaptation is the result of a compromise between its ancestral costs and benefits. Some theorists might even claim that it reflects an optimal compromise.[11]

Now consider a behavioral example, the courtship tactics of the male scorpion fly.[12,13] Males, depending on the level of male-male competition they encounter, use one of three tactics—dead insect, proteinaceous mass, or forced mating—for obtaining copulations. Females prefer mating partners who give them "nuptial gifts," either a dead insect or a proteinaceous mass. Because resources for obtaining the nuptial gifts are limited, males compete vigorously for them. The most successful males use the "dead insect" tactic. The next most successful tactic is to offer a "proteinaceous mass". Males without the resources to employ either of these tactics attempt to force copulations on females. Because all males are capable of using all tactics, the heritability of the behaviors is indicated as zero in FIGURE 1. However, if heritability were actually measured, it might be greater than zero because the mating behavior may depend on traits, such as body size or growth rate, that are heritable.

These examples are instructive because they illustrate three important aspects of adaptations. First, adaptations did something for their ancestral possessors by enabling them to respond to contingencies in their environment, such as dealing with invading parasites and adjusting mating tactics to environmental circumstances. Other examples are: doing the work necessary to find sugar, finding a healthy mate, forming a social contract, or identifying genetic kin. Second, the operation of adaptations involves decision-making. The above examples require decisions about adjusting body temperature in response to invading parasites,[10] becoming motivated to seek sugar, choosing between mates that differ in future health, [14] deciding whether a social contract is well formed,[15] and deciding whether an individual is a genetic relative.[16]

Finally, the operation of an adaptation reflects the costs and benefits that shaped it. The fever adaptation does not "know," and indeed cannot "know," that the invention of antibiotics has altered the costs and benefits of fever for fighting parasites. If it could, it could "refuse" to raise body temperature and avoid the costs of fever. But this would imply an instantaneous Lamarckism that would make natural selection ir-

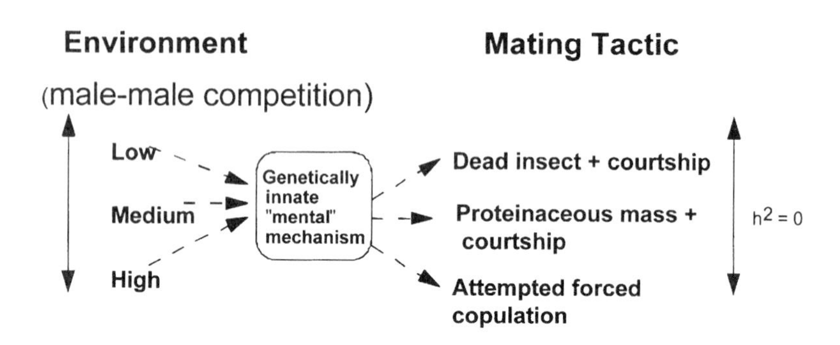

FIGURE 1. Mating tactics in scorpionflies (*Panorpa sp.*). The level of male-male competition determines the reproductive tactic used. (From Crawford.[42] Adapted with permission from the American Psychological Association.

relevant. Similarly, the basic cost-benefit structure of behaviors such as responses to signs indicating another's health (fitness) or of another's ability and willingness to fulfill social contracts, or of another's genetic relatedness can not be changed in response to current circumstances. Only natural selection can change the cost-benefit structure of an adaptation.

These considerations lead to a conceptualization of an adaptation as

> ...a set of decision processes that enabled the cost benefit analysis an ancestral organism carried out in response to a specific set of environmental contingencies, and that organized the effector processes for dealing with those contingencies so that the gene(s) mediating the adaptation could survive and reproduce in competition with alternative gene(s).[17]

Fever, the taste for sugar, waist-to-hip ratio, degree of body asymmetry, recognizing genetic relatives, and forming social contracts provide instances of this definition.

However, I claim that all adaptations must reflect a cost-benefit analysis. Consider, for example, the beaks of a species of Darwin's finches. If the beak of a particular finch is too small, it will not do the job. If it is too large, it will be costly to grow, maintain, and may unbalance the finch in flight and other activities. Therefore, as the beak grows, it must respond, in a cost-benefit way, to the growth of other parts of the finch.

Finally, most evolutionary psychologists argue that because mental adaptations evolved in response to specific ancestral conditions, the human mind is not a *tabula rasa.* For example, Symons writes that "complex, specialized, species-typical brain/mind mechanisms are precisely what a Darwinian view of life should lead us to anticipate."[9] (p. 143) Most evolutionary psychologists would claim that male scorpion flies have at least one specialized mechanism for choosing and implementing the appropriate courtship tactic. To continue this line of reasoning—just as the stomach could not have evolved to be a general digester, because there were no *general* foods to which natural selection could respond—the psyche could not have evolved to be a *tabula rasa,* because there were no *general* mental problems to which natural selection could respond. Hence, when we speak of the difference between current and ancestral environments, we must do so with respect to particular adaptations and the specific conditions they evolved to respond to.[18] Now let us consider the difference between *then* and *now* in a bit more detail.

ADAPTATIONS: THEN AND NOW

The environment of an adaptation includes all the internal and external conditions impinging on the reproduction of the genes mediating its development and functioning.[19] To help understand how adaptations function in ancestral and current environments, it is necessary to distinguish between *innate* and *operational* adaptations, between *ancestral* and *current developmental* environments, between *ancestral* and *current immediate* environments, and between *ancestral* and *current behavior* (FIG. 2).[18] The upper part of this figure, labeled "Then," refers to the period when ancestral forces selected the genes mediating the adaptation. The part of the figure below the bold line, labeled "Now," refers to an infinitesimal segment of the evolutionary time line in which an adaptation actually functions. In most cases "Now" refers to the most recent infinitesimal segment of the time line.

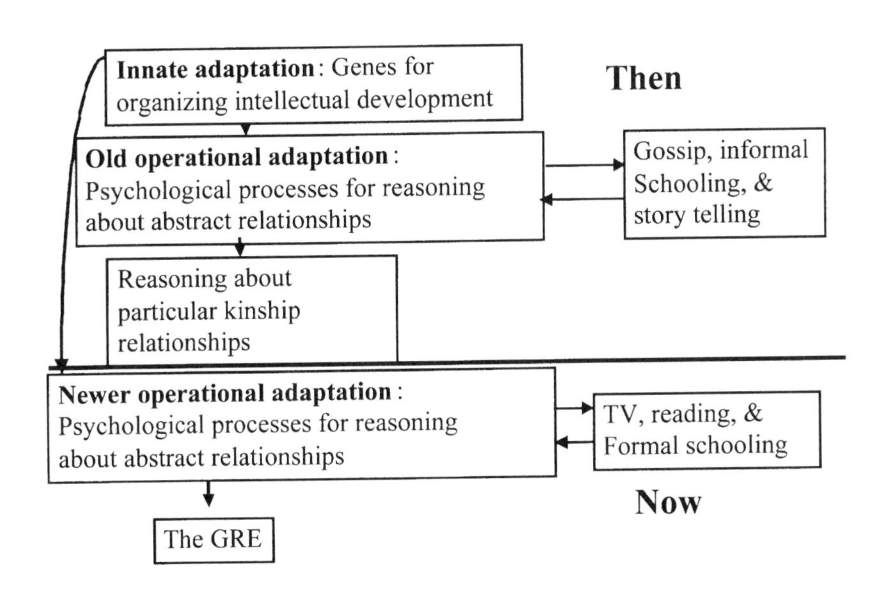

FIGURE 2. Innate and operational operations in ancestral and current environments. Although the innate adaptation is unchanged between "Then" and "Now," both the operational adaptation and behavior may differ in ancestral and current environments. (From Crawford.[18] Adapted with permission from Elsevier Science Publications, Ltd.)

The *innate adaptation* is the information encoded in the genes mediating the development of the *operational adaptation.* It was shaped across evolutionary time, and evolutionary psychologists assume that it changes only very slowly across evolutionary time. The operational adaptation consists of the anatomic structures, physiological processes, and psychological processes that do the actual work of helping the organism do the things it has to do to survive and reproduce. For the male scorpion fly seeking a mate, the innate adaptation is the information in his genes that directs the development of the operational mating adaptation, the decision processes enabling him to adjust his behavior to environmental mating circumstances. For a child learning a language the innate adaptation is the set of genes enabling the language to be acquired. The operational adaptation is the anatomy and physiology and the information-processing decision processes instantiated in them that actually enable the language to be learned.

Now consider the distinction between the immediate and developmental environments. The *immediate environment* of an adaptation refers to the present environmental conditions, either ancestral or current, to which an operational adaptation responds. For the male scorpion fly seeking a mating, it is the level of male-male competition he is experiencing. But, it also includes his internal states, such as energy levels and current physical strength, influencing his response in a particular time or place. For a child encountering a new word or grammatical form in a story told by a Pleistocene elder, or read by a teacher in a large urban school, the immediate environment is the information in the environment the sense organs are responding to, as well the present level of language skills and other internal conditions influencing the child's response to the new information.

The *developmental environment* refers to the succession of immediate environments that have impinged on the formation of the operational adaptation up to a particular time. An understanding of the developmental history of a male scorpion fly's courtship behavior is not necessary for predicting his mating behavior because all adult males are capable of using all three mating tactics without previous experience.[12] But, for understanding the response of a particular child learning a language, knowledge of the developmental history of the child is crucial.[20] The tactics of the male scorpion fly are said to be *concurrently contingent* on environmental events because they depend only on the present state of the environment. Human language learning, in contrast, is said to be *developmentally contingent* on environmental conditions because present learning depends on previously acquired language abilities.[21]

Although most human evolutionists assume that innate adaptations are unchanged in adjacent infinitesimal intervals of the evolutionary time, both the *developmental* and *immediate environments* may differ in these intervals. Hence, both ancestral and current operational adaptations and behavior may differ because of environmental changes that have occurred since an innate adaptation took its present form. It is these changes to which environmental mismatch theorists[22–24] refer when they claim that the current environment is problematic for humans, and that evolutionary psychologists claim are important to consider when studying the evolutionary significance of human behavior. Moreover, operational adaptations and behavior may differ between contemporary cultures because of cross-cultural differences in developmental and immediate environments.

With these considerations in mind, evolutionary psychology can be conceptualized as concerned with: (1) the stresses, the adaptive problems, that existed in ancestral environments; (2) the mental mechanisms that Natural Selection shaped to deal with those stresses and problems; and (3) the way the evolved mental mechanisms function in current environments.[21]

FIGURE 2 illustrates this conception, showing how ancestral and current verbal reasoning processes may differ from ancestral ones even if the genes producing them are the same. For example, our hunter-gatherer ancestors may have had to reason about kinship relations as part of their daily lives. Their learning environment would have included informal teaching, overhearing gossip, observing the behavior and reasoning of other members of their group, and playing games that required intellectual reasoning. One result would have been facility in thinking about complicated problems in kinship. An immediate environment may have been the appearance of a visitor to their group that required a decision on his or her degree of kinship to members of the group. Most of these learning environments exist today, but they have been augmented by formal schooling, reading, and TV. The result may be instances of operational adaptations that differ somewhat from those our ancestors might have developed. Moreover, the operational adaptations of our descendants may differ from ours. Finally, behaviors may not contribute to fitness in particular infinitesimal segments of evolutionary time. We can therefore develop a classification of adaptive functions in ancestral and current environments.

AN EVOLUTIONARY CLASSIFICATION OF BEHAVIOR

TABLE 2 provides the basis of such a classification.[19] The "ancestral" dimension is defined in terms of adaptive and maladaptive, where adaptiveness is defined in terms of expected reproductive fitness in an ancestral environment.[25] Because the current environment refers only to an infinitesimal segment of the evolutionary time line, in which the adaptation may not contribute to reproductive success, current adaptiveness cannot be defined in terms of reproductive success. Current adaptiveness/maladaptiveness is defined in terms of malfunction of adaptations selected because they contributed to ancestral fitness. Although current adaptation malfunction may detract from reproductive fitness, there may be instances where a modern environment is particularly benign, and the malfunction of the adaptation may not detract from current fitness, and may even contribute to it. For example, the mechanisms for bonding to children may malfunction and result in a "parent" bonding to an adopted child. This bonding could contribute to the parent's current fitness if it contributes to the parent's ability to rear other children that share parental genes.

True pathologies are conditions that would detract from reproductive fitness in virtually any environment. They are due to serious organic damage or cultural stresses and deprivations that cause the failure of adaptations essential for survival, growth, or reproduction.[19,21] Huntington's chorea and phenylketonuria, genetically caused mental malfunctions; memory loss and the inability to recognize faces due to damage to physiology and anatomy, and the inability to speak because of the absence of language experience during the early years of life provide examples of true pathologies. These conditions are pathologic in any but the most benign of artificial environments. Although true pathologies do not have an evolutionary history in the usual sense, their study may help us understand the evolution of adaptive systems.

TABLE 2. Adaptations in ancestral and current environments

	Current, funtional	Current, dysfunctional
Ancestral, adaptive	Adaptive-culturally variable	Pseudopathologies
	• courtship rituals	• obesity
	• athletic sports	• prostitution
	• learning languages	• wife abuse
Ancestral, maladaptive	Quasinormal behaviors	True pathologies
	• recreational sex	• Huntington's chorea
	• adoption	• phenylketonuria
	• true altruism	• autism

For example, Simon Baron-Cohen's studies of autistic children help us to understand this "mind-blindness.[26,27]

Pseudopathologies are conditions or behaviors that are problematic in the current environment, although they have their basis in evolved adaptations. Obesity, due to our love for sugar and fat's being expressed in environments rich in foods containing sugar and fat; prostitution, due to the ancestral capacity to trade sex for resources' being expressed in an industrial economy, wife abuse, due exaggerated social cues' suggesting infidelity—these also come to mind. These, and many other currently problematic conditions and behaviors, may have their basis in adaptations that contributed to ancestral fitness. As we move further from our environments of evolutionary adaptedness (EEAs), where the cost-benefit structure of our adaptations evolved, we can expect more to appear.

Quasinormal behaviors are those that would have detracted from fitness in ancestral environments, but because of changes in the environment and/or cultural standards, have become socially acceptable and even encouraged.[15,19] Possible examples include recreational sexual behavior, allowable owing to modern methods of birth control; delayed child bearing and short birth intervals, caused by careers of modern women; adoption of genetically unrelated children, owing to the dearth of "substitute" children from extended family for childless couples; and "true altruism," resulting from the failure of kin-recognition mechanisms to discriminate kin from non-kin in current environments. In these cases the cost-benefit structures of adaptations are not evaluating situations properly, but the costs of the behaviors produced is minimal because of a benign environment.

Finally, there are *adaptive-culturally-variable behaviors*. These behaviors vary across time and space, but still serve their ancestral function.[19,21] Learning of artificial languages, such as Esperanto, is a good example. Murdoch[28] has shown that there are a large number of traits, including age-grading, athletic sports, bodily adornment, community organization, cooperative labor, courtship, division of labor, cleanliness training, gift-giving, government, marriage, and penal sanctions that are characteristic of every known society. Although the form of expression of these traits may differ somewhat from culture to culture (e.g., the athletic sports in different societies differ considerably), the adaptive cost-benefit structures producing them function in a wide variety of circumstances. For a more extensive view of adaptive-culturally-variable behaviors see Brown.[29]

Adaptive-culturally-variable behaviors and pseudopathologies have evolutionary histories. Hence, it should be possible, at least in theory, to trace the evolutionary history of athletic sports, marriage, and government, as well as wife abuse, obesity, and prostitution back through the evolutionary record. The edited books of Barkow *et al.*[30] Batzig,[8] and Crawford and Kirby[31] provide examples and methods of studying adaptive-culturally-variable behaviors and pseudopathologies in humans.

ENVIRONMENTAL INTERVENTIONS

It may be possible to reduce or eliminate some pseudopathologies by appropriate environmental interventions. For example, FIGURE 1 indicates that forced copulation in male scorpion flies might be reduced, or even eliminated, by reducing or eliminating male-male competition. This competition might be reduced by giving all males sufficient resources and/or by segregating them so that they cannot come into direct competition. However, it is unlikely that male-male competition in scorpion flies could be eliminated without very coercive restrictions on males that might lead to other pseudopathologies. For example, males might have to be maintained in individual cages in order to reduce male competition to a level sufficient to eliminate forced copulation. However, these unnatural restrictions might, themselves, cause other pathologies.

Similarly, if male harassment of women has its origin in evolved male adaptations, it may not be possible to eliminate it completely without measures that would be so coercive that they could not be applied in a democratic society. Moreover, if, in some very authoritarian society these coercive measures were implemented, they could produce other, equally serious pathologies, such as depression. If anorexia nervosa, a putative pseudopathology, has its origin in ancestral mechanisms for delaying reproduction when conditions for reproducing are poor, but can be expected to improve,[32–34] it may be difficult to eliminate it from modern industrial environments without introducing environmental interventions that would be unacceptable in a democratic society or that might cause other pseudopathologies.

In general, quasinormal behaviors are not as difficult to deal with as either true pathologies or pseudopathologies. Few of our quasinormal behaviors are mentioned in books on psychopathology or psychiatry. However, there are at least three reasons why quasinormal behaviors can be a source of trouble.

First, quasinormal behaviors may produce conflicting or ambiguous inputs to information-processing mechanisms, both in the individuals exhibiting them, and those who associate with them. The result may be anomalous cost-benefit analyses and emotional conflicts. A woman, who engages in recreational sexual behavior because of the availability of reliable birth control may experience emotional conflict because other adaptations related to sexual behavior, such as those involved in the desire for children and long-term intimacy, may be telling her the behavior is too costly. Moreover, the behavior may bring her into conflict with parents and grandparents who desire children and grandchildren.

Second, because the environment has changed, the cues from the environment that the adaptation used in managing behavior may not be adequate to produce a fully functionally behavior. Adopting a genetically unrelated child can be stressful.

Many adoptive parents report that they do not equate an adopted child with a biological child. The reason may be that some of the ancestral cues involved in a parent's attaching to a biological child may not be present for an adopted child. From an evolutionary perspective, the stress in adopting a child is not caused by a reduction in lifetime reproductive success of the adoptive parent relative to what it would have been had the child been a biological offspring. Instead, it may be due to traits of the adopted child producing inputs to cognitive and perceptual decision processes in the parents, friends, and relatives of the parents, as well as in the child itself, that are interpreted in an ambiguous way, leading to conflict and stress.

Third, no matter how well a particular behavior is accepted in a particular culture, there will likely be some individuals who do not find it conducive to their well-being and happiness. Many of the women in polyandrous societies who do not find husbands, and some of the men who must share wives, may not be as accepting of polyandry as the elders of the society who arrange the marriages. Poor people may not view the costs and benefit of the stock market in quite same way as Wall Street brokers and Japanese tycoons. Grandparents may not be as enthusiastic about their grandchildren's being cared for in day-care centers as are their daughters.

Finally, owing to cultural change, societal standards may change across time, moving a particular behavior in and out of the range of acceptability. Fifty years ago divorce, day-care centers, and homosexuality were not as acceptable as they are today. Twenty years ago, the stock market was not as valued in Russia and China as it is today. Whether quasinormal behaviors do become social problems depends on the values of the societies where they exist, the way those values are enforced, and the speed with which those values are changing.

STUDYING THE EVOLUTIONARY SIGNIFICANCE OF BEHAVIORS

Using Darwin's theory of evolution by natural selection in the study of human behavior is not easy.[35] In the remainder of this article, I outline one approach to validating evolutionary explanations of human behavior. But, first I address the belief that predictions from evolutionary hypotheses should be compared with predictions from non-evolutionary hypotheses. FIGURE 3 may help with the logic.

GOOD EXPLANATIONS ARE COMPATIBLE WITH EVOLUTION BY NATURAL SELECTION

The oval on the right in FIGURE 3 includes the set of all explanations that were constructed with evolutionary theory in mind. For example, it might include explanations of helping that rely on kinship and reciprocity. Evolutionary theory was not used in developing the set of explanations represented in the left oval. For example, it might contain varieties of economic, religious, and political explanations for helping behavior, but many of them will be compatible with evolutionary thinking, while others will not. Hence, the two sets intersect. The intersection of the sets contains two types of explanations: evolutionary explanations that are compatible with non-evolutionary explanations and nonevolutionary explanations that are compatible with evolutionary

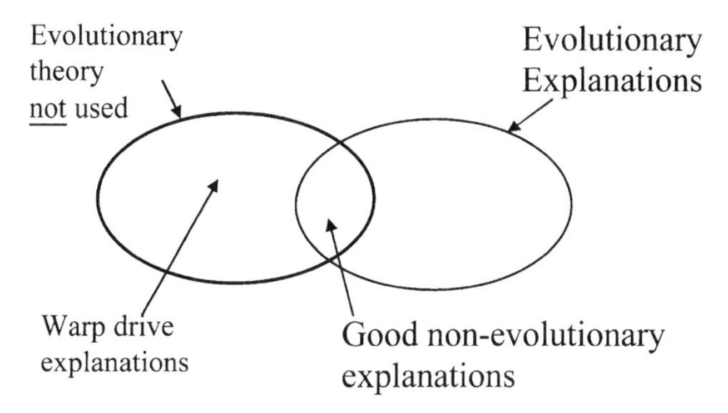

FIGURE 3. The set of evolutionary explanations overlaps with the set of nonevolutionary explanations. The intersection contains good explanations, those that are compatible with evolutionary theory, although it was not used in their construction.

theory. Not only was evolutionary theory not used in constructing the explanations in the part of the left oval that does not overlap with the evolutionary explanations, but also these explanations are not compatible with it. I refer to these as *warp-drive explanations*. (Recall that when the captain of the *Starship Enterprise* wants the ship to break Einstein's theory of relativity, he asks the engineer to put the ship into warp drive.) Explanations of helping behavior that exclude all types of ancestral payback effects would be included in this set. For example, a theory of helping that assumed that empathy existed only to produce prosocial behavior is a warp drive explanation.

Explanations in the overlap are good explanations. They are compatible with evolutionary theory even if the theory was not used in their construction. It is risky to develop an explanation of a particular aspect of the physical world that is not compatible with Einstein's theory of relativity. Similarly, it is risky to develop an explanation of behavioral phenomena that is not compatible with Darwin's theory of evolution by natural selection. This line of thinking suggests that when developing an explanation of behavior it is wise to determine whether it is compatible with evolutionary thinking. If it is not, then some rethinking may be advisable. Hence, evolutionary theory can be a first pass filter for the testing of new explanations of behavior.

TESTING EVOLUTIONARY EXPLANATIONS: FOUR STEPS

There is no culture in which brother-sister, father-daughter, or mother-son incest is an acceptable practice. Some cultures have laws prohibiting these matings, while in others laws are not needed because the practice is unknown or very rare. Close inbreeding is rare in the animal kingdom. Moreover, there is evidence that matings between close relatives produce offspring that are less viable than those from more outbred matings. Hence, it seems reasonable to postulate an evolutionary explanation for avoiding inbreeding.[36] Edward Westermarck[37] argued that intimate contact between individuals during their first few years of life "inoculated" them against sexual interest in each other when they became adults. There is now considerable evidence supporting his theory. I use the example of brother-sister incest avoidance to explain my views on testing evolutionary explanations of human behavior. I claim that four steps are needed to thoroughly validate an evolutionary explanation of a human behavior.

First, it is necessary to get an indication of whether the putative adaptation could have evolved through natural selection, given what we know about ancestral human environments and social structures. Developing a quantitative model of ancestral selection pressures and using it to explore the conditions that could have contributed to the evolution of the supposed adaptation is a good starting point. The dependent variable in the basic model could be lifetime reproductive success. The independent variables for a basic model would be degree of genetic relatedness of mates, ranging from zero for completely outbred mates to 0.5 for full siblings, the reproductive values of the participants (the expected number of remaining offspring to be produced by individuals of age x), and sex. Sex would be included because the costs of incest may be different for males and females. Building more details about possible ancestral selection pressures into the model will improve its usefulness. A more elaborate model might include inclusive fitness as a dependent variable, since incest could contribute to success of genetic kin even if it detracted from the fitness of one or both mates. Independent variables, such as family size, group size, ages of the participants in the incestuous mating, and the harshness of the environment could be included. In any case, systematically varying the values of the independent variables to explore the factors that might have influenced the formation of incest avoidance mechanisms would provide information on the plausibility of the hypothesized adaptation. Although there is extensive evidence for the deleterious effects of brother-sister incest, no one has systematically explored its effects using such a model. For examples of models used in the current context see Refs. 33 and 38.

The purpose of such a model is not to provide a definitive test of an evolutionary hypothesis, but rather to help provide guidance for collecting other evidence relevant to testing it. Across different cultures, there are many reasons for practices relating to the relationships between brothers and sisters. If the Westermarck[37] explanation is valid, some of these practices should reflect evolved mental mechanisms for avoiding brother-sister incest. For example, in societies where there are intimate relations between brothers and sisters as children they should not find each other sexually attractive as adults. Such societies should be less likely to have harsh brother-sister incest rules. However, harsh rules governing relations between brothers and sisters would be more common in societies where brothers and sisters have little intimate contact during childhood. There is some cross-cultural evidence in support of these expectations.

However, neither the modeling nor the cross-cultural studies enable researchers to make statements about cause. A true experiment, where there is random assignment of treatments to subjects, is required to make such statements. FIGURE 4 provides a basic design for such an experiment. There are two groups of subjects in the experiment: full siblings and unrelated individuals matched by age with the siblings.

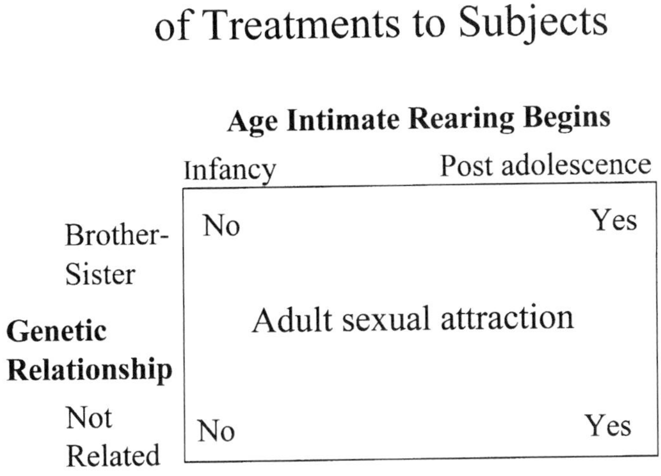

of Treatments to Subjects

Genetic Relationship	**Age Intimate Rearing Begins:** Infancy	Post adolescence
Brother-Sister	No	Yes
	Adult sexual attraction	
Not Related	No	Yes

FIGURE 4. Logic for an experimental test of the Westermarck effect.[37] Pairs of siblings and unrelated individuals are randomly assigned to intimate and nonintimate rearing groups. Individuals from pairs reared together during childhood should not show sexual attraction to each other as adults.

Individuals from each pair are reared either in the same household (sharing the same bathroom, etc.) from infancy or are reared apart until postadolescence. As adults, members of the pairs are tested for sexual interest in each other. If the Westermarck[37] hypothesis is valid, both the siblings and the nonsiblings with intimate rearing should not find each other sexually attractive as adults. However, there should be some sexual attraction between the siblings and the unrelated individuals who did not have intimate rearing as children. There is some evidence for these speculations.[39]

Such an experiment cannot be carried out on human beings. However, there are a number of naturalistic experiments that approximate this design. Children reared in the same Israeli *kibbutz* rarely marry.[40] Taiwanese marriages where infant girls are adopted into families to become wives of the families' sons are less successful than marriages between individuals who did not share a household.[41] Similarly, marriages between patrilineal parallel cousins (children of brothers) in Lebanon are also less successful.[41]

I have presented very stringent conditions for validating an evolutionary hypothesis. My intuition is that they are much more stringent than the current standards in psychology, anthropology, or sociology. I do not know of any case where all four steps have been attempted. I present them as an ideal that researchers should strive for rather than as procedures that must be carried out before any statements about the evolutionary significance of a behavior can be made.

The question raised at the beginning of this paper—How can we set up a society that is founded on moral principles, and yet is pliable and comfortable enough for people to live in so that it will persist?—faces all societies. There are societies where incest is rare and not regarded as an outrage when it does occur. There are societies where brother-sister incest is regarded as a heinous crime requiring severe punishment. We, in the Anglo-American world, seem to be moving toward the latter type of society. An evolutionary analysis of incest and inbreeding avoidance might help us take a more productive approach to dealing with incest.

CONCLUSION

Edward O. Wilson opened *Sociobiology: The New Synthesis* with the following paragraph:

> Camus said that the only serious philosophical question is suicide. That is wrong even in the strict sense intended. The biologist, who is concerned with questions of physiology and evolutionary history, realizes that self-knowledge is constrained and shaped by the emotional control centers in the hypothalamus and limbic system of the brain. These centers flood our consciousness with all the emotions—hate, love, guilt, fear, and others—that are consulted by ethical philosophers who wish to intuit the standards of good and evil. What, we are then compelled to ask, made the hypothalamus and limbic system? They evolved by natural selection. The simple biological statement must be pursued to explain ethics and ethical philosophers, if not epistemology and epistemologists, at all depths.[3] (p. 3)

We live in a troubled world. I believe some of that trouble is generated by our ancestral adaptations' producing thoughts and feelings that are not optimal for the modern world. Some of these thoughts and feelings lead us to fall into naturalistic and moralistic fallacies. Some of these fallacies lead us into destructive and oppressive behaviors. Evolutionary psychology is an exciting discipline in itself. However, I believe it also offers us some hope for better understanding ourselves and producing a better world.

REFERENCES

1. ROBINS, R.S. 1997. Political Paranoia: The Psychopolitics of Hatred. Yale University Press. New Haven, CT.
2. DARWIN, C. 1981. The Descent of Man, and Selection in Relation to Sex. (1871 edition, John Murray. London.) Facsimile reproduction of first edition with an introduction by J.T. Bonner & R.M. May. Princeton University Press. Princeton, NJ.
3. WILSON, E.O. 1975. Sociobiology: The New Synthesis. Harvard, Belknap Press. Cambridge, MA.
4. GRANT, P. 1986. The Ecology and Evolution of Darwin's Finches. Princeton University Press. Princeton, NJ.
5. IRONS, W. 1979. Cultural and biological success. *In* Evolutionary Biology and Human Social Behavior: An Anthropological Perspective. W. Irons & N. Chagnon, Eds.: 284–301. Duxbury Press. North Scituate, MA.
6. ALEXANDER, R.D. 1987. The Biology of Moral Systems. Aldine de Gruyter. New York.
7. SYMONS, D. 1989. A critique of Darwinian anthropology. Ethol. Sociobiol. **10:** 131–144.
8. BARKOW, J., L. COSMIDES & J. TOOBY, Eds. 1992. The Adapted Mind: Evolutionary Psychology and the Generation of Culture. Oxford University Press. Oxford, England.
9. SYMONS, D. 1987. If we're all Darwinians, what's the fuss about? *In* Sociobiology and Psychology. C. Crawford, D. Krebs & M. Smith, Eds.: 121–146. Erlbaum Associates. Hillsdale, NJ.
10. KLUGER, M. 1986. Is fever beneficial? Yale J. Biol. Med. **54:** 89–94.

11. MAYNARD Smith, J. 1978. Optimization theory in evolution. Annu. Rev. Ecol. Syst. **9:** 31–56.
12. THORNHILL, R. 1980. Rape in *Panorpa* scorpion flies and a general rape hypothesis. Anim. Behav. **28:** 52–59.
13. THORNHILL, R. 1984. Alternative female choice tactics in the scorpion fly and their implications. Am. Zool. **24:** 367–383.
14. BUSS, D.M. 1999. Evolutionary Psychology: The New Science of Mind. Allyn and Bacon. Boston, MA.
15. COSMIDES, L. & J. TOOBY. 1989. Evolutionary psychology and the generation of culture. Part II: Case study: a computational theory of social exchange. Ethol. Sociobiol. **10:** 51–97.
16. HAMILTON, W.D. 1964. The genetical evolution of social behaviour. J. Theor. Biol. **7:** 1–52.
17. CRAWFORD, C.B. 1998. The theory of evolution in the study of human behaviour: an introduction and overview. *In* Handbook of Evolutionary Psychology. Ideas, Issues, and Applications. C. Crawford & D. Krebs, Eds.: 3–42. Erlbaum Associates. Mahwah, NJ.
18. CRAWFORD, C.B. 1993. The future of sociobiology: counting babies or studying proximate mechanisms. Trends Ecol. Evol. **8:** 183–186.
19. CRAWFORD, C.B. 1998. Environments and adaptations: then and now. *In* Handbook of Evolutionary Psychology: Ideas, Issues, and Applications. C. Crawford & D. Krebs, Eds.: 275–302. Erlbaum Associates. Mahwah, NJ.
20. PINKER, S. 1994. The Language Instinct: The New Science of Language and Mind. Allen Lane. London.
21. CRAWFORD, C.B. & J.L. ANDERSON. 1989. Sociobiology: an environmentalist discipline? Am. Psychol. **44** (12)**:** 1449–1459.
22. EATON, B., M. SHOSTAK & M. KONNER. 1988. The Paleolithic Prescription: A Program of Diet and Exercise and a Design for Living. Harper and Row. New York.
23. EATON, S.B., M.C. PIKE, R.V. SHORT, N.C. LEE, J. TRUSSELL, R.A. HATCHER, J.W. WOOD, C.M. WORTHMAN, N.G. BLURTON-JONES, M.J. KONNER, K.R. HILL, R. BAILEY & A.M. HURTADU. 1994. Women's reproductive cancers in evolutionary context. Q. Rev. Biol. **69** (3)**:** 353–367.
24. COE, K. & L.B. STEADMAN. 1995. The human breast and the ancestral reproductive cycle. Hum. Nature. **6**(3)**:** 197–220.
25. BURIAN, R.M. 1983. Adaptation. *In* Dimensions in Darwinism: Themes and Counter Themes in 20th Century Evolutionary Thought. M. Grene, Ed.: 287–314. Cambridge University Press. Cambridge, England.
26. BARON-COHEN, S. 1995. Mindblindness: An Essay on Autism and Theory of Mind. MIT Press. Cambridge, MA.
27. BARON-COHEN, S. 1990. Autism: aspecific cognitive disorder of "mind-blindness." Int. Rev. Psychiat. **2:** 79–88.
28. MURDOCK, G.P. 1945. The common denominator of culture. *In* The Science of Man in the World Crisis. R. Linton, Ed.: 124–142. Columbia University Press. New York.
29. BROWN, D. 1991. Human Universals. Temple University Press. Philadelphia, PA.
30. BETZIG, L., Ed. 1997. Human Nature: A Critical Reader. Oxford University Press. New York.
31. CRAWFORD, C.B. & D. KREBS, Eds. 1998. Handbook of Evolutionary Psychology: Ideas, Issues, and Applications. Erlbaum Associates. Mahwah, NJ.
32. ANDERSON, J.L., C.B. CRAWFORD, J. NADEAU & T. LINDBERG. 1992. Was the Duchess of Windsor right? A cross-cultural review of the sociobiology of ideals of female body shape. Ethol. Sociobiol. **13:** 197–227.
33. ANDERSSON, J.L. & C.B. CRAWFORD. 1992. Modelling the costs and benefits of reproductive suppression. Hum. Nature **3:** 299–334.
34. SURBEY, M.K. 1985. Anorexia nervosa and female reproductive strategies. Ethol. Sociobiol. **8:** 47S–61S.
35. WILLIAMS, G.C. 1996. Adaptation and Natural Selection: A Critique of Some Current Evolutionary Thought. Princeton University Press. Princeton, NJ.
36. BOYD, R.J.S. 1997. How Humans Evolved. Norton. New York.

37. WESTERMARCK, E.A. 1925 The History of Human Marriage. Macmillan. London.
38. ANDERSON, J.L. & C.B. CRAWFORD. 1993. Trivers-Willard rules for sex allocation: When are they adaptive in humans? Hum. Nat. **4:** 137–174.
39. FOX, R. 1980. The Red Lamp of Incest. Dutton. New York.
40. SHEPHER, J. 1983. Incest: A Biosocial View. Academic Press. New York.
41. WOLF, A.P. 1995. Sexual Attraction and Childhood Association. Stanford University Press. Stanford, CA.
42. CRAWFORD, C.B. 1989. The theory of evolution: of what value to psychology. J. Comp. Psychol. **10** (1)**:** 4–22.
43. CHAGNON, N. 1988. Life histories, blood revenge, and warfare in a tribal population. Science **239:** 985–992.

Desires in Human Mating

DAVID M. BUSS
Department of Psychology, University of Texas, Austin, Austin, Texas 78712, USA

ABSTRACT: This chapter traces theoretical and empirical progress in the study of human mating over the past few decades. Early pre-evolutionary formulations proposed that men and women were identical in their mating motivations. Most were simplistic, typically postulating a single motive for mating: the search for similarity, equity, or complementarity. Given the large sex differences in human reproductive biology, notably women bearing the burdens of internal fertilization and a greater obligatory parental investment, it would be extraordinarily unlikely that evolution by selection would fail to forge sex-differentiated mating strategies. Empirical research over the past 15 years has robustly confirmed evolutionary predictions in the domains of desire for sexual variety, the importance of fertility cues, and the importance of resource-provisioning. Recent work has revealed a hidden side of women's sexuality—a desire for extra-pair partners and the conditions under which this desire is expressed. We now have the theoretical and empirical outlines of an evolutionary formulation of human mating strategies.

DESIRES IN HUMAN MATING

Desires lie at the foundation of human mating. Desires determine whom we are attracted to as potential partners. Fulfillment of desire is the key to successful mate attraction and successful mate retention, and the key to harmony between the sexes involves the fulfillment of desire. Violations of desires constitute the primary source of conflict between the sexes. Effective means for derogating competitors involve impugning them or besting them on qualities desired by a targeted mate. Because of the centrality of desire for understanding so many aspects of human mating, much early research on the psychology of human mating focused on empirically documenting desires, guided by Darwin's theory of sexual selection[1] in its modern manifestations.[2–4]

When I first started studying human mating, in the early 1980s, little work in psychology existed on the topic and existing theories of mating in the social sciences were remarkably simplistic. Most postulated a single motive in mating, such as the search for similarity, the search for equity, or the search for qualities that embodied an opposite-sex parent. None of these theories provided an explanation for why humans would be motivated in these directions. Why should humans seek similarity or equity? What might be the origins of these motives? What functions would they serve? Perhaps even more remarkable was the fact that men and women were presumed to be identical in their mating psychology. Sex differences were not part of any theories of mating, nor did researchers focus on them in their empirical research.[5]

To an evolutionist, however, it would be astonishing if the sexes were identical in their sexual psychology. Spectacular sex differences in reproductive biology, including the fact that fertilization occurs internally with women and not men, and the greater obligatory parental investment of females impose distinct adaptive problems on the sexes. Could these biological differences, recurring over millions of years of evolutionary history, fail to select for a sex-differentiated sexual psychology?

My first scientific interest in human mating began with testing a few simple predictions based on Trivers' 1972 theory of parental investment and sexual selection. Trivers initially defined parental investment as any investment in offspring that precludes the ability to invest in other offspring. Subsequent definitions of parental investment emphasize the time, energy, or effort expended to aid the survival or reproduction of one offspring at the expense of other forms of investment, including effort allocated to intrasexual competition for alternative mates. Thus, parental investment is defined by decrements in a parent's residual reproductive value, including any reduction in the parent's survival, fecundity, mating success, or ability to invest in relatives.[6]

Trivers reasoned that the relative parental investment of the sexes in their offspring determined which of the two components of sexual selection (preferential mate choice and intrasexual competition) was operative for each sex. He reasoned that the sex that invests more in offspring should be more selective in their choice of mates. The costs of making a poor mate choice are greater for the highest-investing sex. A woman, for example, might risk raising a child alone, without sufficient resources, if she chose a man who abandoned her or proved to be a "slacker." A man who made a poor mate choice, in contrast, might only waste a few hours of time, and hence the costs to him are commensurately lower.

By exercising choice, the higher-investing sex can select mates on various grounds, depending on the particular species, to increase the survival and reproduction of her offspring. This can range from selecting mates with "good genes" to selecting mates that show an ability or willingness to invest in her offspring. The low-investing sex, on the other hand, should be more competitive with members of their own sex for sexual access to the higher-investing sex. The higher-investing sex becomes the valuable and limiting reproductive resource over which the lower-investing sex competes. The intrasexual component of sexual selection, in short, should be engaged most intensely by the lower-investing sex.

However, the two components of sexual selection, mate preferences and intrasexual competition, become connected, or the distinction blurred, because the mate preferences of one sex can determine the content of the competition of the other. If females desire males with territory, for example, then that exerts selective pressure on males to compete with one another to acquire what females desire. Those that succeed in besting their intrasexual competitors in fulfilling these desires are preferentially chosen as mates. Those that fail suffer sexual exclusion. These principles, in the past, have been amply documented in the animal literature,[7] but their application to human behavior is less so. We may ask, are women, being the sex with higher levels of obligatory parental investment, more selective, choosy, and discriminating about who they mate with than men? Do women place a greater premium than men on economic resources in a potential mate, as well as the qualities that lead to resources such as ambition, industriousness, social status, and older age? Do men place a greater premium than women on physical appearance, since appearance provides a wealth of cues to a woman's fertility and reproductive value? In the early 1980s, we did not know the answers to these questions.

My first empirical foray into this arena tested these predictions on samples of subjects from Cambridge, Massachusetts. I asked these individuals to evaluate how desirable each of 76 qualities was in a potential spouse, or someone they might marry. The sex differences emerged, precisely as predicted. Women valued financial resources in a mate significantly more than men did. They also valued qualities that tend to lead to such resources, such as ambition, industriousness, education, and social status. Men more than women valued good looks and physical attractiveness. Although I was delighted by this empirical confirmation, I realized that there were alternative interpretations of the sex differences, and furthermore, that perhaps these sex differences would be found only in the United State or at least only in Western cultures. When I showed these results to my colleagues in psychology and sociology, the dominant response was intense skepticism that these sex differences would prove to be universal. Some said that they were due to patriarchal social systems and would not be found in cultures where the sexes were more egalitarian. Some argued that they were products of Western media or American patterns of socializing children. None but the evolutionists predicted that they would be found in every culture.

UNIVERSAL SEX DIFFERENCES

Because of the strong anti-biological bias in the social sciences, I knew that I would have to conduct a study that exceeded most psychological studies in scope. In psychology, the empirical bar is always set higher for those who propose biological explanations of human behavior, since the default assumption in this century has been that all existing behavioral patterns are forged by the environment during a person's ontogeny.[8] In order to find out whether the sex differences in mate preferences that were documented in American samples were universal or prevalent across the globe, I established the International Mate Selection Project. Over the course of five years, roughly 50 research collaborators, most native residents of different cultures, translated the mate preference instruments, administered them to samples in their native cultures, and then sent me the data. When the dust settled, we had 10,047 participants from 37 different cultures located on six continents and five islands. The samples were diverse, representing different religions, ethnic groups, races, political systems, economic systems, and mating systems.

The samples, of course, were not random samples. They were biased toward the more educated, toward the young, and toward those living in cities. They were nonetheless exceptionally diverse. In the Venezuelan sample, for example, the research collaborator systematically sampled every fifth house from neighborhoods representing different socio-economic groups. The Zulu collaborator from South Africa ventured into shantytowns for data collection. Collaborators from some countries had to conduct the study in relative secrecy, since they lacked government approval. In a couple of cases, my research collaborators had to smuggle the data out of the country. Although the ages of the samples tended toward the young side, they ranged from 14 to 71 years, permitting us to evaluate whether mate preferences varied with age.

Not all of the results from this study confirmed the hypotheses. I had predicted that men would universally value virginity in a potential partner more than women, since virginity would presumably provide a powerful signal of paternity certainty to the man. In fact, this proved to be the case in only 62% of the cultures we studied.

In 38% of the cultures, the sexes did not differ with respect to this issue. Furthermore, the absolute value placed on virginity varied widely from culture to culture. Chinese participants viewed it as indispensable. Swedish and Dutch participants viewed it as irrelevant or unimportant. This suggests that men have evolved different solutions to the adaptive problem of paternity uncertainty. The study also found that men and women were highly similar in their desires for many qualities. Both sexes wanted mates who were kind, understanding, intelligent, exciting, healthy, and dependable. No one wanted mean, stupid, boring, disease-ridden partners.

Despite the sexual similarities on some qualities and the wide cross-cultural variability in how much other qualities were desired, two clusters of sex differences proved to be universal, precisely as predicted. Women more than men in all 37 cultures valued potential mates with good financial prospects. Men more than women across the globe placed a premium on youth and physical attractiveness, two hypothesized correlates of fertility and reproductive value. No longer could the sex differences in mate preferences be viewed as products of the media, Western culture, particular age groups, particular economic or political systems, or particular mating systems.

SHORT-TERM VERSUS LONG-TERM MATING

The findings that the predicted sex differences in mate preferences appeared to be universal emboldened me to explore several complexities of human mating, since documenting sex differences in what people want in a marriage partner merely scratches the surface of human mating. One issue that kept cropping up was the fact that not everyone was looking for a long-term mate. Mating relationships can last for a few months, a few days, a few hours, or even a few minutes. The ends of this temporal continuum can be labeled "short-term mating" and "long-term mating."

This temporal dimension was obviously critical. In long-term mateships, for example, both sexes invest heavily, so according to Trivers' theory of parental investment and sexual selection, both sexes should be highly discriminating about whom they mate with, and their standards should be similar. In the short-term mating context, on the other hand, men can get away with minimal investment, whereas women still risk investing tremendously. Sex differences in choosiness, therefore, should show up maximally in the short-term mating context, and minimally in the long-term mating context.

Research that David Schmitt and I conducted, as well as work by Doug Kenrick, robustly supported these predictions.[9,10] We asked samples of participants to judge how important each of 67 characteristics were in two contexts, as a short-term mate (defined as a one-night stand, brief affair, etc.) and as a long-term mate (defined as a marriage partner). The characteristics spanned a gamut of attributes ranging from adventurous, artistic, and athletic to stylish in appearance, understanding, and well-liked by others. On 41 out of the 67 characteristics, approximately two-thirds, men's standards for a short-term mate were significantly lower than women's standards. In a short-term mate men required lower levels of charm, athleticism, education, devotion, social skills, generosity, honesty, independence, kindness, intellectuality, loyalty, sense of humor, sociability, wealth, responsibility, open-mindedness, spontaneity, courteousness, willingness to cooperate, and emotional stability. There were no characteristics for which men were more exacting than women in the short-term mating context. These findings confirmed the prediction that men, compared with women, relax their standards in short-term mating contexts.

The hypothesis of relaxed male standards in short-term contexts received independent confirmation.[10] Using a unique methodology, Kenrick and his colleagues asked participants to report on what their minimal levels of acceptability would be for characteristics such as intelligence and kindness in different types of relationships. They found that, although both sexes expressed high minimum standards in a marriage partner for these traits, the standards that men imposed for someone with whom they would just have sexual intercourse dropped dramatically, whereas women's standards remained uniformly high for such relationships.

We obtained similar results when we investigated characteristics that might deter someone from mating. Women were far more discriminating than men in the short-term mating context. Women more than men tended to reject short-term partners who were mentally abusive, physically abusive, bisexual, disliked by others, dumb, uneducated, old, possessive, promiscuous, self-centered, selfish, lacking a sense of humor, submissive, short, and wimpy. In the short-term mating context, men apparently are willing to lower their standards to embarrassing levels.

Theoretically, the average number of short-term partners should be identical for the sexes, assuming an equal sex ratio. The reproductive logic of men having evolved a powerful desire for short-term mating is clear. Ancestral men were limited in reproduction by the number of fertile women they could successfully fertilize, hence securing opportunistic copulations when the costs and risks were sufficiently low, would have added to a man's reproductive success. But what's in it for women? Why would a woman risk engaging in short-term mating?

Recently, Heidi Greiling and I have tested several families of hypotheses about the potential adaptive benefits to women of engaging in short-term mating. Symons was one of the first to propose several potential adaptive benefits.[4] He suggested that women might benefit in the following ways by sexual intercourse with men other than their husbands: by exchanging sex for meat, goods, or services (*resource accrual hypothesis*); by becoming impregnated by a man with better genes than her husband (*better genes hypothesis*); or by using the sexual intercourse to get rid of a husband (*mate expulsion hypothesis*), or to by acquire a better one (*mate switching hypothesis*) (see also the related hypotheses of Helen Fisher).[11] Additionally, Symons noted the possibility of a short-term affair by a woman as a revenge for her husband's affair, presumably functioning as a deterrent to his future affairs (*revenge hypothesis*).

Biologist Robert Smith articulated three additional potential benefits:[12] First, the *sexy son hypothesis,* which suggests that a woman, by mating with an especially attractive man, might bear sons who would themselves be especially attractive to women in the next generation and hence increase her production of grandchildren. Second, the *genetic diversity hypothesis* posits that a woman who mates with multiple men will bear children who are more genetically diverse, which could act as a hedge against environmental change. And, third, there is the *fertility backup hypothesis:* that a woman could benefit from an extra-pair mating if her husband were infertile, had reduced fertility, or where the couple had gametic incompatibility.[12]

Another potential benefit noted independently by Robert Smith[12] and Barbara Smuts[13] is the *protection hypothesis*. Men typically provide protection to their mates and children, including defense against predation by non-humans and defense against exploitation by other humans. Because a primary mate cannot always be around to defend and protect, a woman might gain added protection by consorting with another man. Finally, Smith[12] proposed the *status enhancement hypothesis*, whereby a woman might, in principle, elevate her social status among her peers or gain access to a higher social stratum by a temporary liaison with a high-status man.

Several additional benefits have been proposed for women's short-term mating. Geoffrey Miller (personal communication) suggested that women might increase their skills of attraction and seduction through short-term mating (*honing mating skills hypothesis*). Miller (personal communication) and Thornhill[14] also proposed that women might use short-term mating to elevate their self-esteem, thus enabling them to make better mating decisions (*self-esteem hypothesis*).

Schmitt and I[9] proposed that women might use short-term mating as an assessment device to evaluate potential long-term mating partners (*mate assessment Hypothesis*). Greiling[15] proposed several other potential benefits. Women may use short-term mating to clarify their long-term mate preferences (*preference clarification hypothesis*), on the assumption that experience with short-term mates enables a woman to better identify desirable long-term mates. And a woman might use a short-term mating to increase the commitment of a regular mate or a mate with whom she is trying to secure a long-term relationship (*commitment hypothesis*).

Our tests of these hypotheses were necessarily preliminary and limited in many respects. (1) We asked women to evaluate the likelihood of receiving various benefits through extra-pair copulations, benefits such as dinners, sexual orgasms, boosts in self-esteem, revenge on their regular partner, and honing their skills of attraction and seductions. (2) In a separate study, we asked women to evaluate how beneficial each of these items would be, if they were received. (3) Next, we asked women to judge the contexts in which they would be most likely to seek an extra-pair copulation. (4) Finally, we separately explored the perceptions of benefits of extra-pair mating in women who actively pursued short-term matings and in those who did not.

One limitation of the method of inquiry is that women may be unaware of adaptive benefits. For example, when women evaluate an item like "securing orgasms" from affair partners they are in all likelihood unaware of possible *adaptive* benefits that they might obtain, such as an increased likelihood of successful fertilization.[16] Similarly, other hypotheses could not be tested directly, such as those involving better or more diverse genes. Nonetheless, these studies provide preliminary information on what women perceive as beneficial and the contexts in which they believe that they would pursue extra-pair copulations.

Two hypotheses received strong support across studies, the *mate switching hypothesis* and the *resource acquisition hypothesis*. Engaging in an extra-pair mating was perceived to make it more likely that a woman would find a partner whom she felt was more desirable than her current partner, and more likely that a woman would secure a back-up potential mate. Short-term extra-pair mating resulting in discovery of a sexual partner who was interested in a commitment to her, willing to spend a lot of time with her, and able to replace her steady partner was judged to be highly beneficial for women, if received through a short-term extra-pair mating. Contexts most likely to promote an extra-pair mating include a belief that she can find someone interested in her with whom she is more compatible than her current partner who is willing to spend a lot of time with her, and is better looking than her current partner.

These findings provide support for the hypothesis that mate-switching may be a key function of short-term mating for women.

Acquiring resources also emerges as one possible adaptive function of short-term extra-pair mating. Women judged that they are likely to receive jewelry, money, free dinners, or clothing by engaging in an extra-pair mating. These and the possibility of career advancement were judged by women as highly beneficial. Women who actually engaged in short-term extra-pair mating perceive the resource benefit as highly beneficial. Women judged that the likelihood of their engaging in extra-pair mating increased when the current partner could not hold down a job, when someone who has better financial prospects than her current partner and seems interested in her is accessible, and when someone who is more successful than her current partner is available.

Receiving sexual gratification also appears to be a key benefit that emerges across studies. Indeed, we found that the benefit judged to be most likely to be received by women is sexual gratification. Having a short-term partner who cuddled with her and with whom she experienced orgasms and sexual gratification was judged to be highly beneficial. Having a regular partner who was unwilling to engage in sexual relations with her, with whom sexual relations have been unsatisfying for a long time, or with whom sexual relations have been too infrequent were among the contexts most likely to be perceived as prompting a woman to have an extra-pair sexual relationship. Finally, women who engage in short-term mating perceive sexual gratification as more beneficial than women who tend to avoid short-term mating.

Despite the consistency of the importance of sexual problems prompting an affair and sexual gratification being a benefit of an affair, the current studies do not permit inferences about the precise adaptive function attached to sexual benefits. Over human evolutionary history, one benefit might have been a fertility backup. An ancestral woman paired with a man uninterested in sex may have had a more difficult time getting pregnant. If this is correct, then fertility backup is a possible function of women's short-term extra-pair mating. Alternatively, a partner's lack of sexual interest may signal to the woman that he is channeling his sexual interest and perhaps commitment elsewhere, in which case the woman might benefit by doing likewise. If this inference were correct, it would support one variant of the mate switching function. A third possibility is that the sexual gratification a woman might gain from an extra-pair mating is not a "function" at all, but instead merely a "beneficial effect" in current environments that do not provide the same adaptive impetus for short-term mating as prevailed in ancestral environments. The answer to which of these interpretations is correct must await future research.

Much work remains to be done on the underlying psychology and biology of short-term mating. What is clear at this point, is that there is abundant evidence that some women do engage in short-term mating some of the time, and likely have done so throughout human evolutionary history.

TACTICS OF HUMAN MATE-GUARDING: FROM VIGILANCE TO VIOLENCE

If women and men sometimes pursue extra-pair copulations, this imposes adaptive problems on their regular partners. An ancestral man who was indifferent to the sexual contact his wife had with other men would have risked investing in a rival's children. An ancestral woman who was indifferent to the sexual contact her husband had with other woman might have risked the diversion of his resources to that other woman and that woman's children. The recurrence of the threat of infidelity should have selected for the co-evolution of mate-guarding tactics to prevent incurring the costs of a partner's infidelity (for literature on such evidence in animals, see Ref. 7).

Prior to studies conducted by evolutionary psychologists, dozens of empirical studies have explored the psychology of jealousy. The most common finding is that men and women do not differ in either the frequency or magnitude of the jealousy they experience. In one study, 300 participants who were partners in 150 romantic relationships rated how jealous they were in general, how jealous they were of their partner's relationships with members of the opposite sex, and the degree to which jealousy was a problem in their relationship. Men and women reported equal amounts of jealousy, confirming that both sexes experience jealousy roughly equally and do not differ in the intensity of their jealous feelings.[17]

According to an evolutionary psychological analysis, all these studies, although informative about the equality of the sexes in experiencing jealousy, had posed the question in too global a manner. An evolutionary analysis leads to the prediction that, although both sexes will experience jealousy, they will differ in the weighting given to the cues that trigger jealousy. Men are predicted to give more weight to cues of sexual infidelity, whereas women are predicted to give more weight to cues of a long-term diversion of investment, such as emotional involvement with another person.[18, 19]

In a systematic test of the hypothesized sex differences, 511 college students were asked to compare two distressing events: their partner having sexual intercourse with someone else, or their partner becoming emotionally involved with someone else.[19] Fully 83% of the women found their partner's emotional infidelity more upsetting, whereas only 40% of the men did. In contrast, 60% of the men experienced their partner's sexual infidelity as more distressing, whereas only 17% of the women did. This constitutes a huge 43% difference between the sexes in their responses, which is large by any standard in the social sciences. By posing a more precise question—not whether each sex experiences "jealousy," but rather which precise triggers of jealousy are more distressing—the evolutionary psychological hypothesis was able to guide researchers to discover a sex difference that had previously gone unnoticed.

Verbal reports are reasonable sources of data, but ideally, converging evidence from other data sources is more scientifically compelling. To explore the generality of the above findings across different scientific methods, 60 men and women were brought into a psychophysiological laboratory.[19] To evaluate physiological distress from imagining the two types of infidelity, the experimenters placed electrodes on the corrugator muscle on the brow of the forehead, which contracts when people frown; on the first and third fingers of the right hand to measure sweating, that is, the electrodermal response (also known as GSR or galvanic skin response); and on the thumb to measure heart rate. Participants were then asked to imagine either a sexual infidelity ("imagine your partner having sex with someone else ... get the feelings and images clearly in mind") or an emotional infidelity ("imagine your partner falling in love with someone else ... get the feelings and images clearly in mind"). Subjects pressed a button when they had the feelings and images clearly in mind, which activated the physiological recording devices for 20 seconds.

Men became more physiologically distressed by the sexual infidelity than by the emotional infidelity. Their heart rates accelerated by nearly five beats per minute, which is roughly the equivalent of drinking three cups of strong coffee at one time. Their skin conductance increased 1.5 μS (micro-Siemens) with the thought of sexual infidelity, but showed almost no change from baseline in response to the thought of emotional infidelity. Their corrugator frowning increased, showing 7.75 μV (microvolt; as a measure of contraction) in response to sexual infidelity, as compared with only 1.16 μV in response to emotional infidelity.

Women tended to show the opposite pattern. They exhibited greater physiological distress at the thought of emotional infidelity. Women's frowning, for example, increased to 8.12 μV of contraction in response to emotional infidelity, as compared with only 3.03 μV in response to sexual infidelity. The convergence of psychological reactions of distress with physiological patterns of distress in men and women strongly supports the hypothesis that humans have evolved mechanisms specific to the sex-linked adaptive problems they recurrently faced over evolutionary history.

These sex differences have now been replicated in Germany, the Netherlands, Korea, and Japan. The magnitude of the sex difference varies somewhat from culture to culture, large in Korea and Japan and smaller in the Netherlands, but the sex difference remains robust across cultures. In sum, men's jealousy appears to be more sensitive to cues of sexual infidelity and women's jealousy more sensitive to cues of emotional infidelity—these results were found across both psychological and physiological methods as well as across cultures.

The psychology of jealousy produces behavioral output that is presumably designed to deter a regular partner from leaving or committing infidelity that ranges from vigilance to violence.[20] Men tend to engage in intense mate-retention efforts when they are married to partners who are young and physically attractive, two hypothesized cues to a woman's reproductive value and appeal to rivals. Women tend to engage in intense mate-retention efforts when they are married to men who have high incomes and who devote a lot of effort to status-striving, both constituting high mate value. Violence toward partners is an extreme mate-retention tactic, used by men more than women, and tends to be most used by men who lack the economic means to keep a mate through positive incentives.[21]

CONCLUSIONS

Human mating is close to the engine of evolution—differential reproductive success caused by differences in design. Ancestral humans had to solve an astonishing variety of adaptive problems to successfully reproduce. They had to select specific partners, such as those that were reproductively valuable, to best intra-sexual rivals in competing for desirable mates, and to retain mates by continuing to fend off rivals and deterring their mate's attempts to defect. Those who failed at these tasks are not our ancestors. We are the descendants of those who succeeded in overcoming these many hurdles, or at least overcoming them more adeptly than others.

Human mating defies simple characterization. Some continue to argue that people are fundamentally evolved to be monogamous, and that any deviation from monogamy represents a distortion from the basic human mating strategy. Others argue that humans are naturally promiscuous, and that marriage represents an unnatural cultural imposition. Both of these simplistic notions are wrong, at least according to the evidence now available.

Men and women both have short-term and long-term mating strategies within their menu of mating. Which strategies a particular individual pursues depends on contexts, including the sex ratio in the mating pool and the person's desirability, both determining the range of alternatives available. In addition, there are various cultural practices such as laws about who may mate with whom, and the strategies pursued by others in the population. Some individuals sustain or endure lifelong monogamy. Some bounce from mate to mate. Some pursue a mixed mating strategy, with one or more long-term mates along with or alternating with some short-term mating on the side.

The field has come a long way from the pre-evolutionary era in which singular mating motives were posited (e.g., similarity, equity) without an underlying logic and the sexes were regarded as identical in their mating psychology. The conceptual and empirical gains of evolutionary psychology have been substantial. But there remains much work to be done on the details of the underlying psychological mechanisms, the contexts that trigger the activation of each, the role of heritable individual differences, and the underlying neurobiology of these mechanisms. If the next decade offers as much progress as the preceding one, we can look forward to substantial developments in our understanding of the psychology of human mating.

REFERENCES

1. Darwin, C. 1871. The Descent of Man and Selection in Relation to Sex. Murray. London, England.
2. Trivers, R. 1972. Parental investment and sexual selection. *In* Sexual Selection and the Descent of Man: 1871–1971. B. Campbell, Ed.: 136–179. Aldine. Chicago, IL.
3. Hamilton, W.D. 1964. The evolution of social behavior. J. Theor. Biol. **7:** 1–52.
4. Symons, D. 1979. The Evolution of Human Sexuality. Oxford. New York.
5. Eckland, B. 1968. Theories of mate selection. Soc. Biol. **15:** 71–84.
6. Clutton-Brock, T.H. 1991. The Evolution of Parental Care. Princeton University Press. Princeton, NJ.
7. Alcock, J. 1998. Animal Behavior. An Evolutionary Approach, 6th ed. Sinauer. Sunderland, MA.
8. Tooby, J. & L. Cosmides. 1992. Psychological foundation of culture. *In* The Adapted Mind: Evolutionary Psychology and the Generation of Culture. J. Barkow, L. Cosmides and J. Tooby, Eds.: 19–136. Oxford University Press. Oxford, England.
9. Buss, D.M. & D.P. Schmitt. 1993. Sexual strategies theory: an evolutionary perspective on human mating. Psychol. Rev. **100:** 204–232.
10. Kenrick, D.T., E.K Sadalla, G. Groth & M.R. Trost. 1990. Evolution, traits, and the stages of human courtship: qualifying the parental investment model. J. Pers. **58:** 97–116.
11. Fisher, H. 1992. The Anatomy of Love. Norton: New York.
12. Smith, R.L. 1984. Human sperm competition. *In* Sperm Competition and the Evolution of Mating Systems. R.L. Smith, Ed.: 601–659. Academic Press. New York.
13. Smuts, B.B. 1985. Sex and Friendship in Baboons. Harvard University Press: Cambridge, MA.
14. Thornhill, N.W. 1992. Female short-term sexual strategies: the self-esteem hypothesis. Paper presented at the Human Behavior and Evolution Society.
15. Greiling, H. 1993. Women's short-term sexual strategies. Paper presented at the Conference on Evolution and the Human Sciences, London School of Economics. London, England.

16. BAKER, R. & M. BELLIS. 1995. Human Sperm Competition. Chapman Hall. London.
17. WHITE, G.L. 1981. Some correlates of romantic jealousy. J. Pers. **6:** 222–227.
18. DALY, M., M. WILSON & S.J. WEGHORST. 1982. Male sexual jealousy. Ethol. Sociobiol. **3:** 11–27.
19. BUSS, D.M., R.J. LARSEN, D. WESTEN & J. SEMMELROTH. 1992. Sex differences in jealousy: evolution, physiology, and psychology. Psychol. Science **3:** 251–255.
20. BUSS, D. M. 2000. The Dangerous Passion. Free Press. New York.
21. DALY, M. & M. WILSON. 1988. Homicide. Aldine. Hawthorne, NY.

Human Sexual Selection, Good Genes, and Special Design

STEVEN W. GANGESTAD

Department of Psychology, University of New Mexico, Albuquerque, New Mexico 87131, USA

ABSTRACT: Evolutionary psychology seeks to understand the functional design underlying psychological processes and behavior. Theories of selection pressures developed within evolutionary biology are key components of this understanding. Because past selection pressures responsible for current design cannot be directly observed, theoretical understandings of the psychological processes and behavior must be inferred. The most important epistemological concept within evolutionary psychology is that of special design-evidence that a feature exhibits specificity, efficiency, and economy for producing a particular beneficial effect. A variety of sexual-selection processes have been proposed to account for aspects of human mating. These processes are not mutually exclusive. More than one may account for aspects of human mating. A core task of evolutionary psychology within this domain is to identify which processes account for which phenomena. I have attempted to illustrate how the search for special design is central to this endeavor.

SEXUAL SELECTION

Sexual selection is selection due to differential access to mates. Competitive advantage in mating can be expressed as an individual's access to more or better mates. Competitive advantages stem from two basic processes, intrasexual selection and intersexual selection. Intrasexual selection results from differential ability to compete against same-sex rivals (e.g., in agonistic encounters over territory that gives access to mates). Intersexual selection results from differential ability to appeal to the mate preferences of the other sex. Although the selection pressures corresponding to these forms of sexual selection are distinct, in many species they may reinforce one another (e.g., males with intrasexual competitive advantages are also those who can attract females, sometimes by virtue of the fact that they outcompete other males; see, for example, Andersson[1]). While sexual selection may sometimes operate more powerfully on females, in most mammalian species it operates more strongly on males.[2] In this paper, I emphasize sexual selection on men.

A major issue in evolutionary behavioral biology of the past 25 years is the question of what accounts for the mate preferences that drive sexual selection. Two predominant theories emphasize fitness benefits. The *good-genes* view states that females choose males who possess indicators of underlying genetic fitness that can be passed on to offspring and thereby increase the female's inclusive fitness. The *good-provider* view states that females choose males who possess traits that promise material benefits that either enhance the female's own survival (e.g., food[3]; physical protection[4,5]) or the survival of offspring (e.g., food or other forms of direct parental care). (For a fuller discussion of these and additional theories of intersexual selection, see Refs. 1, 6, and 7.)

In the great majority of mammals, males do not provide parental care. Yet in many of these species, females prefer some males to others. The major fitness benefit of the female preferences that drive sexual selection in these instances may be good genes. In a substantial proportion of primates, males do provide parental care. Throughout their evolution, human males may have invested very heavily in offspring, providing food, direct parental care, protection, and skill-training.[8] Within evolutionary psychology, theory and research on human mate preferences has tended to emphasize female choice for males who possess resources that can be invested in offspring.[9–13] That is, theory and research has focused on good-provider sexual selection on males. Little research has focused on good-genes sexual selection. Good-provider and good-genes sexual selection are not mutually exclusive processes, however; possibly, both have operated in human evolution and account for phenomena of human mating. Because an understanding of the dynamics of human mating requires an appreciation of the various forms of sexual selection that may have operated ancestrally, the questions of whether and how good-genes sexual selection has operated are important ones.[14]

THE EVOLUTION OF SEX AND SEXUAL SELECTION

Until recently, quantitative geneticists have been skeptical of good genes sexual selection. This process requires substantial heritable variation in individual fitness: Some mates must be more fit than others due to their genotypes and these advantages must be able to be passed to offspring. Traditionally, however, it has been thought that, because selection removes heritable factors that account for variation in fitness (e.g., deleterious mutations), fitness should have very little genetic variation in natural populations (see, for instance, Refs. 15 and 16). If individuals do not vary in fitness for heritable reasons, good-genes sexual selection cannot operate.[17]

A surprising result within evolutionary genetics of the decade is that, in fact, genetic variation in fitness and fitness-related traits actually have very substantial amounts of genetic variation—indeed, typically more than ordinary traits and traits under stabilizing (as opposed to directional) selection. One standardized measure of genetic variance is the additive genetic coefficient of variation (CV_a), the square root of the genetic variance divided by the population mean of the trait, times 100 (to yield a percentage rather than a proportion measure). Because the CV_a is directly associated with the "evolvability" of a trait (the trait's response to selection), it is relevant to questions of selection.[18] While ordinary morphological traits tend to have CV_as of about 5, fitness traits such as longevity and fecundity tend to have CV_as of 10–20.[18,19] As a CV of 20 translates into nearly a two-and-a-half-fold difference in the trait level of individuals two standard deviations above and below the mean, this amount of variation is very substantial and can produce good-genes sexual selection.[20]

Perhaps as surprising as these empirical findings is the fact that, from a traditional theoretical perspective, these findings should *not* really be surprising. Fisher[21] long ago recognized that genetic variation in fitness is a function of two forces: selection, which removes variation, and factors that oppose selection. The latter factors include mutation, which at equilibrium introduces new (in general, mildly) deleterious variants at the rate at which selection removes them, and rapid changes in the environment altering which genetic variants are selected for and against. The "new" theoretical insight of the past decade or two is that at equilibrium these two sets of opposing forces maintain an amount of genetic variation in fitness consistent with the empirical estimates. Recent modeling of mutation-selection balance suggests that even in *Drosophila*, species with genomes about an order of magnitude smaller than that of humans, individuals have from 20–50 mildly deleterious mutations on average at equilibrium, with a CV of 8–17.[22,23] Mutation-selection balance thus appears to be able to account for at least half of the genetic variation in fitness. Coevolution of individuals and biotic features of the environment, which alters selection pressures, may account for much of the remaining variation in fitness. Important coevolving biotic features probably include parasites (which coevolve with host defense systems[24]) and plant food sources that produce toxins harmful to the ingesting individual which coevolve with the forager's ability to resist the oxidative stress (damage due to free radicals) caused by those toxins.[25]

Not incidentally, these same factors have been identified as causes of the evolution itself. Sexually reproducing individuals may outcompete asexual ones because the sexual recombination of genes can produce offspring who possess high genetic fitness despite the main factors that work against selection, mutation, and rapidly evolving biotic features of the environment.[26] According to these theories of sex, not only is the evolution of preferences favoring mates possessing good genes consistent with the evolution of sex, but also these views imply that the evolution of sex only makes sense in the context of evolutionary pressures favoring mating of individuals who possess genetic benefits, such as good-genes sexual selection.

BIPARENTAL INVESTMENT AND GOOD GENES

In species in which both parents invest in offspring, it makes sense that mate choice is partly based on assessments of the ability and willingness of potential mates to effectively invest in offspring. Biparental care occurs in many species of birds and, in many of those species, evidence suggests that good-provider sexual selection takes place.[27] At the same time, however, good-genes sexual selection might be expected to also take place. In some species, this seems to be the case.

One of the fascinating findings in behavioral ecology of the past decade is that many socially monogamous birds are not sexually monogamous. Extra-pair paternity (EPP) rates (percentage of offspring in a mating pair's nest not fathered by the male of the pair) in these species average over 10% and not uncommonly exceed 20%.[28] At the same time, in nearly half of these species the EPP rate is less than 5%. A key question is what function extra-pair mating serves for females in species in which it occurs. Although a variety of selection pressures may be involved,[28] one function appears to be selection for good genes. In monogamously mating species, a large proportion of males of reproductive age will find a mate. The female mates of many of these males may be able to find an extra-pair partner in her neighborhood who possesses greater genetic fitness than her in-pair mate (particularly if the birds are not highly dispersed), thus creating a selection pressure for females to extra-pair-mate with males of high genetic fitness. If good-genes sexual selection accounts for the high EPP rate in some species, then a higher amount of genetic variation between males might be expected for species with particularly high EPP rates. Petrie, Doums, and Møller[29] found that, indeed, high rates of EPP are associated with greater genetic diversity across species.

Naturally, if females in species with high EPP rates choose males for their genetic quality, they must identify genetic quality on the basis of some honest signal. In many birds, sexually selected traits include bright plumage, which Hamilton and Zuk[24] hypothesized advertises genetic quality (specifically, as a marker of disease resistance). Møller and Birkhead[30] found a relationship between male plumage brightness and the level of extra-pair paternity.

One might wonder whether, in these species with high extra-pair paternity rates and bright males, the sexually selected traits signal willingness and ability to invest in offspring rather than genetic fitness (and hence were selected through good-provider rather than good-genes sexual selection). In species in which extra-pair paternity rates are low (perhaps because of low genetic variance or a feeding niche's imposing dispersal of individuals across a large area and thereby low intraspecific encounter rates), sexually selected traits do appear to be associated with good providing; males in these species tend to do a greater proportion of the offspring feeding. By contrast, in species with high EPP rates, attractive males actually do *fewer* of the feedings than their less attractive counterparts.[27] Presumably, these males enjoy a greater return on their extra-pair mating effort than do less attractive males and, hence, spend a greater proportion of their time and effort seeking extra-pair mates. The primary benefit females garner from extra-pair mating with these males appears to be a genetic benefit for her offspring.

ADAPTATIONISM AND EVIDENCE OF SPECIAL DESIGN

We cannot observe past evolutionary history directly and, hence, cannot observe directly the selection pressures that accounted for evolutionary change and the design of existing organisms. In many species, we can provisionally make the assumption that the past selective environment was much like the current environment and attempt to understand how the past selective environment accounted for current design by observing current selection pressures. We cannot assume, however, that the selective pressures operating on modern humans resembles past selective pressures and hence cannot use the present as a stand-in for the past.[31] How, then, can we explain current design in terms of evolutionary selection pressures? In the current instance, how can we determine whether good-genes sexual selection operated on ancestral humans and partly accounts for the mating psychology of modern humans?

According to the logic of adaptationism, the primary source of evidence about past selection pressures is the *current design of organisms*. Organisms are a product of past evolutionary change and, therefore, are themselves a record of their evolutionary history. While a number of evolutionary forces can and do account for evolutionary change (including random drift, migration, and mutation), natural selection is the only evolutionary force known to account for eminently workable design. Hence, evidence for eminently workable design is evidence that natural selection has been at work.

In his classic treatment of adaptationism, George Williams[32] laid out criteria of *evidence of special design*. Evidence of special design is evidence that a particular trait or set of traits of an organism exhibits specificity, economy, and efficiency for producing a *particular* beneficial effect (i.e., an effect that would have enhanced gene-propagation and led to selection for the trait, also referred to as the function of the trait). Evidence for special design not only demonstrates that natural selection has been at work to produce a trait, but it is also a telltale sign that *particular* selection pressures have been at work—specifically, the selection pressures entailed by the function of the trait (see also Ref. 33).

The task of constructing an argument for special design has been described as a task of reverse engineering. Engineers are faced by a problem to solve and design a mechanism to solve the problem. The resulting mechanism typically exhibits specificity, economy, and efficiency for solving the problem is was designed to solve. It "looks like" it was designed to solve a specific problem. The biologist attempting to understand the evolutionary history of an organism and its features is faced with a "reverse engineering" task. The organism has already been designed. The task is to decide what problem in the ancestral environment of the species it was designed to solve. If good designs typically exhibit specificity, economy, and efficiency for serving the functions they were designed to serve, then it makes sense to try to identify those functions by looking for evidence of specificity, economy, and efficiency.[34]

Did good-genes sexual selection operate on ancestral humans and partly shape the nature of their mating psychology? Specifically, has selection produced preferences in females that, under certain circumstances, favor males with high genetic fitness, which in turn have exerted sexual selection pressures on males? From an adaptationist perspective, to answer these questions we should look for evidence that female preferences and related features of female mating psychology exhibit evidence for special design for the function of mating with males of high genetic fitness.

TESTS OF GOOD GENES SEXUAL SELECTION

Fluctuating Asymmetry as an Indirect Marker of Genetic Fitness?

To test whether females prefer to mate with males of high genetic fitness, evolutionary biologists must have some way of identifying males of high genetic fitness. To do so, biologists often use indirect, fallible measures. One such measure is fluctuating asymmetry (FA). FA is deviation from symmetry on traits that are symmetrical at the population level. Thus, in many bird species wing or tarsus asymmetry would qualify as FA. Asymmetry on such traits is thought to reflect the deleterious effects of developmental perturbations due to genetic or environmental factors (e.g., mutations, toxins, pathogens) and, therefore, maladaptation (for a review, see Møller and Swaddle[35]).

Variation in asymmetry across individuals has two components. First, some individuals are more prone to experiencing developmental error, and those more prone tend to be more asymmetrical. Second, error itself has a stochastic component; it may accumulate and create much asymmetry or cancel out and result in relatively little asymmetry. Only a small portion of the variance in a single trait's asymmetry is of the first sort, systematic differences in individuals' tendency to experience error.

Of that, only a fraction is due to genetic differences between individuals.[36] So a composite of several traits' asymmetries can better tap individual and genetic variation in developmental adaptedness.[37] Research shows that, across a variety of species, individuals who possess low FA have greater levels of fitness traits (e.g., survival, fecundity) than do those who possess high FA[38,39] (see also Refs. 40 and 41).

Research on a large variety of species has also found that females often prefer mating with males who possess low FA.[42] Although relationships between male mating success and asymmetry are often small (correlations of –0.2 or weaker[43]), these relationships must reflect moderate to large associations between underlying developmental imprecision and mating success.[44] One possible reason for female preferences for symmetry is good-genes sexual selection. Ancestrally, females in many species may have been selected to prefer to mate with symmetrical males because of the genetic benefits those males would pass onto offspring. Alternatively, however, preferences for mating with symmetrical males may have arisen because of material benefits those males provided to females or their offspring.

A primary means by which biologists have attempted to decide whether good-genes or good-provider sexual selection is responsible for female preference is to look for evidence of special design. Do the preferences of females appear to be well-designed for garnering genetic benefits? Or, do they appear well-designed for garnering material benefits? One species that serves as a good illustration is the European barn swallow.[44] Female barn swallows prefer to mate with males who possess symmetrical tail feathers. These males do not appear to provide greater material benefits to offspring, as they actually spend less time feeding offspring than do their less symmetrical counterparts and, furthermore, are not more efficient at feeding (due, in part, to the fact that they possess longer tail feathers). Symmetrical males appear to spend more time seeking extra-pair matings and, indeed, have more of them than less symmetrical males. As extra-pair males do not appear to provide any material benefits to offspring or females themselves, female preference thus appears to be designed to garner genetic benefits from symmetrical males rather than material benefits.

Naturally, while good-genes sexual selection may account for female preference for symmetrical males in barn swallows, it need not account for female preference for symmetrical males in all species in which the preference has been observed. Hence, although cross-species comparisons can be useful for testing models of selection pressures and generating ideas about a particular species, evidence for special design must be demonstrated on a species-by-species basis.[27]

PREFERENCE FOR MALE SYMMETRY IN HUMANS

Just as in a variety of other species, human symmetrical males appear to possess a mating advantage over less-symmetrical males. In studies done at the University of New Mexico, we have examined correlations between men's self-reported number of sex partners and a composite of asymmetry summed across multiple traits (e.g., ear, wrist, elbow width, finger lengths; the relations were age-controlled). While men's number of sex partners is hardly a perfect measure of their potential mating success, it probably covaries with their potential mating success considerably. In these studies involving over 500 men, we have observed a weighted correlation of about −0.21, $p < 0.001$ (for reviews, see Refs. 36 and 45). This correlation is small but, once again, must reflect a moderate correlation between underlying developmental imprecision and men's number of sex partners (estimated to be about −0.4[36]).

Two key questions that arise about this association are: (1) What are the proximate factors that lead to this association (e.g., intrasexual competitive advantage of symmetrical men, female preference for symmetrical men)?; and (2) If female preference is at all involved, what are the selection pressures that led to this preference?

It does appear that symmetrical men possess certain forms of intrasexual competitive advantages over less symmetrical men. Symmetrical men are perceived to be more robust and muscular and are less likely to back down to other men.[46] In one study that examined what men said about themselves and a male competitor in a situation in which they competed to be chosen as a lunch date by an attractive woman, highly symmetrical men were more likely to draw direct comparisons between themselves and the competitor.[47] Perhaps as a result of their willingness to engage in direct intrasexual competition and unwillingness to back down to other men, symmetrical college men get into more physical fights and, in particular, initiate more fights than do less-symmetrical men[48] (see also Ref. 49).

While these studies indicate that male intrasexual competition may partly explain the association between men's symmetry and their mating success, they do not rule out a role for female preference. In fact, the impact of male intrasexual competition on symmetrical men's mating success may be partly or fully mediated by female preference for traits advantageous in male intrasexual competition.[46]

FEMALE PREFERENCE AND SPECIAL DESIGN

Women's Preference for the Scent of Symmetry

Here, I focus on one particular female preference in men: the scent of symmetrical men.[50,51] I focus on this preference for two reasons. First, women claim that men's scent affects their attraction to them as much as or more than does their physical appearance. Indeed, scent appears to be a form of "physical" attractiveness that women value more than do men (as opposed to visual physical appearance, which men care about more than women[9,52]). Second, and more importantly, women's preference for a man's scent has special design features that may be key to addressing the question of what selection pressures led to female preference for symmetrical men.

Baker and Bellis[53] found that women's patterns of in-pair and extra-pair copulations differ. Whereas their in-pair copulations tend to occur with approximately equal frequency across the menstrual cycle (or increase in frequency slightly during the non-fertile, luteal phase), their extra-pair copulations occur most frequently during the mid-to-late follicular phase, the time of the cycle when fertility is highest.[54] Baker and Bellis conjectured that this pattern of copulations may be caused by a shift in women's preferences across the menstrual cycle, with increased attention to cues of genetic benefits occurring during the most fertile phase. Because symmetrical men not only have more sex partners in general, but also tend to be chosen as extra-pair partners by women, one possibility is that women tend to prefer cues associated with developmental precision during the fertile phase. If women historically sought extra-pair sex in selective circumstances partly to obtain genetic benefits not provided by an investing partner at some risk of the investing partner's finding out, it would make sense that they would seek those copulations when they could actually receive the indirect genetic benefits passed onto offspring: when they were fertile. Hence, evidence that women prefer to mate with men who possess cues of genetic benefits selectively when they are fertile may qualify as evidence for special female design for obtaining genetic benefits.

Thornhill and I chose to examine this possibility in the context of women's olfactory preferences. As just noted, women claim men's scent importantly affects their attraction to them. Moreover, evidence suggests that women's olfaction changes across the menstrual cycle. For instance, women tend to rate androstenone, a steroid found in men's sweat, more positively near ovulation than during non-fertile phases.[55]

In an initial study,[50] we asked 41 men to wear a T-shirt for two consecutive nights. During the two-day period, they were to wash only with unscented soap, not to wear any fragrances or colognes, not eat certain strong foods, and not sleep with another person. They dropped their shirts off at our lab on a designated morning. Later that same morning and throughout the next day, women came in, smelled each shirt, and rated its attractiveness (a composite of two ratings: pleasantness and sexiness). For each woman, we regressed her ratings on men's symmetry to yield a "preference for symmetry" score (the regression slope, a measure of the change in rating as a function of a change in symmetry). We then examined the correlation of these preference scores with women's estimated fertility based on their self-reported day of the cycle and actuarial data on probability of conception for each day. Across 28 normally ovulating women, the correlation was 0.54, $p < 0.001$. Examination of the bivariate plot revealed that when women's fertility was near-zero (very early and late in the cycle), they had no systematic preference for the scent of either symmetrical or asymmetrical men. As their fertility increased, however, they increasingly preferred the scent of symmetrical men.[36]

A subsequent study replicated and extended that result in a larger sample of about 50 normally ovulating women and 80 men.[51] Women's preference for symmetry correlated 0.42 with their fertility based on the day of their cycle, $p < 0.001$. We asked men how many times they showered and whether they wore any fragrances. The number of times men showered predicted the attractiveness of their scent. When this variable was partialled out and all men who wore fragrances were eliminated from the analysis, the correlation between women's preference for symmetry and their fertility actually increased, $r = 0.48$, $p < 0.001$.

In a third study in our lab, this result was once again replicated, $r = 0.26$, $p < 0.05$. When data from all three studies were pooled, the correlation between women's preference for symmetry and the fertile phase of their cycle was 0.40, $p < 0.0001$. A fourth study, by Rikowski and Grammer,[56] replicated the finding in an Austrian sample.

FIGURE 1 illustrates the changes in preference for symmetry across the menstrual cycle observed within the two published studies from our lab.[50,51] Preference for symmetry peaks at or just before ovulation. During the 5–7 day period prior to ovulation, a period of high fertility risk, women also prefer the scent of symmetrical men.

This feature of women's preferences can be explained as a special design feature evolved to enable ancestral women to obtain genetic benefits from extra-pair mates

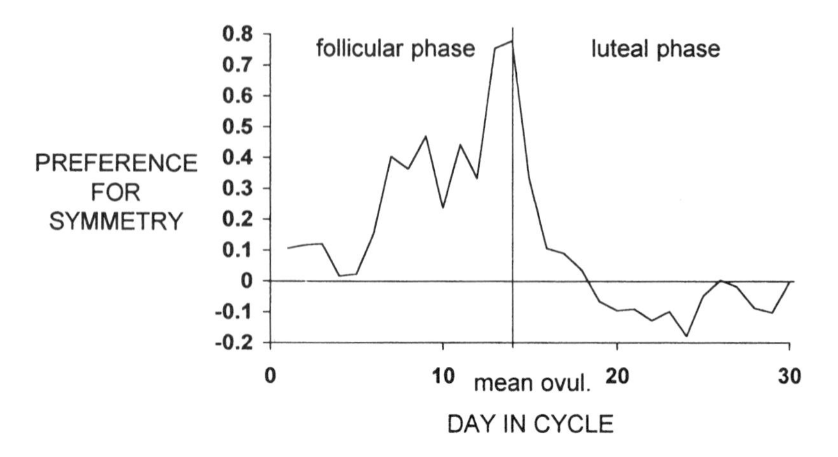

FIGURE 1. Changes in preference for symmetry in the aggregated data from Gangestad and Thornhill[50] and Thornhill and Gangestad.[51] Preference is measured as the regression slope of an individual's scent attractiveness ratings on men's asymmetry times –1. Points represent 3-day moving averages. For the Thornhill and Gangestad data, men's number of showers during the 2-day period of wearing the shirt was partialled out. $N = 77$ women.

while avoiding costs of seeking such benefits during periods of infertility. It is difficult to understand the nature of these preferences otherwise. This special design feature thus suggests that women's preferences for mating with symmetrical men evolved to select for good genes. Additional work should attempt to identify the honest signal of high developmental precision that women detect in men's scent.

OTHER SHIFTS IN WOMEN'S PREFERENCES ACROSS THE MENSTRUAL CYCLE

Our findings have led others to examine changes in female preferences for other features across the menstrual cycle. Penton-Voak *et al.*[57] explored the relationship between female preferences for masculine facial characteristics and menstrual cycle phase. They first averaged digitized faces to create an average male face and an average female face. By combining and contrasting these averaged faces, they could create other faces varying in amount of sexual dimorphism (i.e., degree of feminization vs. masculinization). A sample of women in Japan was asked to pick which male face they found most attractive. Women in the most fertile phase of the cycle (days 6–14) preferred more masculinized faces compared to preferences of women outside the fertile phase. This result was replicated on a sample of women from the UK. In that replication, Penton-Voak *et al.* added another feature: They asked women to rate the faces for attractiveness as a long-term partner and as a short-term partner. Interestingly, during the fertile phase of the cycle women preferred more masculinized faces only within the short-term mating context.

These findings are consistent with the notion that women's preference for more masculinized faces during the fertile phase of the cycle has been designed by selection to garner genetic benefits through opportunistic extra-pair mating. This interpretation requires that at least some masculine facial features are associated with other markers of genetic fitness in men. Scheib *et al.*[58] found evidence that this is, in fact, the case. Additional work should further address these purported relationships.

REFERENCES

1. ANDERSSON, M.B. 1994. Sexual Selection. Princeton University Press. Princeton, NJ.
2. TRIVERS, R. 1972. Parental investment and sexual selection. *In* Sexual Selection and the Descent of Man. 1871–1971. B. Campbell, Ed. Aldine. Chicago, IL.
3. BORGIA, G. 1979. Sexual selection and the evolution of mating systems. *In* Sexual Selection and Reproductive Competition in Insects. M. S. Blum and N. A. Blum, Eds. Academic Press. New York.
4. MESNICK, S.L. 1997. Sexual alliances: evidence and evolutionary implications. *In* Feminism and Evolutionary Biology. P. A. Gowaty, Ed. Chapman & Hall. London.
5. WILSON, M. & S.L. MESNICK. 1997. An empirical test of the bodyguard hypothesis. *In* Feminism and Evolutionary Biology: Boundaries, Intersections, and Frontiers. P. A. Gowaty, Ed. Chapman & Hall. London.
6. KIRKPATRICK, M. & M.J. RYAN. 1991. The evolution of mating preferences and the paradox of the lek. Nature **350:** 33–38.
7. HOLLAND, B. & W.R. RICE. 1998. Chase-away sexual selection: antagonistic seduction versus resistance. Evolution **52:** 1–7.
8. KAPLAN, H. 1996. A theory of fertility and parental investment in traditional and modern human societies. Am. J. Phys. Anthropol. **23:** 91–135.
9. BUSS, D.M. 1989. Sex differences in human mate preferences: evolutionary hypotheses tested in 37 cultures. Behav. Brain Sci. **12:** 1–4.
10. BUSS, D.M. 1994. The Evolution of Desire: Strategies of Human Mating. Basic Books. New York.
11. BUSS, D.M. 1998. Sexual strategies theory: historical origins and current status. J. Sex Res. **35:** 19–31.
12. BUSS, D.M. & D.P. SCHMITT. 1993. Sexual strategies theory: a contextual evolutionary analysis of human mating. Psychol. Rev. **100:** 204–232.
13. KENRICK, D.T., G.E. GROTH, M.R. TROST & E.K. SADALLA. 1993. Integrating evolutionary and social exchange perspectives on relationships: effects of gender, self-appraisal, and involvement level on mate selection. J. Pers. Soc. Psychol. **25:** 159–167.
14. GANGESTAD, S.W. & J.A. SIMPSON. 2000. The evolution of human mating: the role of trade-offs and strategic pluralism. Behav. Brain Sci.: in press.
15. TAYLOR, P.D. & G.C. WILLIAMS. 1982. The lek paradox is not resolved. Theor. Popul. Biol. **22:** 392–409.
16. MAYNARD SMITH, J. 1978. The Evolution of Sex. Cambridge University Press. Cambridge, England.
17. KIRKPATRICK, M. 1986. The handicap mechanism of sexual selection does not work. Am. Naturalist. **127:** 222–240.
18. HOULE, D. 1992. Comparing evolvability and variability of traits. Genetics **130:** 195–204.
19. BURT, A. 1995. Perspective: the evolution of fitness. Evolution **49:** 1–8.
20. KIRKPATRICK, M. 1996. Good genes and direct selection in the evolution of mating preferences. Evolution **50:** 2125–2140.
21. FISHER, R.A. 1930. The Genetical Theory of Natural Selection. Clarendon. Oxford, England.
22. CHARLESWORTH, B. 1990. Mutation-selection balance and the evolutionary advantage of sex and recombination. Genet. Res. **55:** 199–221.

23. CHARLESWORTH, B. & K.A. HUGHES. 1998. The maintenance of genetic variation in life history traits. *In* Evolutionary Genetics from Molecules to Morphology. R. S. Singh & C.B. Krimbas, Eds. Cambridge University Press. Cambridge, England.
24. HAMILTON, W.D. & M. ZUK. 1982. Heritable true fitness and bright birds: a role for parasites. Science **218:** 384–387.
25. VON SCHANTZ, T., S. BENSCH, M. GRAHN, D. HASSELQUIST & H. WITTZELL. 1999. Good genes, oxidative stress and condition-dependent sexual signals. Proc. Roy. Soc. Lond. B **266:** 1–12.
26. KONDRASHOV, A.S. 1998. Deleterious mutations and the evolution of sexual recombination. Nature **336:** 435–440.
27. MØLLER, A.P. & R. THORNHILL. 1998. Male parental care, differential parental investment by females and sexual selection. Anim. Behav. **55:** 1507–1515.
28. PETRIE, M. & B. KEMPENAERS. 1998. Extra-pair paternity in birds: explaining variation between species and populations. Trends Ecol. Evol. **13:** 53–58.
29. PETRIE, M., C. DOUMS & A.P. MØLLER. 1998. The degree of extra-pair paternity increases with genetic variability. Proc. Natl. Acad. Sci. USA. **95:** 9390–9395.
30. MØLLER, A.P & T.R. BIRKHEAD. 1994. The evolution of plumage brightness in birds is related to extra-pair paternity. Evolution **48:** 1089–1100.
31. TOOBY, J. & L. COSMIDES. 1992. The psychological foundations of culture. *In* The Adapted Mind: Evolutionary Psychology and the Generation of Culture. J. Barkow, L. Cosmides and J. Tooby, Eds. Oxford University Press. New York.
32. WILLIAMS, G.C. 1966. Adaptation and Natural Selection. Princeton University Press. Princeton, NJ.
33. THORNHILL, R. 1991. The study of adaptation. *In* Interpretation and Explanation in the Study of Behavior. M. Bekoff & D. Jamieson, Eds. Westview. Boulder, CO.
34. DENNETT, D.C. 1995. Darwin's Dangerous Idea: Evolution and the Meanings of Life. Simon & Schuster. New York.
35. MØLLER, A.P. & J.P. SWADDLE. 1997. Developmental Stability and Evolution. Oxford University Press. Oxford, England.
36. GANGESTAD, S.W. & R. THORNHILL. 1999. Individual differences in developmental precision and fluctuating asymmetry: amodel and its implications. J. Evol. Biol. **12:** 402–416
37. LEUNG, B. & M.R. FORBES. 1997. Modeling fluctuating asymmetry in relation to stress and fitness. Oikos **78:** 397–405.
38. LEUNG, B. & M.R. FORBES. 1996. Fluctuating asymmetry in relation to stress and fitness: Effects of trait type as revealed by meta-analysis. Ecosci. **3:** 400–413.
39. MØLLER, A.P. 1997. Developmental stability and fitness: a review. Am. Naturalist **149:** 916–932.
40. CLARKE, G.M. 1998. Developmental stability and fitness: the evidence is not quite so clear. Am. Naturalist **152:** 762–766.
41. MØLLER, A.P. 1999. Asymmetry as a predictor of growth, fecundity and survival. Ecol. Lett. **2:** 149–156.
42. MØLLER, A.P. & R. THORNHILL. 1997. Bilateral symmetry and sexual selection: a meta-analysis. Am. Naturalist **151:** 174–192.
43. THORNHILL, R., A.P. MØLLER & S.W. GANGESTAD. 1999. The biological significance of fluctuating asymmetry and sexual selection: a reply to Palmer. Am. Naturalist **154:** 234–241.
44. MØLLER, A.P. 1994. Sexual Selection in the Barn Swallow. Cambridge University Press. Cambridge, England.
45. GANGESTAD, S.W. 2000. Sexual selection, good genes, and human mating. *In* Anthology of Evolution and Human Behavior. H. Holcomb, Ed. In press.
46. GANGESTAD, S.W. & R. THORNHILL. 1997. Human sexual selection and developmental stability. *In* Evolutionary Personality and Social Psychology. J.A. Simpson & D.T. Kenrick, Eds. Erlbaum Associates. Hillsdale, NJ.
47. SIMPSON, J.A., S.W. GANGESTAD, P.N. CHRISTENSEN & K. LECK. 1999. Fluctuating asymmetry, sociosexuality, and intrasexual competitive tactics. J. Pers. Soc. Psychol. **76:** 159–172.

48. FURLOW, B., S.W. GANGESTAD & T. ARMIJO-PREWITT. 1998. Developmental stability and human violence. Proc. Roy. Soc. Lond. B **266:** 1–6.
49. MANNING, J.T. & D. WOOD. 1998. Fluctuating asymmetry and aggression in boys. Hum. Nature **9:** 53–65.
50. GANGESTAD, S.W. & R. THORNHILL. 1998. Menstrual cycle variation in women's preference for the scent of symmetrical men. Proc. Roy. Soc. Lond. B **265:** 927–933.
51. THORNHILL, R. & S.W. GANGESTAD. 1999. The scent of symmetry: a human sex pheromone that signals fitness? Evol. Hum. Behav. **20:** 175–201.
52. HERZ, R.S. & E.D. CAHILL. 1997. Differential use of sensory information in sexual behavior as a function of gender. Hum. Nature **8:** 275–286.
53. BAKER, R.R. & M.A. BELLIS. 1995. Human Sperm Competition: Copulation, Masturbation, and Infidelity. Chapman & Hall. London.
54. JÖCHLE, W. 1973. Coitus induced ovulation. Contraception **7:** 523–564.
55. GRAMMER, K. 1993. 5–α-androst-16en-3α-on: a male pheromone? A brief report. Ethol. Sociobiol. **14:** 201–214.
56. RIKOWSKI, A. & K. GRAMMER. 1999. Human body odour, symmetry, and attractiveness. Proc. Roy. Soc. Lond. B. **266:** 869–874.
57. PENTON-VOAK, I.S., D.I PERRETT, D.L. CASTLES, T. KOBAYASHI, D.M. BURT, L.K. MURRAY & R. MINAMISAWA. 1999. Menstrual cycle changes face preference. Nature **399:** 741–742.
58. SCHEIB, J.E., S.W. GANGESTAD & R. THORNHILL. 1999. Facial attractiveness, symmetry, and cues of good genes. Proc. Roy. Soc. Lond. B **266:** 1913–1917.

Mental Traits as Fitness Indicators

Expanding Evolutionary Psychology's Adaptationism

GEOFFREY MILLER

Centre for Economic Learning and Social Evolution (ELSE), University College London, Gower Street, London WC1E 6BT, England, UK

ABSTRACT: According to most evolutionary psychologists, human psychological adaptations can be recognized by criteria such as high efficiency, high complexity, high modularity, low phenotypic variance, low genotypic variance, low heritability, universality across cultures, and universality across individuals. These criteria are appropriate for adaptations that have been shaped through stabilizing selection for survival utility. However, they are often inappropriate for adaptations that have been shaped by sexual selection through mate choice as reliable signals of heritable fitness. If some psychological adaptations evolved as sexually selected fitness indicators of this type, we should expect them to violate many standard criteria used by evolutionary psychology to distinguish adaptations from non-adaptations. This paper addresses the problems raised by new developments in sexual selection theory and animal signaling theory for evolutionary psychology's adaptationism. It suggests that our adaptationist criteria must recognize two typical kinds of psychological adaptations: naturally selected survival mechanisms and sexually selected fitness indicators.

INTRODUCTION: THE STANDARD ADAPTATIONIST CRITERIA

Adaptation has been the key concept in evolutionary theory ever since Darwin.[1] Evolutionary psychology has rightly stressed that "psychological adaptation" should be the key concept in any science of human nature.[2–5] Yet evolutionary psychology also recognizes that not all human behavior is the direct outcome of an evolved psychological adaptation. Many behaviors are individually acquired. Others are pathologic results of genetic mutation or neurological damage. The central methodological challenge in evolutionary psychology has been the identification of criteria that distinguish psychological adaptations from non-adaptations.

The stakes are high in this game of criterion-setting. If a human mental trait is accepted as a legitimate psychological adaptation, it can be admitted into the pantheon of human nature. Its biological legitimacy renders it worthy of intense study. It becomes a defining feature of the human condition. On the other hand, if a class of human behavior is not accepted as the product of a legitimate adaptation, it may be marginalized to the netherworld of the merely individual or the merely cultural. Assuming psychology is striving to be a nomothetic science that seeks lawful knowledge about human nature, and that seeks consilience with the rest of biology, the limits of adaptationism set, to a first approximation, the limits of psychology itself. Behaviors that do not emerge from psychological adaptations tend to be culturally local, historically transitory, or pathological—the stuff of cultural criticism, market research, or psychiatry.

This raises problems for certain human behaviors and psychological phenomena that are culturally, socially, sexually, economically, and emotionally important, but that do not fit the current standard criteria for psychological adaptations. These marginalized behavioral phenomena include things like art, music, humor, sports, religion, intelligence, creativity, and kindness. Basically, the problem is that some people are very much better at these things than others. Yet if they were legitimate psychological adaptations, standard evolutionary psychology predicts a uniformity of functional design that would forbid such extravagant variation.[6–9]

Many of our most cherished human abilities do not seem to qualify as adaptations according to the adaptationist criteria that have become standard in evolutionary psychology.[3–5,10–14] These criteria usually include the following: (1) high efficiency, (2) high complexity, (3) high modularity, (4) low phenotypic variance, (5) low genotypic variance, (6) low heritability, (7) universality across cultures, (8) universality across pre-history and history, (9) universal, spontaneous development in all normal environments according to standardized developmental stages, (10) a functional design that would, on average, have promoted survival or reproductive success under ancestral conditions. As with psychiatric disorders, an adaptation need not fit all ten major diagnostic criteria, but it is expected to fit most of them. These adaptationist criteria have evolutionary rationales largely derived from natural selection theory rather than sexual-selection theory or signaling theory. To assess these criteria, I will first review the basic concept of a sexually selected fitness indicator, and then see whether the traditional criteria are applicable to such indicators.

INDICATORS AS ADAPTATIONS

Over the past few years, biologists studying sexual selection and animal signaling systems have recognized a new class of adaptations called indicators.[13–19] These often look rather different from standard naturally selected mechanisms that solve standard survival problems. The evolved function of indicators is basically to advertise an individual's fitness to other individuals. Usually, the incentives for doing this are to deter pursuit by a predator, to intimidate a sexual rival, or to attract a sexual mate.

In all three cases, strategic issues arise concerning the reliability of fitness indicators. Every individual would simulate high fitness if it could. Such simulation would deter predators from pursuit by making the individual appear difficult to catch. Similarly, apparent high fitness would discourage sexual rivals and attract sexual partners. This is because mate preferences generally evolve to favor fitness indicators that could result in one's offspring inheriting better than average genes, which would be manifest in higher than average fitness. However, if all animals could produce an appearance of high fitness by using a particular indicator, there would no longer be any reason for other animals to pay any attention to that indicator.[7,19] The indicator would no longer convey reliable fitness information, and so would offer no good basis for mate choice. Thus, over the long run, indicators must be reliable in order to be effective as signals.

There are basically just two ways to make fitness indicators reliable. They can evolve as either *strategic* handicaps or *revealing* handicaps.[18] A *strategic* handicap is an indicator that has higher relative costs for a low-fitness individual than it does for a high-fitness individual. For example, luxury goods in modern consumerist societies function as strategic handicaps that reliably indicate the wealth of their owners.[20] A poor individual cannot afford a Ferrari, whereas a rich individual can, so legitimate ownership of a Ferrari reliably indicates wealth. The strategic handicap idea depends on the notion that fitness is relatively fungible like money such that it can be reallocated from one trait to another. This reallocation could happen during the life of the individual (by directing nutrients and energy from one trait to another), or over evolutionary time, through heritable modifications in a body's growth and maintenance priorities.

Revealing handicaps are rather different. They cannot be faked because of some fundamental biological correlation between a component of fitness and an element of the signal. For example, the ability to win a gold medal in the Olympic decathlon is a reliable indicator of physical fitness. At the moment, there is no way that a human with high mental ability, but moderate physical ability (such as Bill Gates) could transfer some excess mental energy or excess money into physical energy to win such a contest. Nor could such a person simply buy a gold medal and pretend to have won, because too many spectators watch the Olympics. Revealing handicaps are reliable because fitness is not completely fungible within a lifetime, and because some biological constraints are resistant to change over evolutionary time. Biologists debate whether specific displays like orange-red carotenoid colors are strategic handicaps, revealing handicaps, or neither,[21] but few challenge the importance of reliability in sexual signaling.

Perceptual issues also arise concerning the discriminability of fitness indicators. A signal is useless if receivers of the signal cannot discriminate between the signal and its absence.[17] Generally, the most useful signals for deterring predators, intimidating rivals, and attracting mates will be those that can be perceived at a distance through visual, auditory, or olfactory channels. The most useful signals for advertising fitness, which is a continuous variable, may often have continuously variable elements that can be easily discriminated, such as color intensity, sound loudness, or pheromone concentration. Thus, indicators must vary within a population in order to convey fitness information. The variation must not be subtle but obvious. It must be perceivable at a distance. It must be variation by design, not by accident. Indicators are adaptations that evolved precisely in order to display maximum perceivable variation within a population.

ADAPTATIONISM FROM A SEXUAL SIGNALING VIEWPOINT

Given the elements of sexual selection theory and animal signaling theory, we are now in a position to critically assess the standard adaptationist criteria proposed by evolutionary psychology for identifying psychological adaptations. My strategy will be to ask which of these criteria would succeed in identifying a sexually selected fitness indicator as a legitimate biological adaptation. If a criterion is systematically biased to exclude such indicators, then we have a methodological problem on our hands.

THE ENGINEERING CRITERIA

The engineering criteria (efficiency, complexity, and modularity) derive from Darwin's desire to explain the appearance of complex organic design through a natural selection process that requires no designer. Yet the assessment of these engineering criteria depends on two difficult steps: (1) postulating some adaptive problem that the adaptation has evolved to solve, and (2) assessing the likelihood that the adaptive problem could have been solved "by chance," without specific selection pressures having shaped the adaptation. If the adaptive problem is misidentified, the wrong assessment may be given about whether a trait is an adaptation. For morphological traits, it may be reasonably easy to discern whether a trait is too complex, too efficient, or too well designed to be due to "chance." But for psychological capacities, it is often difficult to determine whether the capacity is too well designed to be a "chance" side-effect of other adaptations, such as adaptations for skill learning.

The criteria of efficiency, complexity, and modularity probably still apply to sexually selected fitness indicators, but nobody knows yet quite how. The proper use of these criteria depends on seeing sexually selected indicators as adaptations for courtship and mating, and not as side-effects of survival adaptations. In the past, Herbert Spencer's memorable but misleading phrase "survival of the fittest" led many researchers to seek survival functions for psychological adaptations. When no plausible survival function can be found, the trait may often be dismissed as a non-adaptation. For over a century, this led to almost every sexually selected trait's being dismissed as non-adaptive.[22]

EFFICIENCY

Only recently have biologists started to understand animal signaling well enough to imagine ways of assessing the efficiency of fitness indicators.[17,18] A major point of confusion is the requirement that strategic handicaps must be costly in order to be reliable. From the signaling point of view, the high fitness costs of strategic handicaps are what make them efficient as fitness indicators. But from a traditional adaptationist viewpoint, these high fitness costs look inefficient. The potential for confusion is clear if we take an example of conspicuous consumption like Ferrari-ownership. If one asks whether a Ferrari is an efficient mode of transportation, the answer is surely not: it is very poor value for money, imposes high insurance and maintenance charges, and gets poor gas mileage. But if we ask whether a Ferrari is an efficient indicator of wealth, the answer is certainly yes. It is very easy to buy one if you can afford it (Ferrari dealerships are reasonably common and very friendly to the rich), but impossible if you cannot. Even if a poor man steals a Ferrari, he could not afford the maintenance, insurance, and gas costs for very long. The Ferrari is also efficient from the signal-assessor's point of view: it is visible from a distance, easily discriminable from other cars, and commonly understood to be expensive. The assessment of an adaptation's efficiency depends critically on knowing what the adaptation's function is. This is doubly true for fitness indicators, which look ridiculously wasteful and inefficient in every domain other than fitness-signaling.

COMPLEXITY

The complexity criterion also applies to fitness indicators in a rather different way than it applies to ordinary adaptations. Basically, ordinary adaptations evolve complexity because it is a complicated matter to achieve a significant fitness-enhancing effect in a complex world. For example, predators evolve complex bodily and behavioral adaptations for catching prey because prey avoid being caught and their reluctance must be overcome by orchestrating a complex series of worldly events including tracking, identification, pursuit, capture, dismemberment, swallowing, and digesting. To a large extent, ordinary adaptations have to be complex because the world offers little help in solving an animal's adaptive problems.

The complexity that selection demands of fitness indicators has a rather different texture. Indicators promote an animal's fitness by influencing mate-choice mechanisms in the opposite sex. Their effects are psychological, not physical. This means that sometimes the complexity of a signal system can be spread between the behavioral adaptations of the signaler and the perceptual psychology of the receiver.[14] For example, receivers often have an interest in perceiving signals such as fitness indicators. Females evolved to perceive and judge male courtship displays, because the fitness of their offspring depended on their finding a high-quality mate. Sometimes, very simple (but costly) signals can succeed because receivers have evolved to internalize a lot of tacit knowledge about the signaling system, particularly the fitness information conveyed by signals. A diamond engagement ring is not a particularly complex artifact, but as a sexual signal, it conveys a rich set of information about its sender and his intentions to its receiver, because the receiver already knows a lot about the cost of diamonds and the conventions of marriage. By pushing the complexity of the signal system into the heads of sympathetic receivers, the signal itself could be quite simple. If we then assessed this engagement-ring signal narrowly, according to traditional complexity criteria, we might be rather unimpressed. However, if we view the signal in context as part of a system that resides in the heads of receivers and signalers, we may be more generous in accepting it as a well-designed adaptation.

For fitness indicators that aim to create an impression of how an animal ranks along a single quantitative variable, there is not really much information to convey, so the signal itself need not be very complex. Nor need the signal-production equipment be very complex. It only needs to create a discriminable signal perceivable at a reasonable distance that reliably indicates a single quantity. If reliability were not an issue, such signals could be extremely simple and extremely cheap. Most of a fitness indicator's complexity arises from the reliability requirement. The peacock's tail is complex not because it has to transmit a lot of information, but because it has to work very hard to show that its information is credible. Sometimes, the reliability of fitness indicators is guaranteed by their raw physical size: unfit individuals cannot spare the matter and energy to grow such indicators. But often, indicators evolve to indicate fitness by advertising a component of fitness called developmental stability.[23,24] This refers to an animal's ability to grow an organ according to a precise design despite perturbations by genetic mutations, environmental damage, and developmental accidents. One convenient way to advertise developmental stability is by growing bilaterally symmetric displays. Perfect symmetry indicates high developmental stability. Random deviations from perfect symmetry, called "fluctuating asymmetry," are markers of lower fitness.[26] Although very subtle asymmetries all over the body can be measured by scientists with calipers, more pronounced asymmetries on sexual ornaments appear to be perceivable by animals choosing mates.[24] Developmental stability can also be advertised by other morphological traits: regularly spaced stripes, radially symmetric dots, uniform planes of color, regular patterns of hair growth, even teeth, smooth complexion. Less well understood are the means whereby certain behaviors can advertise the developmental stability of underlying brain structures.

Thus, the pressures to advertise developmental stability may become the principal source of complexity in the fitness indicator. Often, this results in a characteristic pattern of complexity, in which discrete elements are repeated in such a way that another animal may easily notice deviations from regularity. The elements themselves must include enough structural complexity that one can be compared with another. At the behavioral level, this may lead to indicators that incorporate rhythmic elements and repeated motifs, as in the songs and dances of birds and humans. From the viewpoint of signaling theory, repetitions across space (bilateral symmetry, radial symmetry, stripes) and across time (rhythm, repetition) are efficient ways to indicate developmental stability, a major component of fitness. But from the viewpoint of traditional criteria for measuring organic complexity, perfect repetition is comparatively uninteresting, because it can be generated by simple developmental mechanisms. Here again we have a difference between adaptationist criteria applicable to fitness indicators versus those applicable to other traits.

MODULARITY

One of evolutionary psychology's most distinctive ideas is the expectation that human minds are massively modular, composed of hundreds of distinct psychological adaptations that evolved to solve distinct ancestral problems of survival and reproduction. The rationale for massive modularity has been the supposed trade-off between generality and efficiency: "As a rule, when two adaptive problems have solutions that are incompatible or simply different, a single general solution will be inferior to two specialized solutions. In such cases, a jack of all trades is necessarily master of none, because generality can be achieved only by sacrificing effectiveness."[2] Just as there is a different software product available for every distinct computational problem, we expect evolution to have produced a different psychological adaptation for every sufficiently distinct adaptive problem. Modularity is obvious for morphology: animals have distinct limbs, senses, and organs to do different things. Mental modularity has been less obvious to psychologists, but evolutionary considerations of functional efficiency suggest the mind should be at least as modular as the body.

These modularity arguments remain compelling for most types of adaptation. However, fitness indicators raise some problems for modularity. The whole point of fitness indicators is that they should tap into individual differences in general fitness. This typically requires that an indicator have some profound overlap with a wide range of adaptations at some fairly fundamental level. A totally modular indicator that had no functional overlap with other adaptations could not function as a reliable indicator at all. This is because an animal's "fitness" is a statistical abstraction across the efficiency levels of all of the animal's distinct adaptations. Such an abstraction is possible when there are genetic and phenotypic covariances between adaptations.[26] General fitness, considered from a factor-analytic viewpoint, does not exist apart from these covariances between adaptations. To advertise general fitness, then, requires somehow tapping into the efficiency levels of a wide range of functionally distinct adaptations. If an indicator could not work around the selection pressures in favor of functional specialization and modularity, it could not work as an indicator. Total modularity would make indicators totally unreliable. (This does not mean that indicators are "general-purpose devices," whatever that might mean. On the contrary, they may be highly specialized to perform the function of sending signals regarding one's fitness to particular types of receivers under particular conditions).

Typically, indicators work by tapping into lower-level developmental or physiological mechanisms that are expressed in a range of adaptations. We already saw how symmetric sexual ornaments could tap into a fitness component called developmental stability that is manifest in almost all morphological and neurological structures. If some psychological adaptations evolved principally as fitness indicators, we might expect them to tap into fitness components of a more psychological or neurophysiological nature. In particular, we would expect such indicators to capture individual differences in the efficiency of a wide range of psychological adaptations. The adaptations, including the indicators, would be modular at the functional level, but they would overlap considerably at lower levels of implementation, such as elementary cognitive operations or basic neural signaling effects. The overlap would represent what we mean by general fitness, applying to psychological traits.

The resulting cognitive architecture would present two very different faces to psychologists. To those interested in human universals, the mind would look highly modular, with distinct psychological adaptations shaped by survival, social, and sexual selection for different functions. But to those interested in individual differences, the mind would look like a tightly knotted network of intercorrelations. This seems to be a reasonable model of the mind as we know it. Evolutionary psychologists have powerful theoretical and empirical arguments for characterizing the mind as highly modular.[27] Yet psychometricians ever since Spearman in 1904 have collected a vast amount of data showing that individual differences in the functional efficiencies of different mental abilities are often highly intercorrelated.[29] When the functional intercorrelations are subject to any reasonable method of factor analysis, a "*g* factor" or "general intelligence" factor always emerges. From the viewpoint of sexual selection theory, this *g* factor simply reflects the psychological and neurological components of general biological fitness, and the mental traits that we praise as indicating high intelligence are simply fitness indicators that evolved through social and sexual selection to display that *g* factor. This may resolve the apparent conflict between massive modularity at the level of psychological adaptations and massive intercorrelations in functional efficiency at the level of individual differences.

THE VARIANCE CRITERIA

The next three criteria (low phenotypic variance, genotypic variance, and heritability) depend on a theoretical argument dating to R. A. Fisher.[30] The argument goes as follows: The reason for expecting low variance in adaptations is the optimizing power of selection. Selection always maximizes fitness, by definition. But every particular trait has costs. These costs imply that for almost every trait, there will be an intermediate optimum at which fitness benefits are maximized relative to fitness costs. (This is obvious to engineers: in a world of limited resources, the best we can do is to optimize designs given the costs of components.) Thus, at evolutionary equilibrium (i.e., for most traits, most of the time, in most species), each trait will be subject to stabilizing (variance-reducing) selection that favors this optimum design. If selection is reasonably strong relative to mutation, the species should converge on this optimum fairly quickly. At the genetic level, this convergence usually implies the elimination of most polymorphisms at loci relevant to the trait, and fixation on just one optimal set of alleles.

Thus, stabilizing selection should tend to eliminate genetic variation underlying the trait. Without any genetic variation in the trait, heritability should not be higher than zero.[31] Moreover, stabilizing selection should tend to make the trait's expression resistant to environmental perturbations. The trait's development should become strongly canalized. This should lead to low levels of phenotypic variation as well.[32] In summary, every adaptive trait should have an intermediate optimum, and at evolutionary equilibrium, stabilizing selection should minimize genotypic and phenotypic variance in all such traits.

This standard evolutionary genetics view predicts low phenotypic and genotypic variance and low heritability in all adaptations that are under reasonably strong selection. When we see human traits that show dramatic individual differences in ability and high heritability, these criteria would lead us to doubt their adaptive significance. This creates problems for evolutionary psychology because almost every human mental trait ever assessed shows at least moderate heritability,[33,34] and heritabilities can be quite high for traits such as intelligence and language ability that were presumably strongly selected in our lineage.[35] Such data suggest that the theoretical argument for low variance in adaptations must be wrong. But how is it wrong?

A major problem is the existence of mutation. Biologists have realized that mutation is a strongly corrosive force in evolution.[36–39] Work done over the last twenty years has shown mutation to be much more significant than expected, undermining the minimum-variance arguments derived from population genetics. The new mutationist view suggests that every trait is subject to a balance of forces between mutation and selection. Mildly harmful mutations are constantly arising in the DNA sequences of the many genes (quantitative trait loci) that underlie complex traits. Almost all mutations impair functioning more than they help it, so mutation is generally "negatively biased," reducing each adaptation's efficiency below optimum.

For ordinary traits, mutation's ubiquity does not matter a great deal. Stabilizing selection presumably still operates on such traits to minimize genotypic and phenotypic variation. We simply expect low variance in adaptations rather than zero adaptations. Most importantly, we still expect lower variance in adaptations than in non-adaptations, which are not subject to such strong stabilizing selection.

However, for traits that function as fitness indicators, mutation forces us to step through the looking glass into a wonderland of counterintuitive effects. If mildly harmful mutations are ubiquitous, then we expect fitness itself to remain genetically heritable most of the time, in most species.[36,38] If fitness is usually heritable, then fitness is usually worth advertising with fitness indicators, especially to potential sexual partners. And if fitness is usually heritable, those potential sexual partners will have good reasons to pay attention to fitness indicators because the mutation loads of their offspring will depend on their mate choice decisions. As several biologists have realized, this can lead to situations where fitness indicators amass higher, not lower levels of genotypic and phenotypic variance.[37,39]

Especially relevant here is the "genic capture" model developed by Locke Rowe and David Houle.[39] They proposed that fitness indicators should be favored that capture the greatest proportion of an animal's total fitness in the manifest display. Fitness indicators should evolve higher fitness-dependence and fitness-sensitivity. One way for indicators to do this is to evolve extreme sensitivity to an animal's energy budget, so animals with high energy reserves can afford a very impressive indicator, while those with low energy reserves may not display the indicator at all. Another way to increase fitness-sensitivity is for an indicator to recruit a large number of genes in its development. The larger the number of genes, the better the indicator gets at revealing overall mutation load across genes. (Heritable fitness can be interpreted as total mutation load, to a first approximation.) Genic capture refers to this postulated evolutionary process whereby fitness indicators come to depend upon, and hence represent the mutation load of, a larger and larger number of genes. Extremely useful indicators would represent a large "mutational target size": they could be disrupted by harmful mutations at a very large number of loci. (Since about half the human genome appears to be expressed in the human brain, the mutational target size of the brain is enormous. This may be why human psychological adaptations make such good fitness indicators.)

The genic capture model predicts that fitness indicators should evolve high genetic variance and high phenotypic variance. These can be measured with coefficients of variation (dimensionless measures that result from dividing the standard deviation in a metric trait by the mean of the trait). Møller and Pomiankowski[26] found that in barn swallows, tails have higher coefficients of variation than wings, because tails are sexually selected as fitness indicators while wings are subject to stabilizing survival selection. Coefficients of variation are only meaningful for metric traits that can be measured on a ratio scale with a true zero point. Evolutionary psychologists should make it a high priority to develop ratio measures of human mental traits (if such a thing is possible), so we can compare coefficients of variation across traits and across species. (IQ and personality trait measures are not true ratio scales, but some physiological correlates of mental traits could be measured on a ratio scale).

The prediction about heritability is less clear. If a trait evolves to indicate an animal's current "condition" (e.g., energy reserves, parasite load), and if that condition depends more on the local environment than on the animal's genotype, then the trait may show low heritability. But if a trait evolves principally to indicate heritable fitness (e.g., mutation load), then the trait should show very high heritability. Unfortunately, it is much easier to measure heritability for human mental traits (which are not very informative about adaptive function) than to measure their coefficients of variation (which are). In any case, the standard argument that adaptations should show low variance and low heritability is clearly wrong for fitness indicators.

THE UNIVERSALITY CRITERIA

During most of the 20th century, the human sciences used the most conservative and uninformative criteria for identifying human mental adaptations: the universality criteria. According to the standard social science model[5] widely accepted in anthropology and psychology, genetically evolved aspects of human nature should appear uniformly across all historical epochs, all cultures, and all normal humans. Anything else must be attributed to learning, culture, or socialization.

These universality criteria excluded from human nature any psychological adaptations that evolved to show specific effects according to age or sex, or that evolved some strategic sensitivity to local social conditions, local mating systems, demographics, or ecological environments. This left very little human psychology in the category of adaptation. Worse, "evolved" became confused with "innate," so any adaptation that was not fully functioning at birth was considered a result of environmental learning or conditioning. Moreover, cultural anthropologists attained academic status largely by trading in behavioral exotica, presenting different cultures in the most alien light possible, and minimizing commonalities. Despite these hurdles, some anthropologists managed to identify a number of human universals.[40]

Evolutionary psychologists are somewhat ambivalent about universality criteria.[11] When a measurable behavioral pattern, facial expression, verbally expressed emotion, or pattern of childhood development appears to be genuinely universal across time and culture, we are happy to cite that universality as evidence for an underlying psychological adaptation. But when overt behavior varies, we seek universality at the more abstract level of a postulated psychological adaptation that is sensitive to biologically significant environmental variables.[5,11,41] This strategy of looking for universals at a variety of levels of description has allowed evolutionary psychology to claim a larger share of the human mind for the adaptationist program.

However, universality criteria are very tricky to apply to behavioral adaptations that evolved as fitness indicators. One reason is that fitness indicators evolve to amplify apparent individual differences in fitness. That is their principal function. If they presented a uniformity of signals within the species, they would be useless for discriminating between individuals. Universality would undermine discriminability. Therefore, we expect fitness indicators to show the opposite of universality with respect to signal quantity and quality.

Also, behavioral fitness indicators such as bird song are subject to strategic control by an animal's nervous system. Animals can make cost-benefit assessments of when it is worth producing the fitness-indicating behavior. Because these behaviors are costly by design (so they work as strategic handicaps), but bring high potential reproductive rewards, many animals may find themselves balanced on a cost-benefit knife-edge. Small changes in environmental factors such as food availability or population density may produce large changes in the frequency of a fitness-indicating behavior. Also, because individuals will differ in fitness, placing them at different points on the cost-benefit curve, there will be large individual variations in the amount of behavior produced. The strategic sensitivity of fitness indicators, coupled with their high costs and high potential benefits, may often lead to large individual differences in the quantity and quality of behavioral output. For fitness indicators, we should not expect a stable, universal pattern of behavioral output.

In the case of humans, strategic sensitivity adds a third difficulty. We appear to have evolved a number of behavioral fitness indicators that operate through different display channels: art, music, dance, sports, religious ritual, conspicuous consumption, and so forth. Suppose individuals can assess their relative strengths and weakness in different display domains, and focus their energies on the domain in which they are most likely to excel. We may all be capable of rudimentary display behaviors in every domain, but we may specialize during adolescence and young adulthood. Especially when sexual competition resembles a winner-take-all contest, there are strong pressures to specialize; so one has a reasonable chance of winning high status for one class of display behaviors, even if one is below average in all other classes. This can lead to each individual's avoiding all display domains other than his or her favorite, in order to create a positive impression and avoid embarrassment. The result can be a pattern of behavioral variation across individuals that looks like a diverse set of learned skills. Yet each "skill" may depend on a psychological adaptation that evolved as a fitness indicator. Different cultures may also privilege certain classes of display behavior over other classes, leading to great diversity across time and cultures in the allocation of effort between different fitness indicators.

To survive, one must do many things reasonably well. To advertise one's fitness though, it is sufficient to do one thing extremely well. Animals usually resemble each other quite closely in their survival behaviors, but diverge dramatically from each other in their display behaviors. This display divergence occurs between species, between cultures, and between individuals. Display divergence undermines the usefulness of universality criteria for identifying human psychological adaptations that evolved as fitness indicators.

CONCLUSION

The identification of psychological adaptations is the heart of evolutionary psychology. Reasonable criteria have been developed for identifying adaptations that evolved to fulfill many survival and social functions. However, these criteria are not very applicable to adaptations that evolved as fitness indicators to deter predators, intimidate rivals, or attract mates. If evolutionary psychology does not expand its view of adaptation, these fitness indicators will continue to be overlooked. Since these fitness indicators are likely to encompass exactly those mental traits that show the highest individual differences and the most dramatic display behaviors, analysis of these indicators may have the most immediate relevance to applied areas such as education, economics, clinical psychology, and human mate choice. The development of new and better criteria for identifying psychological adaptations, including fitness indicators, should be a major step in evolutionary psychology's methodological maturation over the coming years.

REFERENCES

1. Williams, G.C. 1966. Adaptation and Natural Selection. Princeton University Press. Princeton, NJ.
2. Cosmides, L. & J. Tooby. 1994. Origins of domain specificity: the evolution of functional organization. *In* Mapping the Mind: Domain Specificity in Cognition and Culture. L. A. Hirschfeld & S. A. Gelman, Eds.: 85–116. Cambridge University Press. New York.
3. Tooby, J. & L. Cosmides. 1990. The past explains the present: emotional adaptations and the structure of ancestral environments. Ethol. Sociobiol. **11** (4/5): 375–424.
4. Tooby, J. & L. Cosmides. 1990. On the universality of human nature and the uniqueness of the individual: the role of genetics and adaptation. J. Personality **58:** 17–67.

5. TOOBY, J. & L. COSMIDES. 1992. The psychological foundations of culture. *In* The Adapted Mind: Evolutionary Psychology and the Generation of Culture. J. H. Barkow, L. Cosmides & J. Tooby, Eds.: 19–36. Oxford University Press. New York.
6. MILLER, G.F. 1997. Mate choice: From sexual cues to cognitive adaptations. *In* Characterizing Human Psychological Adaptations. G. Cardew, Ed. Ciba Foundation Symposium **208:** 71–87. Wiley. London.
7. MILLER, G. F. 1998. Review of "The handicap principle." Evol. Hum. Behav. **19(5):** 343–347.
8. MILLER, G.F. 1998. How mate choice shaped human nature: a review of sexual selection and human evolution. *In* Handbook of Evolutionary Psychology: Ideas, Issues, and Applications. C. Crawford & D. Krebs, Eds.: 87–129. Erlbaum Associates. Mahwah, NJ.
9. MILLER, G.F. 2000. The Mating Mind: How Sexual Choice Shaped the Evolution of Human Nature. Doubleday. New York.
10. BUSS, D.M. 1995. Evolutionary psychology: a new paradigm for psychological science. Psychol. Inquiry **6** (1)**:** 1–30.
11. PINKER, S. 1997. How the Mind Works. Norton. New York.
12. THORNHILL, R. 1997. The concept of an evolved adaptation. G. Cardew, Ed.: 4–13 *In* Characterizing Human Psychological Adaptations, Ciba Foundation Symposium **208**. Wiley. London.
13. SYMONS, D. 1990. Adaptiveness and adaptation. Ethol. Sociobiol. **11(4/5):** 427–444.
14. TURKE, P.W. 1990. Which humans behave adaptively, and why does it matter? Ethol. Sociobiol. **11(4/5):** 305–339.
15. ANDERSSON, M.B. 1994. Sexual Selection. Princeton University Press. Princeton, NJ.
16. GRAFEN, A. 1990. Biological signals as handicaps. J. Theor. Biol. **144:** 517–546.
17. HAUSER, M. 1997. The Evolution of Communication. MIT Press. Cambridge, MA.
18. JOHNSTONE, R.A. 1995. Sexual selection, honest advertisement, and the handicap principle: reviewing the evidence. Biol. Rev. **70:** 1–65.
19. ZAHAVI, A. & A. ZAHAVI. 1997. The Handicap Principle: A Missing Piece of Darwin's Puzzle. Oxford University Press. New York.
20. YEBLEN, T. 1899. The Theory of the Leisure Class. Macmillan. New York.
21. OLSON, V.A. & I.P.F. OWENS. 1998. Costly sexual signals: are carotenoids rare, risky, or required? Trends Ecol. Evol. **13** (12)**:** 510–514.
22. CRONIN, H. 1991. The Ant and the Peacock: Altruism and Sexual Selection from Darwin to Today. Cambridge University Press. Cambridge, England.
23. GANGESTAD, S.W. & R. THORNHILL. 1997. Human sexual selection and developmental stability. *In* Evolutionary Social Psychology. J.A. Simpson & D.T. Kenrick, Eds.: 169–195. Erlbaum Associates. Mahwah, NJ.
24. MØLLER, A.P. & J.P. SWADDLE. 1997. Developmental Stability and Evolution. Oxford University Press. New York.
25. THORNHILL, R. 1998. Darwinian aesthetics. *In* Handbook of Evolutionary Psychology: Ideas, Issues, and Applications. C. Crawford & D. Krebs, Eds.: 543–572. Erlbaum Associates. Mahwah, NJ.
26. MØLLER, A.P. & A. POMIANKOWSKI. 1993. Fluctuating asymmetry and sexual selection. Genetica **89:** 267–279.
27. HOULE, D. 1991. Genetic covariance of life history traits: what genetic correlations are made of and why it matters. Evolution **45:** 630–648.
28. HIRSCHFELD, L.A. & S.A. GELMAN, Eds. 1994. Mapping the Mind: Domain Specificity in Cognition and Culture. Cambridge University Press. New York.
29. JENSEN, A. 1998. The *g* Factor: The Science of Mental Ability. Praeger. London.
30. FISHER, R.A. 1930. The Genetical Theory of Natural Selection. Clarendon Press. Oxford, England.
31. CHARLESWORTH, B. 1987. The heritability of fitness. *In* Sexual Selection: Testing the Ideas. J.W. Bradbury & M.B. ANDERSSON, Eds.: 21–40. Wiley. Chichester, England.
32. BULL, J.J. 1987. Evolution of phenotypic variance. Evolution **4:** 269–279.
33. BAILEY, J.M. 1998. Can behavior genetics contribute to evolutionary behavioral science? *In* Handbook of Evolutionary Psychology: Ideas, Issues, and Applications. C. Crawford & D. Krebs, Eds.: 211–233. Erlbaum Associates. Mahwah, NJ.

34. PLOMIN, R., J. RIES, G. MCCLEARN & M. RUTTER. 1997. Behavioral Genetics, 3rd ed. W. H. Freeman. San Francisco, CA.
35. MILLER, G.F. & P.M. TODD. 1998. Mate choice turns cognitive. Trends Cogn. Sci. **2** (5)**:** 190–198.
36. KONDRASHOV, A. 1988. Deleterious mutations as an evolutionary factor III. Mating preference and some general remarks. J. Theor. Biol. **131:** 487–496.
37. POMIANKOWSKI, A. & A.P. MØLLER. 1995. A resolution of the lek paradox. Proc. Roy. Soc. Lond. B **260** (1357)**:** 21–29.
38. RICE, W.R. 1988. Heritable variation in fitness as a prerequisite for adaptive female choice: the effect of mutation-selection balance. Evolution. **42:** 817–820.
39. ROWE, L. & D. HOULE. 1996. The lek paradox and the capture of genetic variance by condition dependent traits. Proc. Roy. Soc. Lond. B **263:** 1415–1421.
40. BROWN, D. 1991. Human Universals. McGraw-Hill. New York.
41. BUSS, D.M. 1989. Sex differences in human mate selection: evolutionary hypotheses tested in 37 cultures. Behav. Brain Sci. **12** (1)**:** 1–49.

The Optimal Number of Fathers

Evolution, Demography, and History in the Shaping of Female Mate Preferences

SARAH BLAFFER HRDY

Department of Anthropology, University of California, Davis, Davis, California 95616, USA

ABSTRACT: Around the world polygynous marriage (one man, several women) is vastly more common than polyandrous marriage (one woman, several men), and women tend to be more cautious about entering into sexual relationships than men are. Such patterns are often assumed to reflect essential differences between the sexes. However, the same dichotomy between "ardent" males and "coy" females is not found in other primates. Furthermore, under a range of circumstances females enhance their reproductive success by mating with multiple partners and use *polyandrous mating* (soliciting copulations from several or more males) to circumvent male-imposed costs on their free choice of mates. The existence of one-male mating systems does not prove that females "naturally" gravitate to them. Typically monandrous (copulating with just one partner) mating systems are maintained by one male excluding rivals or by other circumstances that distort female options. As with many other animals, primate females (including women) can benefit reproductively from polyandrous matings. Understanding this takes us beyond narrow research programs intent on demonstrating "universal" differences between the sexes, and allows us to study females as flexible and opportunistic individuals who confront recurring reproductive dilemmas and tradeoffs within a world of shifting options.

MODELS THAT PRESUME "ARDENT" MALES AND "COY" FEMALES

According to Darwin's theory of sexual selection, males compete among themselves for access to females, and then females choose the one best male. As Darwin put it, the female "with the rarest exception, is less eager (to mate) than the male...." The female generally "requires to be courted; she is coy, and may often be seen endeavoring for a long time to escape...."[1] (p. 273) A century later, textbooks with chapter titles like "The Reluctant Female and the Ardent Male"[2] perpetuate this essential dichotomy between the sexes. Because sperm-producing males invest less in offspring than ovulating and gestating females do, and because of the time that must elapse between female conceptions, males benefit from mating with as many partners as they can and are naturally eager to do so, while females cannot benefit from philandering and extra fertilizations in this same way.[3] This presumption of monandrous females coupled with males who ranged from monogamous to polygynous shaped our reconstructions of early hominid mating systems

To this day, it remains axiomatic in many circles that females do not benefit from multiple partners—especially not in humans where male protection and provisioning are essential for offspring survival. It is assumed that mothers lose, and cannot possibly gain from behaviors that reduce male certainty of paternity, (e.g., see Symons[4] [p. 299] for an explicit statement of this widely held assumption often left unstated). This is why it is often assumed that men must have an insatiable desire for sexual variety, in contrast to women, who should be indifferent to it.[5] (p. 473) The reason men desire many partners—while women desire only one–is that supposedly a prehistoric man "who slept with fifty women could have sired fifty children," while a woman who slept with many partners "would have no more descendants than a woman who slept with one."[6] (p. 30)

At one level, such arguments are indisputable. No one can reasonably deny a generalized male eagerness to mate evident in many different species, nor fail to note that some females are sexually discriminating, even to the point of being obligately monandrous. The pronghorn antelope provides the very model of a sexually selected Darwinian mammal. Having scrutinized the performances of males in her vicinity, the female pronghorn makes sure that she is in the custody of the most vigorous male available during the brief period when she is ready to conceive, and then mates just once, only with him[7] (esp. pp. 214–230). After all, she descends from a long line of ancestresses who had one clear priority: to produce offspring capable of outrunning the cheetah that once coursed across North America, and exercised a voracious selection pressure on pronghorns.

Longstanding selection pressures that favor the most viable offspring explain why females "free" to choose (*sensu* Gowaty) among progenitors should be more fertile and have more viable offspring. In the clearest demonstration to date, Marion Petrie has shown how peahens comparison-shop and then mate with the peacock whose train is most elaborate.[8] Chicks sired by the male with the largest eyespots grew larger and survived better. Since peacocks contribute nothing to offspring beyond their genes, the most plausible interpretation is that the fanciest males also provided the most viable genes—as predicted by sexual selection theory. The problem does not reside with Darwin's theory, but with the practice of generalizing from the female pronghorn or peafowl (females with clear priorities and quite a few options) to females generally, including females whose options are more constrained.[9–11] Hence, when we presume that women are modest and sexually discriminating because "that's the way all females are...." we close the case too soon, leaving out history relevant to both the evolution and also the development of the behavior we are studying, in particular all the tactics and stratagems both by males (and also by other females) that interfere with female choice or create circumstances that override a straightforward quest for good genes.

It should not surprise us therefore to learn about another of Marion Petrie's research findings: across a broad sample of birds that live in socially monogamous pairs rates of extra-pair paternity (based on DNA matching) were highest in populations with the most genetic variation between males.[12] Populations with the highest incidence of "infidelity" were those in which outside partners were likely to be most genetically different from the female's mate. Being paired with an individual who, from the female's perspective, is a suboptimal male—whether it is because he is genetically "inferior," immunologically inappropriate, too close a relative, or whatever —is one obvious rationale for a female to seek extra-pair copulations. There is a burgeoning literature on sperm competition.[13–16] What is often overlooked, however, is that without selection pressure on females to mate polyandrously, strong selection pressures on males to produce voluminous and competitive sperm would never have been at work in the first place. Indeed, one of the more plausible rationales for the rare evolution of intromittent penises in a species of weaverbird is that selection for this mode of sperm delivery was produced by polyandrous mating by the anything-but-coy females in that species.[17] If this hypothesis holds up, it would be ironic that penises—viewed by many as the essence of ardent maleness—would have evolved to help males cope in spite of female promiscuity.

In what follows, I first summarize comparative evidence across animals that illustrates why when females can *not* have their first choice (which would be freedom to choose the father with the most viable genes in a world where the mother and her offspring are kept safe and guaranteed access to the resources they need), they resort to "Female Plan B," seeking benefits available from mating with a range of males. Next, I return to the primate order to examine specific problems female primates have in exercising free mate-choice, and to features of female sexuality (defined here as readiness to copulate) that I assume evolved to counteract and overcome these obstacles. In particular, I will argue that polyandrous mating was an important element in the strategic repertoire primate mothers use to keep their infants alive, and that a polyandrous (as opposed to monandrous or "coy") heritage is central to the psychophysiological legacy that our prehominid ancestors brought to the hominid experiment. Finally, I review ethnographic evidence demonstrating that polyandrous tendencies are more widely expressed in the human species than is apparent from modern cross-cultural surveys taken from the ethnographic present.

Instead of attributing monandrous mate preference in women to some essential female nature, this alternate view of female primate sexuality requires us to consider recent history (measured in thousands and hundreds of years) as well as the evolutionary history of those populations.

BENEFITS OF POLYANDRY—COMPARATIVE EVIDENCE

Once sociobiologists began to consider seriously the possibility that females might benefit from polyandrous mating, one of the first stereotypes to crumble was the assumption that males are unique in seeking sexual variety for its own sake (again see Symons[18] for a clear statement of that widely held assumption). Recent experiments with pseudoscorpions (*Cordylochernes scorpiodes*) reveal females actively seeking sperm from sequential partners. Typically, females paired with the same male prefer a respite one-and-a-half hours after mating, and then are eager to resume mating after 48 hours. Given a chance to mate with a different male, however, the proportion of females accepting sperm from an additional male was as great after an hour-and-a-half as after 48 hours. No comparable quest for novelty was detected for males. Males remained eager to mate again and again with the same female.[19] Furthermore, subsequent experiments demonstrated that females receiving sperm from two different males had a significantly higher reproductive success than did females receiving an equivalent number of sperm packets *all from the same male*, probably due to increased genetic compatibility between partners.[20]

Similar preferences for "novel" (read outbred?) males are reported for free-ranging primates.[21, 22] (p. 166 ff) As early as the 1970s genetic studies using protein polymorphism data to perform paternity exclusions for a troop of Japanese macaques revealed that 29% of infants were sired by males from outside the troop.

Similarly, among chimps at the Tai site in Cote d'Ivoire, half of all infants were sired by males from other communities. Reports from chimps in Tanzania and Guinea confirm this pattern of extra-community paternity. Apparently, furtive matings permit female Japanese macaques and chimps to circumvent constraints of breeding options imposed by cliques of locally dominant males.[21] (p. 137, n13).[23] New genetic evidence for hominoid primates reveals that proteins linked to sperm production have evolved faster in humans and chimpanzees than among gorillas, suggesting that sperm competition characterized our hominid ancestors as well as the ancestors of modern chimps.[101] If human ancestors were characterized by sperm competition it strengthens the likelihood that early human females were mating polyandrously. But why? Let us first consider comparative evidence for other animals.

Abundant evidence now exists for a wide range of animals that females free to mate with a range of males are more fertile and their offspring more viable.[20,24,25] Among prairie dogs, for example, females who escape being monopolized by a single male, and manage to mate with three or more males, are more fertile and produce significantly larger litters than do mothers who mated with only one male.[25] Because prairie dog litters may be sired by multiple progenitors, such litters will be genetically more diverse with attendant protection against lineage extinction (due to parasites, for example).[26] Maternal fecundity is correlated not only with the number of males the female mates with, but also correlated with the mother's body size. Maternal body size is a factor not just because big mothers are more fertile, but also because, as Hoogland points out, large females are better at avoiding domination by males who might otherwise constrain their mate choices.[25]

In line with conventional Darwinian thinking, a prairie dog male benefits from monopolizing access to a female. But there is an added twist. The male's mate does not always benefit from being so managed. Discrepant interests between males and females explain why females able to resist male control should be more fertile or produce more viable offspring. But improving their odds in the genetic lottery of sexual recombination is not the only incentive for mothers to engage in polyandrous matings. Females also benefit in ways that have nothing to do with which sperm actually fertilizes her egg. Other-than-genetic benefits include the chance to exchange sexual access for immediate benefits—such as nutrients—or for future benefits such as eliciting male protection, support, or tolerance for subsequently born infants. In order for polyandrous tendencies to evolve, benefits must on average outweigh costs in terms of energy, exposure to sexually transmitted diseases or punishment by possessive mates.

A classic example of immediate benefits from mating *other* than fertilization, would be katydids, where males squeeze out a large sperm packet full of nutrients and then transmit it to the female who converts those resources into progeny. Other exchanges of sex for resources (or social support) can be widely documented among primates, both in primates like chimps and humans, where males hunt, and in those like bonobos, where hunting is rare.[27–29]

But can sexual relations with a female alter a male's behavior toward offspring she subsequently bears? In many primates (34 different species, so far) infanticide is one of the more toxic effects of sexually selected competition between males. Among langur monkeys, for example, males who enter the breeding system from outside may kill unweaned infants.[30] Over an 18-year-long study of langurs at Jodhpur, in the largest such study ever undertaken, Sommer[31] reports that 33% of all infants die by being killed when their mothers are intercepted by males they have never mated with. Infanticide effectively cancels the mother's last mate choice, distorts her options for scheduling the next conception, and imposes pressure on her to conceive after a shorter interval than might otherwise be physiologically optimal for her, constraining her to breed with the male at hand rather than waiting for a better alternative. Recent DNA evidence collected by Carolla Borries and colleagues in the first langur field study to ascertain paternity reveals that none of the victims were attacked by genetic fathers. Males who either were or might be the father (this based on both DNA evidence and behavioral observations to ascertain which males mated with the mother when she was fertile) refrain from attacking offspring of that female. At Borries's site, where males are sometimes able to remain near the mother, possible fathers actually help her to protect her infant. Since all mothers mate with multiple males, none of the protectors could be certain of paternity, yet a possibility of paternity was sufficient to alter the male's subsequent behavior towards her offspring,[32,33] presumably because past sexual history with the mother provides some sort of cue that elicits tolerant versus destructive behavior towards her infant.[a] Because there are both practical and ethical constraints on doing such experiments with primates, the only rigorous research on cues that promote switches from infanticidal to nurturing behavior in males has been done with rodents.[34] Although we are ignorant of the exact processes involved in the case of monkeys, it seems unlikely that the transformation in male behavior is due to any conscious decision.

Langurs are not the only primates where males with only a fractional probability of paternity help protect a former mate's offspring. Some savanna baboon males who mate with a female subsequently stay close. These "possible fathers" look out for their offspring[35] and intervene if an infant, possibly theirs, is threatened by another male.[36] I believe that sexual swellings actually evolved among primates precisely to facilitate breeding with several "possible fathers."

Just how effective male proximity is for keeping babies alive is hard to quantify. The task is simplified when, as in humans and some birds, males provision, because observers can measure how much food is brought to immatures cached in a centralized homebase or nest. The best evidence for how mothers benefit from manipulating information about paternity derives from a type of European sparrow known as the dunnock (*Prunella modularis*). Dunnock females are typically polyandrous, males (if they can be) are polygynous. Alpha and beta males calibrate the number of mouthfuls of food they bring chicks in accordance with how often they managed to copulate during the period when the female was fertile.[37,38] As predicted by the hypothesis that females manipulate the information available to males about paternity,[30] (pp. 32–35) DNA fingerprinting revealed that dunnock males were often, but not always, accurate in their paternity "assessments."

The most striking similarity with primates, however, is found in a close relative of dunnocks (*Prunella collaris*) that also lives in multi-male, multi-female breeding groups. These birds have converged upon a baboon-like solution for making sure that fertile females mate with several males. The female's cloacal region protrudes and turns scarlet, increasing the odds that multiple males will be drawn into the web of

[a]The best evidence for this is that even a strange infant, temporarily kidnapped from another troop, is not attacked so long as it remains in the possession of a female who is familiar to the male.

possible paternity.[39] The more males—up to three—provisioning chicks, the larger the number of chicks surviving to fledge.[40,41]

TRAITS FACILITATING POLYANDROUS MATING ARE PROMINENT IN PRIMATES

In the Primate order, sexual swellings have evolved at least three different times, and characterize some 25 species. "No case," Darwin wrote, "interested and perplexed me so much as the brightly colored hinder ends and adjoining parts of certain monkeys."[42] (pp 18–19) I doubt, however, that Darwin would have remained puzzled for long if he had read Parish and de Waal's descriptions of chimp and bonobo sexual behavior [this volume and references therein, p. 97]. A maximally swollen female chimp mates 1–4 times an hour with thirteen or more partners. Over her lifetime, she will engage in some six thousand or more copulations (estimate from Gombe, cited in Wrangham[43]) with dozens of partners, in order to produce no more than five or so surviving offspring.[44]

Let us assume that sexual swellings did evolve to insure that female primates mate with multiple partners. Some years ago, I attempted to make sense of the confusing diversity of sexual patterns in Old World monkeys and apes—both those with and those without sexual swellings—by substituting this new assumption for the old assumption that each female was selected to mate with the one best male.[45,46] I assumed that by and large these females were resorting to a different strategy. The "goal" for them was to mate polyandrously with a range of partners. How to manage this became the "problem" females had to "solve." Exactly how they solved it depended on phylogenetic constraints, current mating system, and demographic conditions.

Where multiple males are permanently in residence, the most efficient solution is for females to compress mating into a discrete period around ovulation and to conspicuously advertise estrus so that males have to follow the female around and compete among themselves for the opportunity to mate, and then their "goal" accomplished, to return to business as usual, namely, foraging. In most primates, however, one dominant male excludes competing males; females have only occasional (often furtive) opportunities to mate with subordinate or outside males. Under these circumstances, one way for females to solve the problem of mating with a range of males is to exhibit the same midcycle peak in libido universally found in primates, but to also solicit sex on a less cyclical, more "situation-dependent" basis.[b] The absence of any discrete signal of ovulation visible at a distance would be an asset under such circumstances.

[b]Libido is an old psychological term for sexual drive; primatologists pefer "sexual proceptivity." Such desire is presumed to have evolved because it increased a fertile female's chances of conceiving. However, many primates (not only women) exhibit "proceptive behavior," actively solicit males, or copulate even at times when they are not ovulating. This flexible capacity to mate on a situation-dependent basis across the cycle leads to a great deal of nonconceptive sexual behavior between potentially fertile males and females who are not currently fertile. Given this situation, it is the biological equivalent of apples versus oranges to compare the "sex drive" of a potentially fertile male with a nonovulating female, or to assume that the urge to mate derives from the same "motivation" or evolved for the same reason in both sexes.

FIGURE 1. Reconstructions of early hominids routinely depict one or several females who are invariably mated with a single male, as in the case of this pair of australopithecines sauntering across the diorama at the American Museum of Natural History in New York City. In fact, we know remarkably little about the mating systems of these creatures. (Reproduced with permission from the American Museum of Natural History; photograph by D. Finnin and C. Chesek).

When ovulation is not advertised by conspicuous swellings, only a resident male able to monitor a female across cycles has reliable cues (olfactory as well as visual?) as to when she is actually fertile. Among langur monkeys, for example, there is no conspicuous visible sign at ovulation. Instead females present their rumps and shudder their heads with variable and idiosyncratic intensity. Most solicitations occur at midcycle, but females have the potential to also solicit males and mate on a situation-dependent schedule (cf. Refs. 47–51). Some years ago, Kim Wallen reviewed experimental results that provide indirect support for the hypothesis that there is more to primate mating than conception. When groups of macaque females (who do not exhibit discrete sexual swellings at midcycle as chimps do) were caged with a single male, they basically played the game by the endocrinological book. Female proceptivity peaked at midcycle, and mating was confined to this midcycle period of "estrus." However, when females were caged with multiple males, the patterning of sexuality in these macaques became more flexible and they solicited sex across the follicular phase of the cycle, with dominant females taking precedence over subordinates in mating with the most males (Figure 4 in Wallen[52]). (See Bercovitch[53] for discussion of the especially variable and complex expression of sexual swellings in the genus *Macaca*, which includes interesting exceptions to general patterns described here).

Extraordinarily enterprising bonobo females combine elements of both visible swellings plus periods of sexual receptivity that last for weeks. But it is human females who (like langurs) do not have a conspicuous physical sign around ovulation, who fall at the extreme edge of the primate continuum of flexible receptivity. Women exhibit a midcycle peak in libido but are capable of copulating throughout the cycle[54] (for broader literature review see Table 3 in Hrdy[46]). Not only does human female behavior and the cues that she exhibits to males change, but even the criteria by which females assess males over the menstrual cycle change, so, for example, women prefer men with more "masculine" faces at midcycle, more "feminized" faces at other endocrinological phases (see Penton-Voak *et al.*[55] and Gangestad [this volume, p. 50] for a discussion of cycle-dependent scent preferences in females).

Many people still assume that our hominid ancestors had sexual swellings that were lost over the course of human evolution, some say to promote pair bonding.[56] In fact, swellings are more likely to have been independently evolved in the line leading to chimps and bonobos. Sexual swellings are scarcely detectable in the other Great Apes or among the last surviving relicts of the genus *Homo*—modern humans. "Concealed ovulation" (or more accurately, ovulation without advertising) in our own species is not so much a new trait as an extreme manifestation of an old one.

WHY IS POLYANDRY SO RARE IN HUMANS—OR IS IT?

Wherever primates are well studied, there turn out to be remarkably few populations where females do not, when feasible, solicit strange or "extra-group" males.[57] Even in famously monogamous species like titi monkeys or siamangs, females solicit outsiders when they can.[36,58] From the sexual swellings and prominent clitoris of a chimpanzee, to the semi-continuous, situation-dependent receptivity of a tamarin, female primates apparently evolved to draw multiple males into the web of possible paternity when feasible. When, in 1981, I proposed that such a polyandrous tendency (however subdued) was part of the legacy that prehominid females brought to the human experiment, the idea was rejected not only by feminists uncomfortable at the prospect of assigning biologically based predispositions to either sex, but also by evolutionary psychologists, who deemed the idea of polyandrous potentials in human females impossible on theoretical grounds because paternal provisioning was viewed as essential to female reproductive success, and males capable of assessing the mother's recent sexual history ought to "diminish their parental investments as their confidence in paternity wanes."[4] (p. 299) "Why," Don Symons, a founding father of evolutionary psychology, inquired, "should a female be better off with ... three males, each of which invests one-third unit [than] with one male which invests one unit?" He concluded that there is only "dubious evidence that this [assertively sexual female] nature exists and no evidence that women anywhere normally tie up multiple male parental investments by confusing the issue of paternity..."[4]

Across cultures, formal polyandrous marriages are indeed exceedingly rare (fewer than 2% of human cultures are so classified). But informally, polyandrous arrangements are far more common due to extramarital affairs, to a shortage of women[59] or inability of one man to provide security,[60] to a husband's "sharing" his wife with kin, age-mates or allies (which by some estimates is found in one-third of all human cultures),[61] (p. 334) or due to women's taking up with sequential mates over a lifetime.[62,63] Because so little attention has been focused on these topics, however, it can be difficult to learn from the ethnographic record whether a woman was seduced, raped, complicitous, or the initiator, or whether the husband was duped or supportive. For husbands are not always prohibitively jealous of their wives (e.g., see Smedley[60] for an African case study and Crocker and Crocker[64] for a South American one). That is, mothers—and sometimes husbands as well—behave as if they were aware that male solidarity could be critical to their well being, or that having several "fathers" could promote the survival of offspring that statistically are more likely to have been sired by a woman's husband (or by his kin) than by an unrelated progenitor.

All foragers, and hence all early humans, were cooperative breeders in the sense that no mother could hope to successfully rear successive children unless she had direct and substantial assistance from others.[65] In this respect, humans are different from other extant apes, for whom provisioning (mostly by mothers) ends at weaning. In humans, by contrast, provisioning goes on and on, long past weaning, sometimes past adolescence, past marriage, and even past the time that an offspring begins to breed. Among many hunter-gatherers, youngsters 15 years and older are still consuming more calories than they collect.[66] Mothers by themselves—especially if they have new infants—cannot successfully rear offspring without assistance from others. Not all of this assistance comes from husbands, or even necessarily from men. Caretaking assistance by pre-reproductive group members and provisioning help from other mothers and especially post-reproductive kin (often referred to as "grandmothers" since mother's mother, mother-in-law or aunt sometimes provide critical help) is increasingly well documented for foraging societies.[65,67,68]

What is important about "polyandrous motherhood"[c] (anthropologist Jane Guyer's term) is not just the spectacle of women "having fun," but the more enduring vision of mothers making do. My goal here is not to rewrite ethnography in the wake of our society's changing attitudes towards female sexuality, but to point out how new assumptions about the potential benefits of polyandry (some of them introduced into evolutionary biology by feminists) can increase our awareness of female strategies. Once we broaden our definition of polyandrous behavior to include situations where one mother is linked to several men—husbands, fathers, and possible fathers —polyandry is not so rare after all (see Tew,[69] Smith,[70] Muller,[71] and Guyer[62] (pp. 231–252) for both pre- and postcolonial West African societies; Hakansson[72] for densely populated areas of East Africa; Crocker and Crocker,[64] Hill and Hurtado,[63] and Beckerman *et al.*[73] for tribal South America; pre-twentieth century ethnographic accounts like those for the Huron, cited in Hartung,[74] for North America; Berndt and Berndt[75] for aboriginal Australia; Befu[76] and Shih[77] for traditional societies in Central Japan and southwestern China; as well as Hrdy[65] for additional examples from contemporary mother-centered families in rural and urban Africa and the Americas, as well as the Caribbean). Wherever power relations between the sexes permit it— which among humans is more likely to be the case among matrilocal women, who tend to have greater reproductive autonomy—and wherever ecological or economic

[c]*Polyandrous motherhood* is a relatively new term used by anthropologists[62] to cope with discrepancies between formal marriage labels and the actual lives of women rearing children fathered by different men, or children whose genetic paternity is unclear. A woman may be married to a man other than the genetic "father" of a given child or find herself eliciting assistance from several men—not necessarily her husband.

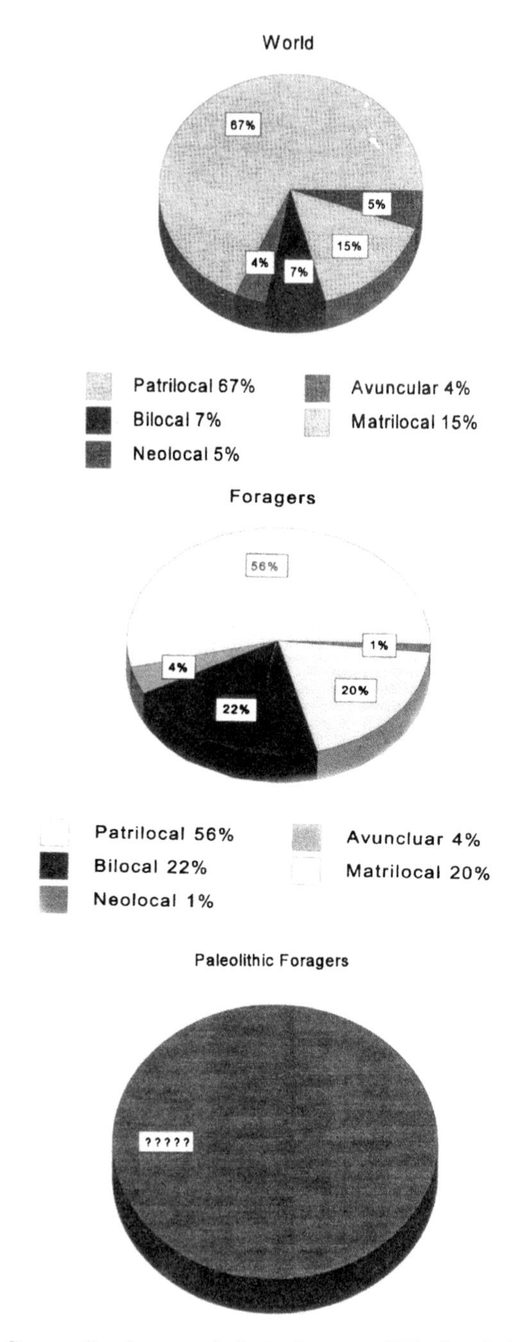

FIGURE 2. Cross-cultural surveys indicate that some 67% of societies (World) exhibit patrilocal residence patterns. This proportion dropped to 56%, however, when anthropologist Carol Ember[91] included only foraging societies (Foragers) subsisting as our Pleistocene ancestors did. The actual residence patterns of Paleolithic foragers are unknown.

circumstances make polyandrous matings more beneficial than monandrous pairing, we would expect mothers to hedge their bets by trading off certainty of paternity for the advantages to be obtained from "several fathers."

Take the Aché of eastern Paraguay.[67] At any one time, the majority of marriages are monogamous. Yet each of these unions at some point is likely to be polygynous or polyandrous. For marriage among foragers is inherently unstable, especially when unions are passing through a polygynous or polyandrous phase. The marriage dissolves from internal tensions due to male jealousy or to intolerance between co-wives. Sixty percent (11 of 18) of Aché men spent some (typically brief) amount of time in polyandrous marriages. Over their lives, most Aché women have children with two or more men (see p. 229; see also Sangree[63]). Ultimately, in spite of the obvious commonalities of interest between a husband and a wife and in spite of all the efficiencies that trust and long-term pair bonds can offer, these unions are perpetually at risk due to tensions between the preoccupations of fathers, whose top priority is often access to a new mate (hence quantity of offspring sired), compared to the concerns of mothers whose top priority is more often the quality and the prospects for those offspring they commit to (discussed further in Hrdy[65]).

This does not mean that fathers are unimportant. Far from it. The record on that is all too clear: children without male protection and provisioning suffer terrible costs from malnutrition, infanticide, and pedicide.[67] This is not an "anti-family" message. To my knowledge, monogamy, with its emphasis on shared interests between the sexes, has always provided the best antidote to the more toxic effects of sexual selection. For a mother with the luxury of choosing her mate, under circumstances where both parents are likely to be committed to investing in the offspring, monogamy may well be the woman's optimal strategy.

The point is not that males don't matter, but rather that there was never much evidence or a very strong theoretical basis for assuming that mothers in the Pleistocene could count on fathers to give a higher priority to provisioning children they already have rather than seeking additional mates any more than mothers today can count on them to do so. Instead, what impresses behavioral ecologists like Kristen Hawkes, James O'Connell, and Nicholas Blurton-Jones is how often men today (in the case of their studies of hunters among African foragers) seem more interested in maximizing prestige (which translates into more sexual partners) than in actually provisioning families. They emphasize the impracticality of foraging decisions, particularly men's obsession with large and prestigious prey like eland, even when higher returns in terms of protein can be obtained by targeting more abundant, but less prestige-enhancing small prey.[68,78] It is telling, for example, that among people like the Aché, hunters lose interest in their wives right after birth—at just the time when a women most needs to be provisioned. In the pungent idiom of the Aché: men don't like being around new mothers because "their bodies smell (of milk)..."[67] While men tend to find very pregnant and postpartum wives less sexually attractive, women have increased libido in the first and second trimesters of pregnancy[79] but reduced libido in the months post partum (e.g., Barrett *et al.*[80])—just when they presumably (especially in foraging societies) are *most in need of provisioning*. In other words, nothing about this pattern conforms to predictions generated by the model that either women's sexuality (willingness to engage in sex) or their sexual attractiveness evolved to insure male provisioning after birth.

If paternal provisioning were absolutely essential for survival of offspring, fathers themselves should have been selected long ago to find babies and new mothers irresistibly attractive. But there is little evidence that they do. Rather, it is just when mothers need protection and provisioning most that men seem sexually least interested in wives and most likely to seek new sexual partners. The unreliability of some (many?) fathers[d] would be a compelling reason for women who anticipate unpredictable provisioning to hedge their bets by lining up support from an array of allomothers (individuals other than the mother who help care for her offspring). Such allomothers might include her own kin as well as "possible" fathers and their kin.

Is there, then, never any reason—apart from capture, cloistering, clitoridectomies, constant surveillance, or monopolization of the resources women need to reproduce—for a woman to freely choose to remain with one man and be faithful to him? Of course there is: when spouses are compatibly matched, when the man is committed to staying, and especially when shared stakes in offspring or other endeavors are high enough. This is one reason why rates of DNA-detected misattributed paternity are inversely correlated with socioeconomic status.[81,82]

There are also,internalized reasons for women—even those without these incentives—to behave modestly. In many societies, a girl is taught that her status and that of her children depends on her "reputation" (one reason, other than claustration, why rates of misattributed paternity would be so low in populations such as orthodox Jews).[83] So too do women behave modestly when they are convinced from an early age that demons, damnation, or other punishments await those who transgress normative sex roles.[65] But otherwise (especially in societies that are matrilocal, bilocal, or neolocal, but even occasionally in those that are patrilineal), informal polyandry is more common.

At this point, some readers may be wondering about the bottom line: can polyandrous matings and confusion of paternity ever increase a woman's reproductive success? To date, the best-documented cases derive from lowland South America. In this part of the world there is a commonly accepted belief that fetuses are "built up" in a woman by multiple applications of semen from several different men (a biological fiction known to anthropologists as *partible paternity*).[73] A belief in partible paternity characterizes societies ranging over a vast area from central and eastern Brazil (the Mehinacu, the Kaingang, the Araweté, and the Curripaco) northeastward to the Bari and Yanomana of Venezuela, east to the Matis of Peru, all the way south to the Aché of Paraguay. A belief in partible paternity encompasses people belonging to at least six different language groups, tribes separated by thousands of miles, who presumably diverged from one another long ago. Such a belief, where it exists, reduces potential costs to mothers from polyandrous mating.[73]

Among the matrilocal hunter-gatherer-horticulturist Canela, virtually every child has several co-fathers. Indeed, the Canela are unusual for casting the web of possible paternity across more than a dozen different candidates since women engage in publicly sanctioned unions with many men, often having sexual intercourse with them as part of a designated ceremony.[64] Virtually every Canela child born has more than one possible father. Elsewhere in this "partible paternity zone," children are more

[d]This paper focuses on maternal rather than paternal perspectives; I do not discuss variation in parenting behavior by men.

likely to have only a couple of possible "fathers" or else only one. In these cases, it is possible for researchers to compare the survival chances of children who have attributed to them different numbers of possible fathers.

Behavioral ecologists Kim Hill and Magdalena Hurtado[67] (p. 444) report that 63% of Aché children from their demographically reconstructed (pre-contact) forest sample had one or more secondary fathers. Children with one primary and one secondary father had the highest survival rates, while those with only one, or with more than two (i.e., too many possible fathers), survived less well. Among the Bari, 80% of children (156 out of 194) with paternity ascribed to several "fathers" survived to age fifteen, compared to only 64% (404 out of 628 of children) with only one father a difference significant at the 0.001 level.[84] Beckerman *et al.*[73] attribute this greater survival to the gifts of food co-fathers provide.

Having several presumptive fathers is likely to be especially advantageous where one man may not be able to reliably provision a family, or where fathers are critical for offspring-survival but are also likely to die. (Throughout this area fatherless children are less likely to survive). Other demographic contingencies—such as a shortage of wives—can also increase pressure for polyandrous unions. Consider for example a case reported among the Yanomana, a people famous for the polygynous marriages of powerful males who accumulate many wives. Napoleon Chagnon's research provides sociobiologists their "chestnut" case for a traditional society in which a man's dominance status correlates with his reproductive success. What is often overlooked, however, is that (as with the Aché) a comprehensive view of Yanomana family systems must also include not only a wife's extra-pair matings, but also occasional polyandrous phases in the family dynamic. During the years just after the anthropologist John Peters contacted the Shirishana Yanomana, a period characterized by a shortage of women, there were nine polyandrous marriages and five monogamous ones.[59,85] (Although all the relevant parties lived together, these polyandrous marriages were informal and transient, so that the distinction between polyandrous marriage and polyandrous mating is not clear-cut.) All marriages begin monogamously. Thereafter, an extra wife will be added if such a woman is available and the husband prevails. But if wives are in short supply, it may be that an extra husband (who presumably has no better option than to marry polyandrously) is added. Furthermore it must be noted that if the first husband has a good chance of being the father of offspring sired and the additional father enhances the probability of their survival, or if the first husband benefits from the alliance with another man, paternal as well as maternal interests may be served by this arrangement. No doubt the belief in partible paternity facilitates such polyandrous unions. Nevertheless, monogamy among these people, was the most stable marital form, an uneasy compromise between maternal and paternal interests.

Everywhere, polyandrous unions and communal sharing of wives are fragile arrangements, especially after contact with outside groups. Among the Canela, there were both internal and external pressures that discouraged their persistence (e.g., disapproval by outside government agents and domestic changes within families as Canela men obtained jobs in the wage economy).[64] It is unusual in any traditional society for publicly sanctioned informal polyandry to survive contact with economic systems that produce competition for defensible resources. Even among people who persist in believing that paternity is partible among a wife's different sexual partners, patrilineal ownership of the means of production (probably a relatively recent innovation in the Amazonian partible paternity zone) can lead to a new puritanism. As ethnographer Paul Valentine describes for the Curripaco, these people continue to believe that infants are composites built up by multiple inseminators. Yet patrilineal ownership of productive land along the river has since developed among these people, making husbands increasingly intolerant of infidelity by wives—which persists, but in secret. At the root of this change, I suspect, is newly valuable property and the patrilineal transmission of this property. A desire to avoid confusion or conflict over patrilineal resources provides one reason why, if a Curripaco man dies, his widow is supposed to remain chaste or else marry a kinsman from the husband's patrilineage.[86]

Across cultures, polyandrous matings range from the extremes of publicly sanctioned ritual couplings among the Canela, or the wife-sharing of clan-based groups like the Masai, to the furtive unions that characterize all but the most coercively patriarchal societies. Through time and across space a broad range of female predispositions can be documented in ethnographic, historical, and even pre-historic accounts that linger on as folklore about the Maenads and their ilk. Species differences notwithstanding, across primates and across populations, the main factors determining how monandrous primate females are have less to do with the fact that they are the ovum-producing sex, than with their ecological and historical circumstances. Key variables include how much autonomy the female's local alliances permit her, and how successful males in her population are (and have traditionally or historically been) in excluding rivals and controlling female movements. A reliable generalization across primates, including humans, is that females who remain among their kin in female philopatric (or "matrilocal") arrangements have greater autonomy than those who live patrilocally.[87,88]

Until recently, I, like most sociobiologists, assumed that the female philopatry typical of social mammals, including most species of Old World monkeys, had been replaced by male philopatry among apes, and that this patrilocal way of life was "species-typical" and "universal" among both chimps and humans.[89] (p. 125) Many of those applying evolutionary perspectives to human behavior still take it for granted that in almost all traditional societies "sons stay near their families and daughters move away...."[5] (p. 477) It is a conclusion that initially rested on two points: the importance of closely bonded male relatives in chimps[90] and the finding that 70% of cultures in the ethnographic record are patrilocal.[91] Since 80% of patrilocal societies are polygynous, the presumption about male patrilocal residence seemed consistent with presumptions about uni-male polygynous family systems, and led to the conviction that early human mating systems could safely be assumed to be patrilocal and polygynous. Today, however, these assumptions are far from secure.

As evidence on chimp demography and genetics accumulates from long-term field studies, the residence patterns of chimps and other apes are looking a lot more complicated than previously assumed. If they can, female chimpanzees who find themselves on secure, food-rich territories stay near their mothers. Of 14 Gombe Stream females whose lives have been monitored since birth, six have remained, five transferred to new communities, and three have disappeared. Conversely, of 11 adult females present in 1995, five were natives, six were immigrants (see note 22 in Pusey *et al.*[92]). Furthermore, at the Tai field site (but not at Gombe), average degrees of genetic relatedness among adult males are no higher than among females.[24] Perhaps more to the point for those interested in maternal strategies, philopatric females (who also tend to be socially dominant) breed at an earlier age, produce offspring after shorter intervals, and produce offspring with high survival rates. The all-time record for female reproductive success among wild chimps (seven offspring) is held by Flo's daughter Fifi, who inherited her mother's territory (see also Harcourt *et al.* [93] (p. 267) for gorillas).[45,92] The moral is clear: those who can, stay; those who can't, migrate away to breed.

When we turn to the human ethnographic record, patrilocal residence and polygynous marriages do indeed predominate. But this record post-dates massive population shifts caused by rapidly expanding populations of post-Neolithic agriculturists and herders. No doubt inter-group raiding for women pre-dated the Neolithic, but defensible land and other material resources along with increasing rates of population growth would have intensified the pressure on men to remain near kin, enhancing patrilocal allegiance and the formation of fraternal interest groups.[91] The need to defend local resources makes sons the sex with greater resource-holding potential, and in patrilocal situations, the sex with the most reliable allies. Male offspring are then the obvious candidates to receive resources that are transmitted across generations, eventually leading to patrilineal inheritance and the development of related patriarchal institutions.[94]

Well suited to inter-group raiding, patrilineal groups expanded into areas that 10- and 20,000 years ago were occupied by hunter-gatherers living under variable conditions, often at very low densities. If we confine our surveys to hunter-gatherers still living more nearly as Pleistocene foragers did (for example, excluding those who depend on horses to hunt) 56% as opposed to 71% of societies are patrilocal (see Figure 2 in Ember).[95] The rest are matrilocal or, more commonly, bilocal. Wherever foragers live at low densities, or in unpredictable environments (e.g., with variable rainfall), kin ties are utilized to migrate away from adversity and to gravitate towards ecological, social, and reproductive opportunities. Both men and women should prefer locales with available resources. Mothers, however, might prefer groups offering allomaternal assistance in childrearing, while fathers might have quite different priorities (e.g., availability of fertile women).

I do not doubt that some early hominids lived patrilocally, relied on male-biased inheritance of status and hunting grounds, and developed many of the essential ingredients of patriarchal mindsets. But more and more I am impressed by how flexible and opportunistic many primates, including human foragers, are. What strikes me is how unwise it was to project a breeding system derived from one type of patrilocal and patrilineal human society onto bipedal (and hence "hominid") ancestors subsisting primarily on seeds and fruits 4 million years ago, or onto anatomically modern members of the genus *Homo* hunting and gathering and beginning to move out of Africa 100,000 years ago, or beginning to people the Pacific land masses and the New World 50- to 20,000 years ago. I can not think of any reason why the mating systems and preferences of these people would be less variable and less flexible than those of foragers today, or less variable than other "weedy" or highly adaptable primates like baboons, langur monkeys, or chimpanzees (formerly far more widely spread across Africa than they are today). If anything, greater control over their environment should have made humans more variable.

AS POWERFUL AS EVOLUTIONARY THEORY IS, WHY DO WE STILL NEED HISTORY?

Why does history matter for reconstructing the mating preferences of our ancestors? There are several reasons. Across primates, whether a female lives matrilocally or migrates out to breed has important implications for her freedom of movement and reproductive autonomy.[87,96] In matrilocal societies with bilateral inheritance like the Canela have, the mother's brother figures more importantly in the lives of young people than does their genetic father. Property passes through the mother to her brother's sons, rather than from a father to his own son. Although it has become virtually dogma among those applying evolutionary theory to human behavior that matrilineal arrangements developed as cultural adaptations to protect lineages from the consequences of female infidelity, I now think it likely that we had the sequence backwards. Uncertain paternity, we all assumed, promoted the development of matrilineal inheritance in the 15% or so of human societies in the world today where that system still prevails (see Hartung[74] for classic treatment; see also p. 272 in Daly and Wilson[2]and p. 432 in Pinker[5]). But matrilocal residence is a necessary precondition for the development of matrilineal systems,[97] and if (as I am now convinced) women in matrilocal societies have the most social leverage and reproductive autonomy, the opposite scenario seems just as plausible: women would be most likely to mate polyandrously with several men where support from matrilineal kin (including help provisioning young) provided them the social leverage to do so. Since I assume such patterns were more common prior to the Neolithic than afterwards (meaning prior to the introduction of herding, agriculture, settled living, higher population densities, and the greater emphasis on defendable property that these entail), history is essential to this interpretation.

In a species as opportunistic as human primates are, with outcomes so often dependent on which individuals happen to have the most leverage at the moment, history is enormously relevant for explaining phenomena like female mate preferences. Consider the case of women's preferences for "wealthy" providers, by now widely documented. It is often claimed that such preferences reflect innate female proclivities and supposedly evolved in their current form during humanity's "Environment of Evolutionary Adaptedness."[98] But are these preferences really innate? Or do they reflect women's adjusting to their circumstances? If the former, we have to explain why females evolved a preference for "wealthy" men (i.e., men with more resources than other men), a status that men in African foraging societies (like the !Kung San or the Hadza) scrupulously avoid. Furthermore, in sedentary, nonforaging societies, where wealth may indeed be a factor in women's choice of husband, wealth tends to be accumulated over time and thus concentrated in the hands of older men. How then to explain an evolved preference in women for older men who, even if still potent, might deliver along with their sperm an added load of genetic mutations?[99] Simplistic assertions about females preferring wealthy or dominant males to the contrary, we know a great deal more about how males compete with one another for access to mates than we know about the underlying criteria for female mate preferences, especially in situations where female choices are not constrained by male monopolization of resources. If, on the other hand, preferences for wealthy men are viewed as opportunistic (and quite possibly recent) adjustment to circumstances (discussed as the "patriarchal constraints" hypothesis in Hrdy[46]), we acknowledge that under some ecological, demographic, and historical circumstances women prefer men with access to the most resources without claiming to have demonstrated the existence of innate universal preferences. For, if preferences for men with resources is a response to patriarchal social structures (meaning patrilocality, patrilineal inheritance and institutions, and belief systems biased in favor of male reproductive interests and control of resources), and if patriarchal social organizations are only one possible type of human social arrangement, it does not follow that those same preferences will be found in societies where historically women's choices have been less constrained.

Supposedly evolutionary psychologists have already taken my challenge into account:

> An obvious retort is that women value wealthy and powerful men because it is the men who have the wealth and power. In a sexist society women have to marry up to get them. That alternative has been tested and refuted. Women with large salaries, postgraduate degrees, prestigious professions, and high self-esteem place a greater value on wealth and status in a husband than other women do. So do the leaders of feminist organizations. Poor men place no higher value on wealth or earning power in a wife than other men do. Among the Bakweri in Cameroon, the women are wealthier and more powerful than the men, and they still insist on men with money. (Pinker,[5] p. 482)

In other words, Pinker claims that data from the Bakweri provide the test case demonstrating an innate preference of women for men with property, as opposed to good genes, good sense, dependable character, or some other trait. So what is known about the Bakweri? Few cases would serve better to make my point that we can not claim to understand women's mate choices without taking into account the context—economic and historical—in which female mate preferences were expressed. For the Bakweri, as was also true in much of the U.S. until the 1870s and in England even later, are characterized by patrilineal inheritance of property. A woman's status and that of her children were largely determined by the status of the man she married. As late as the 1960s when this report on Bakweri land tenure was published:

> [a Bakweri] woman could not inherit land, nor could land used by her be inherited by anyone other than a male member of her husband's lineage...[100] (p. 319)

Bakweri women had the right to work the land, and may in fact do most of the work, but ownership depended on her husband's holdings. Even though a woman was able to earn in her own right, she might well perceive that she and her children had a stake in her husband's holdings. So far, the only thing the Bakweri case demonstrates is that there is a longstanding legal tradition in place that improves the odds that women continue to choose males on the basis of wealth.

From the perspective of men able to hold onto property, patrilineal inheritance has obvious reproductive advantages. It may even serve maternal interests if bands of related men protect her and her children from marauding males from other groups. But it is a way of life built around the assumption that the optimal number of "fathers" for any infant born to his mate will always be the same, just one—him. For women, however, not only the identity of the father, but the optimal number of "fathers" depends on circumstances. Whenever extensive and exclusive paternal investment is essential to produce quality offspring of enviable status, or where harsh penalties attend adultery, the mother's optimal number of fathers is likely to be the same as his, but otherwise, not necessarily.

The question then becomes: at what points in human evolution and history did patrilineal interests start to prevail? Are the consequences now inscribed in the genome of our (by bonobo standards) relatively chaste and extremely modest species? Or did evolution produce females more sensitive in this respect so that they could adapt quickly to local circumstances and customs that have long varied, and still do vary? This is one of the areas of mate preferences that we know least about, all too often overlooked in our eagerness to document essential male-female differences or to demonstrate just how "natural" patriarchal arrangements are. Yet just as social scientists can not hope to understand human affairs without taking into account evolution, I am convinced that evolutionists cannot do so without taking into account history.

ACKNOWLEDGMENTS

I am indebted to human behavioral ecologists Kristen Hawkes and Steve Beckerman, as well as to all those who participated in the 1999 AAAS conference entitled *Partible Paternity* organized by S. Beckerman and P. Valentine. I am also thankful to fellow sociobiologist P.A. Gowaty for inspiring me to think about constraints on female choice in new ways. And I thank A. Harcourt, J. Hartung, D. Hrdy, D. Judge, M. Borgerhoff-Mulder, Ray Hames, W. Skinner, R. Stallman, and M. Towner for valuable discussion and criticism.

REFERENCES

1. Darwin, C. 1871 [1974 reprint]. The Descent of Man and Selection in Relation to Sex. Gale Research Co. Detroit, MI.
2. Daly, M. & M. Wilson. 1978. Sex, Evolution and Behavior. Thompson/Duxbury Press. North Scituate, MA.
3. Trivers, R. 1972. Parental investment and sexual selection. *In* Sexual Selection and the Descent of Man. B. Campbell, Ed. Aldine. Chicago, IL.
4. Symons, D. 1982. Another woman that never existed. Quart. Rev. Biol. **57(3):** 297–300.
5. Pinker, S. 1997. How the Mind Works. Norton. New York.
6. Pinker, S. 1998. Boys will be boys: an evolutionary explanation for presidents behaving badly. New Yorker (Feb. 9): 30–31.
7. Byers, J.A. 1997. American Pronghorn: Social Adaptations and the Ghosts of Predators Past. University of Chicago Press. Chicago, IL.
8. Petrie, M. 1994. Improved growth and survival of peacocks with more elaborate trains. Nature **371**: 598–599.
9. Gowaty, P.A. 1996. Battles of the sexes and origins of monogamy. *In* Partnerships in Birds: The Study of Monogamy. J.M. Black, Ed.: 21–52. Oxford University Press. Oxford, England.
10. Gowaty, P.A., Ed. 1997. Feminism and Evolutionary Biology: Boundaries, Intersections and Frontiers. Chapman and Hall. New York.
11. Gowaty, P.A. 1997. Sexual dialectics, sexual selection, and variation in reproductive behavior. *In* Feminism and Evolutionary Biology. Chapman and Hall. New York.
12. Petrie, M., C. Doums & A.P. Møller. 1998. The degree of extra-pair paternity increases with genetic variability. Proc. Natl. Acad. Sci. USA **95:** 9390–9395.
13. Smith, R. 1984. Human sperm competition. *In* Sperm Competition and the Evolution of Mating Systems. R. L. Smith, Ed.: 601–609. Academic Press. New York.
14. Baker, R.R. & M.A. Bellis. 1995. Human Sperm Competition: Copulation, Masturbation and Infidelity. Chapman and Hall. London.

15. EBERHARD, W.G. 1996. Female Control: Sexual Selection by Cryptic Female Choice. Princeton University Press. Princeton, NJ.
16. THORNHILL, R. & S.W. GANGESTAD. 1996. The evolution of human sexuality. Trends Ecol. Evol. **11 (2):** 98–102.
17. WINTERBOTTOM, M., T. BURKE & T.R. BIRKHEAD. 1999. A stimulatory phalloid organ in a weaver bird. Nature **399:** 28.
18. SYMONS, D. 1979. The Evolution of Human Sexuality. Oxford University Press. Oxford, England.
19. ZEH, J.A., S.D. NEWCOMER & D.W. ZEH. 1998. Polyandrous females discriminate against previous mates. Proc. Natl. Acad. Sci. USA **95:** 13732–13736.
20. NEWCOMER, S., J.A. ZEH & D.W. ZEH. 1999. Genetic benefits enhance the reproductive success of polyandrous females. Proc. Natl. Acad. Sci. USA **96:** 10236–10241.
21. HRDY, S.B. 1977. The Langurs of Abu: Female and Male Strategies of Reproduction. Harvard University Press. Cambridge, MA.
22. SMALL, M. 1993. Female Choices: Sexual Behavior of Female Primates. Cornell University Press. Ithaca, NY.
23. GAGNEUX, P., D.S. WOODRUFF & C. BOESCH. 1999. Female reproductive strategies, paternity and community structure in wild West African chimpanzees. Anim. Behav. **57:** 19–32.
24. MADSEN, T., R. SHINE, J. LOMAN & T. HAKANSSON. 1992. Why do female adders copulate so frequently? Nature **355:** 440–441.
25. HOOGLAND, J. 1998. Why do Gunnison's prairie dogs copulate with more than one male? Anim. Behav. **55:** 351–359.
26. BAER, B. & P. SCHMID-HEMPEL. 1999. Experimental variation in polyandry affects parasite loads and fitness in a bumblebee. Nature **397:** 151–153.
27. PARISH, A.R. & F.B.M. DE WAAL. 1992. Bonobos fish for sweets: the female sex-for-food connection. Abstracts XIVth Congr. Internatl. Primatol. Soc. Strasbourg, France.
28. DE WAAL, F.B.M. & F. LANTING. 1997. Bonobo: The Forgotten Ape. University of California Press. Berkeley, CA
29. KNIGHT, C. 1991. Blood Relations: Menstruation and the Origins of Culture. Yale University Press. New Haven, CT.
30. HRDY, S.B. 1979. Infanticide among animals: a review, classification and examination of the implications for the reproductive strategies of females. Ethol. Sociobiol. **1:** 3–40.
31. SOMMER, V. 1994. Infanticide among the langurs of Jodhpur: testing the sexual selection hypothesis with a long-term record. *In* Infanticide and Parental Care. S. Parmigani & F. vom Saal, Eds. Harwood Academic Publishers. Switzerland.
32. LAUNHARDT, K., C. EPPLEN, J.T. EPPLEN & P. WINKLER. 1998. Amplification of microsatellites adapted from human systems in faecal DNA of wild Hanuman langurs (*Presbytis entellus*). Electrophoresis **19:** 1356–1361.
33. BORRIES, C., K. LAUNHARDT, C. EPPLEN & P. WINKLER. 1999. DNA analyses support the hypothesis that infanticide is adaptive in langur monkeys. Proc. Roy. Soc. Lond. B **266:** 901–904.
34. PERRIGO, G. & F. VOM SAAL. 1994. Behavioral cycles and the neural timing of infanticide and parental behavior in male house mice. *In* Infanticide and Parental Care. S. Parmigiano & F. vom Saal, Eds.: 365–396. Harwood Academic Publishers. Switzerland.
35. ALTMANN, J. 1980. Baboon Mothers and Infants. Harvard University Press. Cambridge, MA.
36. PALOMBIT, R. 1999. Infanticide and the evolution of pair bonds in nonhuman primates. Evol. Anthropol. **7(4):** 117–129.
37. BURKE, T., N.B. DAVIES, M.W. BRUFORD & B.J. HATCHWELL. 1989. Paternal care and mating behaviour of polyandrous dunnocks *Prunella modularis* related to paternity by DNA fingerprinting. Nature **338:** 249–251.
38. DAVIES, N.B. 1992. Dunnock Behaviour and Social Evolution. Oxford University Press. Oxford, England.
39. NAKAMURA, M. 1990. Cloacal protuberance and copulatory behavior of the alpine accentor (*Prunella collaris*). The Auk **107:** 284–295.
40. NAKAMURA, M. 1998. Multiple mating and cooperative breeding in polygynandrous alpine accentors. I. Competition among females. Anim. Behav. **55:** 259–275.

41. Nakamura, M. 1998. Multiple mating and cooperative breeding in polygynandrous alpine accentors. II. Male mating tactics. Anim. Behav. **55:** 277–289.
42. Darwin, C. 1876. Sexual Selection in Relation to Monkeys. Nature **15:** 18–19.
43. Wrangham, R. 1993. The evolution of sexuality in chimpanzees and bonobos. Hum. Nature **4(1):** 447–480.
44. Wallis, J. &. Y. Almasi. 1995. A survey of reproductive parameters in free-ranging chimpanzees (*Pan troglodytes*). Paper presented at the 18th Annual Meeting of Am. Soc. Primatol., June 21–24, 1995.
45. Hrdy, S.B. 1986. Empathy, polyandry and the myth of the coy female. *In* Feminist Approaches to Science. R. Bleier, Ed. Pergamon Press. New York.
46. Hrdy, S.B. 1997. Raising Darwin's consciousness: female sexuality and the prehominid origins of patriarchy. Hum. Nature **8:** 1–49.
47. van Noordwijk, M. 1985. Sexual behaviour of Sumatran long-tailed macaques (*Maca fascicularis*). Z. Tierpsychol **70:** 177–196.
48. Andelman, S. 1987. Evolution of concealed ovulation in vervet monkeys (*Cercopithecus aethiops*). Am. Naturalist. **129(6):** 785–799.
49. Takahata, Y. 1980. The reproductive biology of a free-ranging troop of Japanese monkeys. Primates **21:** 303–329.
50. Buchanon-Smith, H. & T.R. Jordan. 1992. An experimental investigation of the pair bond in the Callitrichid monkey. Int. J. Primatol. **13(1):** 51–72.
51. Palombit, R. 1992. Pair bonds and monogamy in wild siamangs (*Hylobates syndactylus*) and whitehanded gibbon (*Hylobates lar*) in northern Sumatra. Ph.D. thesis, University of California, Davis, CA.
52. Wallen, K. 1990. Desire and ability: hormones and the regulation of female sexual behavior. Neurosci. Biobehav. Rev. **14:** 233–241.
53. Bercovitch, F. B. 1999. Sex skin. Encycl. Reprod. **6:** 437–443.
54. Stanislaw, H. & F.J. Rice. 1988. Correlation between sexual desire and menstrual cycle characteristics. Arch. Sex. Res. **17(6):** 499–508.
55. Penton-Voak, I.S., D.I. Perrett, D.L. Castles, T. Kobayashi, D.M. Burt, L.K. Murray & R. Minamisawa. 1999. Menstrual cycle alters face preference. Nature **399:** 741-42.
56. Lovejoy, O. 1981. The origins of man. Science **211:** 241–250.
57. van Noordwijk, M. & C. van Schaik. 2000. Reproductive patterns in mammals: Adaptations against infanticide? *In* Infanticide by Males and Its Implications. C. van Schaik & C. Janson, Eds. Cambridge University Press. Cambridge, England.
58. Mason, W. 1966. Social organization of the South American monkey, *Callicebus moloch*: a preliminary report. Tulane Studies Zool. **13:** 23-28.
59. Peters, J.F. & C.L. Hunt. 1975. Polyandry among the Yanomana Shirishana. J. Comp. Fam. Stud. **6:** 197–207.
60. Smedley, A. 1980. The implications of Birom ciscisbeism. J. Comp. Fam. Stud. **XI(3):** 345–357.
61. Broude, G.J. 1994. Marriage, Family and Relationships: A Cross-Cultural Encyclopedia. ABC-CLIO. Santa Barbara, CA.
62. Guyer, J. 1994. Lineal identities and lateral networks: the logic of polyandrous motherhood. *In* Nuptiality in Sub-Saharan Africa—Contemporary Anthropological and Demographic Perspectives. C. Bledsoe and G. Pison, Eds.: 231–252. Clarendon Press. Oxford, England.
63. Sangree, W.H. 1980. The persistence of polyandry in Irigwe, Nigeria. J. Comp. Fam. Stud. **XI(3):** 335–343.
64. Crocker, W. & J. Crocker. 1994. The Canela: Bonding through Kinship, Ritual and Sex. Harcourt Brace. Fort Worth, TX.
65. Hrdy, S.B. 1999. Mother Nature: A History of Mothers, Infants, and Natural Selection. Pantheon. New York.
66. Kaplan, H. 1997. The evolution of the human life course. *In* The Biodemography of Longevity: Between Zeus and the Salmon. K. Wachter & C. Finch, Eds.: 175–211. National Academy Press. Washington, DC.
67. Hill, K. & A.M. Hurtado. 1996. Aché Life History: The Ecology and Demography of a Foraging People. Aldine de Gruyter. New York.

68. Hawkes, K., J.F. O'Connell, N.G. Blurton-Jones, H. Alvarez & E.L. Charnov. 1998. Grandmothering, menopause, and the evolution of human life histories. Proc. Natl. Acad. Sci. USA **95:** 1336–1339.
69. Tew, M. [subsequently Douglas, M.] 1951. A form of polyandry among the Lele of the Kadai. J. Afric. Institute **XXI(1):** 1–12.
70. Smith, M. G. 1953. Secondary marriage in northern Nigeria. Africa **23:** 298–323.
71. Muller, J.C. 1980. On the relevance of having two husbands: contributions to the study of polygynous-polyandrous marital forms on the Jos Plateau. J. Comp. Fam. Stud. **XI(3):** 359–369.
72. Hakansson, T. 1988. Bridewealth, Women and Land: Social Change among the Gusi of Kenya. Uppsala Studies in Cultural Anthropology 10.
73. Beckerman, S., R. Lizarralde, C. Ballew, S. Schroeder, C. Fingelton, A. Garrison & H. Smith. 1998. The Bari partible paternity project: preliminary results. Curr. Anthropol. **39:** 164–167.
74. Hartung, J. 1985. Matrilineal inheritance: new theory and analysis. Behav. Brain Sci. **8:** 661–688.
75. Berndt, R.M & C.H. Berndt. 1951. Sexual behavior in Western Arnhem Land. Viking Fund Publications in Anthropology. No. 16. The Viking Fund. New York.
76. Befu, H. 1968. Origins of large households and duo-local residence in Central Japan. Am. Anthropol. **70:** 309–319.
77. Shih, Chuan-Kang. 1993. The Youngning Moso: sexual union, household organization, and ethnicity in a matrilineal duo-local society in southwest China. Ph.D. dissertation, Stanford University, Stanford, CA.
78. Hawkes, K., J.F. O'Connell & N.G. Blurton-Jones. Hadza hunting and the evolution of the nuclear family. Unpublished ms. University of Utah.
79. Masters, W.H. & V.E. Johnson. 1966. Human Sexual Response: 158–159. Little, Brown. Boston, MA.
80. Barrett, G., E. Pendry, J. Peacock, C. Victor, R. Thakar & I. Manyonda. 1999. Women's sexuality after childbirth: a pilot study. Arch. Sex. Behav. **28(2):** 179–191.
81. Baker, R.R. 1999. Sperm wars: a study of multiple mating in Britain. Paper presented at the AAAS Meeting, Anaheim, CA, Jan. 24.
82. Cerda-Flores, R.M., S.A. Barton, L.F. Marty-Gonzalez, F. Rivas & R. Chakraborty. 1999. Estimation of non-paternity in the Mexican population of Nuevo Leon: a validation study with blood group markers. Am. J. Phys. Anthropol. **109:** 281–283.
83. Boster, J. S., R. R. Hudson & S. J. C. Gaulin. 1999. High paternity certainties of Jewish priests. Am. Anthropol. **100(4):** 967–971.
84. Beckerman, S. 1999. The concept of partible paternity among native South Americans. Paper presented at AAAS Meeting, Anaheim, CA, Jan. 24, 1999.
85. Peters, J.F. 1982. Polyandry among the Yanomana Shirishana Revisited. J. Comp. Fam. Stud. **13:** 89–95.
86. Valentine, P. 1999. Fathers that never exist: exclusion of the role of shared father among the Curripaco of the Northwest Amazon. Paper presented at AAAS meeting, Anaheim, CA, Jan. 24, 1999.
87. Hrdy, S.B. 1981. The Woman that Never Evolved. Harvard University Press. Cambridge, MA.
88. Ross, M.H. 1986. Female political participation: a cross-cultural explanation. Am. Anthropol. **88:** 843–858.
89. Wrangham, R. & D. Peterson. 1996. Demonic Males: Apes and the Origins of Human Violence. Houghton Mifflin. Boston, MA.
90. Rodseth, L., R. W. Wrangham, A. Harrigan & B. B. Smuts. 1991. The human community as a primate society. Curr. Anthropol. **32:** 221–254.
91. Witkowsi, S. R. & W. T. Divale. 1996. Kin groups, residence and descent. *In* Encyclopedia of Cultural Anthropology, Vol. 2. D. Levinson & M. Ember, Eds.: 673–680. Henry Holt. New York.
92. Pusey, A., J. Williams & J. Goodall. 1997. The influence of dominance rank on the reproductive success of female chimpanzees. Science **277:** 828–831.
93. Harcourt, A., P.H. Harvey, S.G. Larson & R.V. Short. 1981. Testis weight, body weight and breeding system in primates. Nature **293:** 55–57.

94. Hrdy, S.B. & D.S. Judge. 1993. Darwin and the puzzle of primogeniture: an essay on biases in parental investment after death. Hum. Nature **4:** 1–46.
95. Ember, C. 1975. Residential variation among hunter-gatherers. Behav. Sci. Res. **3:** 199–227.
96. Smuts, B. 1992. Male aggression against women: an evolutionary perspective. Hum. Nature **3:** 1–44.
97. Aberle, D.F. 1961. Matrilineal descent in cross-cultural perspective. *In* Matrilineal Kinship. D. M. Schneider & K. Gough, Eds.: 666–727. University of California Press. Berkeley, CA.
98. Buss, David. 1994. The Evolution of Desire. Basic Books. New York.
99. Crow, J. 1999. The odds of losing at genetic roulette. Nature **397:** 293–294.
100. Ardener, E., S. Ardener & W.A. Warmington. 1960. Plantation and village in the Cameroons: some economic and social studies. Oxford University Press. Oxford, England. [Published for Nigerian Institute of Social and Economic Research.]
101. Wyckoff, G.J., W. Wang & C-I. Wu. 2000. Rapid evolution of male reproductive genes in the descent of man. Nature **403:** 304–309.

The Other "Closest Living Relative"

How Bonobos (*Pan paniscus*) Challenge Traditional Assumptions about Females, Dominance, Intra- and Intersexual Interactions, and Hominid Evolution

AMY R. PARISH[a,b] AND FRANS B. M. DE WAAL[c]

[a]*Department of Anthropology, University College London, Gower Street, London WC1E 6BT, England*

[c]*Living Links Center, Yerkes Regional Primate Center, and the Psychology Department, Emory University, Atlanta, Georgia, USA*

ABSTRACT: Chimpanzee (*Pan troglodytes*) societies are typically characterized as physically aggressive, male-bonded and male-dominated. Their close relatives, the bonobos (*Pan paniscus*), differ in startling and significant ways. For instance, female bonobos bond with one another, form coalitions, and dominate males. A pattern of reluctance to consider, let alone acknowledge, female dominance in bonobos exists, however. Because both species are equally "man's" closest relative, the bonobo social system complicates models of human evolution that have historically been based upon referents that are male and chimpanzee-like. The bonobo evidence suggests that models of human evolution must be reformulated such that they also accommodate: real and meaningful female bonds; the possibility of systematic female dominance over males; female mating strategies which encompass extra-group paternities; hunting and meat distribution by females; the importance of the sharing of plant foods; affinitive inter-community interactions; males that do not stalk and attack and are not territorial; and flexible social relationships in which philopatry does not necessarily predict bonding pattern.

INTRODUCTION

> Chimpanzees and bonobos provide two kinds of connections between humans and the rest of the animal world. One is historical: they suggest what our ancestors were like and how we have evolved from a chimpanzee-like form around 6,000,000 years ago. The other is conceptual: they offer the opportunity to understand the functional significance of traits they share with us. The flowering of behavioral diversity between populations is one such trait.[1] (p. 6)

The study of wild-living chimpanzees (*Pan troglodytes*) is a relatively young discipline, having begun in earnest only in the 1960s. In just under forty years, however, field research projects on the behavioral ecology of chimpanzee populations have multiplied from three to more than forty-five.[1,2] The realization that chimpanzees possess tremendous behavioral, genetic, demographic, and morphologic variability across populations has rapidly replaced the initial perception that chimpanzees are static, forest-dwelling, arboreal, vegetarian, peaceful apes. This diversity has been

[b]Address for correspondence: 961 Sapphire Street, San Diego, California 92109, USA.

characterized as the "main finding on chimpanzees of the last decades."[3] (p. 455) Relatively simplistic "species-typical" generalizations require revision to acknowledge tremendous variation both within and between populations. And yet the urge to compare and quantify chimpanzee social systems with our own makes it difficult to resist characterization of "the chimpanzee"—particularly when those stereotypes mirror traditional assumptions about the last common ancestor (e.g., male-bonded, male-dominated, physically aggressive societies).

Another species exists in the genus *Pan*, and this confounds generalization even further. This species, the bonobo (*Pan paniscus*), is equally complex, equally genetically related to humans,[4,5] and therefore, equally relevant to an understanding of human evolution. Patterns of sociality among bonobos differ from those in chimpanzees, however, in startling and dramatic ways. With so much variation within and between populations of both species, simplistic characterization of humanity's "closest living relative" becomes daunting.

The problematic nature of "species-typical" descriptions is not particular to the study of chimpanzees and bonobos. Intensive field research on a number of primate species has unearthed diversity in social systems that either contradicts or complicates more simplistic traditional descriptions. For instance, until recently, primatology textbooks described gorillas as terrestrial and folivorous, gibbons as living in "monogamous" nuclear family units, and orangutans as solitary and asocial. Yet recent observations reveal that some gorilla populations are arboreal and frugivorous,[6] that individuals in some gibbon groups engage in extra-pair copulations and form flexible living arrangements involving multiple adult individuals of the same sex,[8–10] and that orangutan females in some populations coalesce and socialize when ecologically feasible.[11,12] The focus in primate research now emphasizes behavioral flexibility, behavioral diversity, and local environmental differences.[1,13,14]

Long-nurtured ideas about our closest relatives aren't easily relinquished, however. In the same way that paleontologists prefer their fossil finds to belong to a human ancestor rather than to an extinct side-branch, experts on ape behavior sometimes claim that their subjects are the only or best model for the last common *Pan*–human ancestor. Although bonobos are occasionally proposed for this distinction,[15,16] chimpanzee models have long reigned supreme in this arena. This is due both to the paucity of information on bonobos and to the salience of particular features of chimpanzee sociality in supporting favored assumptions about the last common ancestor. Recent discoveries of social systems in bonobos, also "our closest relative," which are based upon sex rather than warfare, fruit sharing rather than hunting and meat sharing, life-long maternal influence, and female rather than male dominance have met with a mixed reception. While they have delighted some, they have obviously disturbed others.

At least four strategies have emerged to keep bonobos at a distance and thus preserve chimpanzee-based scenarios of human evolution. The first strategy is to describe the bonobo as an interesting but specialized anomaly than can be safely ignored as a possible model of the last shared ancestor.[17] The second and third strategies are to argue that the differences between chimpanzees and bonobos are inflated. Bonobos, it is argued, are more similar to chimpanzees than is typically acknowledged.[18] Conversely, chimpanzees are arguably more like bonobos.[3,19,20] Finally, the very data themselves are either called into question because of "contextual biases [which] ... represent the situating of ideas and interpretations of evidence in terms of the perspective the researcher brings to the research"[18] (p. 406) or dismissed out of hand simply because some revelations stem from data collected on captive bonobos (ibid.).

Several of these positions have some merit. Chimpanzees and bonobos are much closer to each other genetically, morphologically and phylogenetically than either is to humans.[4] Obviously, we expect similarities between two closely related species within the same genus. Equally, we expect that variation in ecological opportunity and constraint will have led to diverse selection pressures and consequent differences in behavior after speciation. Substantial differences between closely related species are already well documented for other primate genera: hamadryas and savannah baboons diverge significantly in phenotype and behavior.[21,22] Likewise, stumptail and rhesus macaques are different in many regards including temperament and dominance style, despite their status as congeners.[23] Likewise, brown and white-fronted capuchins live in the same forest, yet differ in degree of competition among males, female choice, and sexual coercion.[24]

These differences between closely related species offer a caution in terms of extrapolating about our own ancestors: while pattern-matching between extant species and human behavior is undoubtedly intriguing, without an understanding of the causes and value of *variation* in the behavior pattern, little can be inferred with respect to the human evolutionary *process*. At present, the task of identifying which traits are typical within and across populations, let alone shared or not among the three species, is hampered by a paucity of data on bonobos in particular. This article discusses relatively new and sometimes contentious information on dominance patterns and social systems that are of relevance in assessing commonality among the members of the *Pan–Homo* clade.

DOMINANCE AMONG BONOBOS

Despite good and widespread evidence that females behave towards males in ways consistent with the behavioral characteristic typically termed "dominance,"[25–27] categorization of bonobos as a species with "female dominance" is resisted in some quarters. The literature abounds with equivocation. Females are variously described as "co-dominant"[17] (p. 205), "almost co-dominant"[28] (p. 142), "about the same rank" as males[29] (pp. 188–189), or having "close to" male status[30] (p. 174), and "appropriate[ly] respect[ful]" of males.[29] (p. 146) More than a few researchers conclude that dominance relationships are "not clear and invariable" in this species[29] (p. 146) or that a "narrowing status gap" exists.[31] (p. 2) Apparent female dominance is explained away as "female feeding priority coupled with male social dominance"[32] (p. 415) and females are described pejoratively as "irritable", "troublesome"[29] (pp. 146, 188–189) or "daring."[33] (p. 68) Males, in contrast are "tolerant" of females[33] (p. 68), "allow" females to have the upper hand[18] (p. 404), or are "henpecked."[29] (p. 146) Because males remain in control and defer by choice, their puzzling behavior (rather than their plight) can be comfortably explained as "strategic male deference"[34] or even "chivalry."[32] (p. 415)

Consider the following: Three separate instances occurred in the wild in which a female: (*a*) attacked a male after he aggressively interrupted her mating with another (lower-ranking) male; (*b*) "savagely attacked" the male she had been mating with when he was threatened by a higher-ranking male; and (*c*) "screamed furiously and attacked" a male who had rejected her invitation (presentation) for sexual interaction. Although the latter male fled, other females joined in the pursuit. He eventually found safety in a tree and "escaped disaster."[29] (p. 146)

These situations suggest that females are very much in control of their reproductive and social interactions. Yet intersexual interactions in this group are summarized in non-definitive terms where females are active or assertive in sexual interactions and are still not perceived (by human observers!) as clearly dominant, such that: "High-ranking males usually receive appropriate respect from lower-ranking males, and certainly from females. Females, however, can get irritable, and if they do, even high-ranking males cannot touch them."[29] (p. 146)

Are chimpanzees males merely "irritable" when they launch aggressive attacks on, displace, or claim resources from females? Were the roles reversed, such that males had "aggressed" and females submitted, male dominance would clearly spring to mind. The dismissive nature inherent in much of the interpretation of the data is not parsimonious to say the least.

Unconventional interpretations of female dominance in the context of feeding exist in the literature as well. In a comparison of chimpanzees and bonobos, Stanford[18] suggests that the dominance patterns of bonobos more strongly resemble those of chimpanzees when feeding priority is considered separately from "social dominance". This opinion is based upon a single abstract[34] that is unsupported by any peer-reviewed presentation of data. That the report is incorporated into and relied upon (and reported to "have shown" male deference rather than female dominance) in a major comparative review of the genus *Pan*[18] is surprising.

Others, however, acknowledge a more active female role. A description of typical feeding interactions provided by T. Furuichi, a field researcher working at Wamba, is illustrative:

> Especially when feeding, females have priority of access to desirable feeding sites. Males usually appeared ... first, but they *surrendered* when females arrived. Females fed in the central part of the feeding site in aggregation. Males with mothers in the unit-group could feed centrally, but those without mothers could not. Although males rarely showed submissive behaviors to individual *young* females, they behaved quite submissively to the female aggregation, and females sometimes formed alliances and attacked males.[30] (p.195 [emphasis added])

Males may locate food (e.g., fruit trees—although 20% of parties at Lomako contain only females who, presumably, also locate food),[35] but females in the wild claim and control it, occupy the feeding site, control the party composition, favor sons of female group-mates, discriminate against motherless males (and thereby even control mating opportunity for males), and attack males. While male-to-female aggression both within and between groups is "mild," female-to-male aggressive episodes are "fierce" and involve chasing, beating, and biting.[36] (p. 180) Mothers intervene in, and sometimes decide the outcome of, male-male aggression. Rank in fully adult males is often dependent on that of their mothers.[30,37,39] Likewise, in captivity, females control access to desirable food, share it more often with each other than with males, engage in same-sex sexual interactions with one another, prefer to associate and affiliate with other females, and form alliances in which they cooperatively attack males and inflict blood drawing injuries.[26,27]

Even in terms of meat-eating and -acquisition (a "male" activity often given a central role in models of human evolution), bonobos depart from conventional wisdom.

TABLE 1. Observed behaviors in bonobos: proposed and parsimonious explanations

Phenomenon	Proposed explanation	Parsimonious explanation
Females chase males from food	Males defer to females	Females dominate males
Females associate	Females tolerate each other's presence	Females desire one another's company
Sexual interactions encourage peace	Interactions are dominance, not sex	Tension-reduction
Absence of lethal aggression	Aggression just has not been observed	Bonobos are more peaceful
Absence of infanticidal acts	Infanticide just has not been observed	Infanticide not advantageous, paternity-certainty low

In the wild, females hunt, possess and distribute meat.[40,41] They share with each other, but mostly not with males, even though, in one case, "the highest-ranking male of the group had a temper tantrum on a branch below the feasting females."[41] (p. 409)

Is intersexual interaction in bonobos best explained as "strategic male deference" or female dominance? Researchers with the most field experience offer an unequivocal appraisal: females dominate males. Barbara Fruth characterizes the pattern thus: "Females show a high degree of association, form coalitions, and dominate the society."[35](p. vii) She bases her conclusion on 4,400 field hours and 1,200 hours of direct observation in the Lomako Forest between 1990 and 1994.

Likewise, T. Kano, the premier field worker and expert on wild-living bonobos, has recently updated his assessment and forcefully endorsed a female dominance characterization of bonobo social systems. He argues that since almost all agonistic episodes and most dominance interactions occur in the feeding context, it is meaningless to separate dominance in this context from that in others. Furthermore, he notes that *in any event*, no difference exists between dominance interactions in feeding and non-feeding contexts: males submit to "dominant females" in both situations.[42]

A pattern of reluctance to consider, let alone acknowledge, female dominance in bonobos exists, as reviewed here, but this seems to be largely limited to those least unacquainted with the existing data on bonobos in captivity and the wild. A comparison of observed phenomena with parsimonious and proposed explanations (TABLE 1) illustrates the pattern. One wonders whether the lament that primatologists rarely consider the influence of male behavior on female behavior,[43] actually betrays exactly the opposite deficit when it comes to "man's" closest relative.

SOCIAL SYSTEMS COMPARED: THE TRADITIONAL VIEW

The reluctance to acknowledge female dominance in bonobos can be partially understood in terms of historical background and theoretical expectation. Since the early 1980s, primate social systems have been analyzed in terms of female reproductive strategies in relation to food distribution: Ecology influences female distribution (and hence female-female relationships). The distribution of females then is the primary determinant of the distribution of males (and hence male-male and male-female relationships).[44] Patterns of dispersal are predictive of patterns of bonding.

Given the predictions of kin selection, a connection between philopatry, consanguinity, and cooperation is expected.[45]

Social groups in primates in which females are lifelong residents of their natal groups and display differentiated female relationships (e.g., based on grooming or dominance) are classified as "female-bonded." Since no ape species is female-philopatric, the Hominoidea have traditionally been classed as "non-female-bonded" (which carries with it the implication that female relationships are "uniformly unimportant and undifferentiated."[44] At least some chimpanzee societies appear to conform to the predictions of the model,[46–49] while others may not.[20,50] Bonobos almost certainly do not, as delineated below.

Chimpanzees

Until recently, *Pan* social systems seemed to fit the predictions derived from kin selection and female-bonding theory. In traditional descriptions of chimpanzees, males are the philopatric sex and also the sex that forms intense life-long cooperative bonds. These bonds are presumed to confer inclusive fitness benefits. The females, by virtue of being the dispersing sex, are unrelated and avoidant, neutral, or aggressive towards one another. Males are often physically aggressive to females, and females spend the majority of their non-estrous time foraging within solitary ranges accompanied only by dependent offspring.

Bonobos

As in chimpanzees, females are the dispersing sex . In contrast to chimpanzees, male-male sociality is diminished in bonobo society. This is puzzling given male inter-relatedness. Males and females associate and affiliate (e.g. groom) on a regular basis, regardless of female reproductive state (estrous, non-estrous, pregnant, lactating).[30] These aspects of intersexual behavior in bonobos appear to parallel aspects of the "human pair bonds" central to many models of human evolution.[51–53]

Humans

In humans, the ancestral suite of social characteristics is often assumed to involve closed social networks coupled with female exogamy and a consequent lack of alliances among women.[54–56] Surveys of contemporary human societies reveal that approximately 70% have patrilocal residency patterns as opposed to matrilocal or neolocal residency.[57] These residency patterns are roughly equivalent to male philopatric groupings in apes. Apes and humans are thought to share features of female sociality that differ from those in "female-bonded species" like Old World monkeys: that is, Hominoid females may have tolerant relationships with a potential for friendliness, but they rarely form coalitions.[56]

SOCIAL SYSTEMS COMPARED: THE REVISED VIEW

Many of these characterizations of social systems just elucidated demand revision or qualification. Although both chimpanzee and bonobo males are philopatric,[58] most often, but not always, in conjunction with female dispersal,[59] the relationships between dispersal pattern, bonding, and even relatedness do not always follow theoretical prediction.

Chimpanzees

In the case of chimpanzees, the connection between male philopatry and male relatedness is negated in at least some communities by a recently discovered female mating strategy. Female chimpanzees in the Taï Forest, Ivory Coast, routinely give birth to infants sired by males from other communities.[60] Non-community males have sired half the offspring in the study group over a five-year period. This extra-group mating behavior may be a general feature of chimpanzee mating systems as it also occurs in two other chimpanzee study groups (in Gombe[61] and in Bossou[62]), although males are, on average, still related on the order of half-siblings at Gombe.[58]

This finding has extraordinary implications for male relatedness: Taï Forest males are no more related to one another than are the females in the group, despite their philopatry.[63] Cooperative behavior, then, is unlikely to stem from kin selection for inclusive fitness benefits. Decreased average relatedness in both sexes may in part explain the more "bisexual bonding" patterns in the Taï community, which are described by Boesch.[20,64] In Gombe, the potential for extra-group paternities may be especially desirable given that half the females in this community do not disperse .[59]

Bonobos

As in the chimpanzee examples described above, molecular analysis reveals that three of ten juvenile bonobos in the Lomako Forest study population have no potential father within the community. In the remaining seven, all but one male in the group can be excluded as a potential father. If that male did indeed father those infants, then the reproductive variance among males appears remarkably high. As the male is a potential, rather than a definite father, the possibility remains that even more (40 to 100 percent) of the infants born to community females were not sired by community males.[65]

Thus, the relatedness-philopatry connection may also be decoupled in bonobos due to extra-group paternities. Likewise, the expected bonding-philopatry relationship is *certainly* decoupled in bonobos, but not in the direction previously assumed. Association and affiliation between males and females is not the most prevalent category of association. The intersexual interactions that were once perceived as pair bonds have been revealed with further study to be enduring mother-son bonds. In fact, bonds between males and females (particularly young females) are actually rather weak. This suggests that male-female pair bonds are not responsible for social cohesiveness in bonobos.[30]

Instead, the closest bonds among *unrelated* individuals are maintained between females who are remarkably skillful in establishing and maintaining strong affiliative relationships with each other despite being unrelated.[66–69,26,27] In a study of the bonobos housed at the San Diego Wild Animal Park,[70] we found that two-thirds of the time females spent affiliating was with female partners. Franz[71] reports similar findings for captive groups ($n=4$): the oldest adult females are highest in rank and are the "center of social interaction." The dominance structure is reflected in grooming, such that most positive social interactions are directed to higher-ranking individuals. "Social relationships are female centered and structured by a linear but not unidirectional despotic rank order."[71] Overall then, bonds among females enable them to dominate males on a routine and systematic basis that extends beyond the realm of feeding priority in both captive[25–27] and wild[35] populations.

That unrelated females can form such close positive relationships is a surprise given the traditional parameters for "female-bondedness." In fact, it is so unexpected that, as with female dominance, initial interpretation avoided the most parsimonious explanation. Instead of a female *preference* for association with other females, perhaps females merely "tolerated" one another's proximity in pursuit of their presumed ultimate goal: enticing males to travel with them (the logic being that males are more attracted to more females). Likewise, apparently affiliative interaction such as female-female sexual interaction would then regulate competition rather than maintain an actual bond.[72] This assessment of female-female interaction in *Pan paniscus* females preserves the classic female-/non-female-bonded dichotomy in the original model of primate social systems. At the same time, the imagined "true" primary bond in bonobos, that between males and females, is resuscitated. Such intersexual affiliation resonates with models of early human evolution focused on heterosexual pair bonds.

In fact, it is female-female relationships that are of central importance in understanding bonobo social organization. The origins of unique aspects of female sociality (and perhaps sexuality) may be more related to selection for enhanced female-female relationships, rather than originating as a secondary consequence of male-female relationships.

Humans

Although nearly three-quarters of the world's cultures are patrilocal today, of the hunter-gatherers still living as our ancestors did, only 57% are patrilocal. The remaining 43% are matrilocal or more often flexibly bilocal.[73,74] Smuts[75] points out that others estimate even lower rates of patrilocality in the "simplest" foraging societies.[76-78] Other lines of evidence suggest that hunter-gatherer females may not have routinely dispersed. Vigilant *et al.*[79] uses mitochondrial DNA sequencing techniques to examine the rate of accumulation of base changes in African foragers. They report that female lineages moved their home bases during their hunter-gatherer existence as little as 13 meters per year. This suggests that female dispersal coupled with male philopatry might not be as ubiquitous in human history as would be convenient for many traditional models of human evolution. The genetic structure and levels of dispersal in aboriginal populations are similar to those in macaque populations (a genus characterized by female philopatry).[80]

DISCUSSION

Mating Strategies, Social Relationships, Social Systems: A Female Role

We believe that chimpanzees and bonobos differ in important ways.[81–83] TABLE 2 enumerates some of the areas where differences and similarities between bonobos and chimpanzees are obvious and salient features of their respective social systems.

The list is not exhaustive and is meant to be critical rather than encyclopedic. Nor is it meant to suggest total exclusivity. There may be exceptions to some characterizations. Nonetheless, on balance, the list provides a general overview of the two species' attributes. Principally, the table highlights the obvious: neither species is the sole link to the last common ancestor. There exists a suite of traits among us, some of them inherited from the last common ancestor, some of them lost in the meantime in one, two or all three of today's living species, and some of them unique in that they developed after speciation. While all traits are obviously ecologically dependent, particular solutions may have become characteristic of one species and not another.

Chief among the salient differences between the species are differences in social interaction. Until intensive study of bonobos began to yield results, there was no evidence that either female bonding or female dominance over males occurred *routinely* within any of the living Hominoidea. Among other striking differences, intergroup interactions in bonobos rarely involve *contact* aggression, but instead rely upon vocal exchange, and bonobos have yet to involve "intercommunity warfare" as seen in chimpanzee populations. In fact, most encounters are affinitive.[36,39,42] Even more remarkably, females freely mate with males from other groups in the presence of males from their own communities,[36] a nearly unimaginable scenario for chimpanzees. Likewise, territoriality in bonobos is much relaxed relative to that in their congener. More than 66% of the home range of one Wamba community overlaps with those of other groups.[84] Finally, an obvious chimpanzee/bonobo difference exists in sexual behavior: all possible age and sex combinations participate in bonobo sexual interactions. Sex is routinely used for non-reproductive goals (tension-reduction, reconciliation, bartering for social favors, sex for food exchanges).[25,68,85]

At the same time, bonobos and chimpanzees are very similar: They share the same genus, the same fission/fusion community/unit-group social structure, and they can interbreed in captivity and produce viable offspring.[86] The data discussed in this paper suggest that bonobos and chimpanzees may share something else in common: female mating and social strategies and counter-strategies that are more complex and variable than previously recognized. Their proactive role, unrecognized in many models of human evolution, obviously discomforts some. Yet it is probably not surprising to others that these strategies exist (e.g., see Refs. 87–89; and this volume, p. 75).

It is difficult to tease apart the degree to which similarities and differences between bonobos and chimpanzees are the result of subtle variation in ecological and environmental influence rather than "species-typical" characteristics. Although the emerging patterns of intraspecies diversity warn against "essentializing" either species in the genus *Pan,*[90] it must also be acknowledged that there are some areas in which overlap is not apparent. For instance, bonobo females engage in a unique sexual behavior termed genito-genital (GG) rubbing in which they embrace ventro-ventrally and rub their genital swellings together with rapid sideways movements.[68] Female bonobos in every group ever observed (captive or wild) engage in GG rubbing on a routine basis, in contrast to chimpanzees, who do not GG-rub.

In other instances, there may be overlap in the *range* of a given behavior, but great differences in the norm of its occurrence. For instance, females can affiliate in both species. In chimpanzees, this pattern is mostly manifested in captivity (suggesting release from ecological constraint),[27] but is typical of and well established in every captive and wild population of bonobos on which there are data.

TABLE 2. Comparison and contrasts between chimpanzees and bonobos

Characteristics	Chimpanzees	Bonobos
Distribution	Wide/Equatorial Africa	Limited/Couvette Centrale
Dispersal pattern	Male philopatry/female dispersal	Male philopatry/female dispersal
Community social structure	Yes	Yes
Fission/fusion groups	Yes	Yes
Territoriality	Defended	Large overlap
Intercommunity interaction	Aggressive	Peaceful
Dominance rankings	Males dominant	Females dominant
Vocalizations	Lower (no overlap)	Higher (no overlap)
Locomotion	More terrestrial	More arboreal
Male-male association	Frequent	Less frequent
Male-female association	Cycle-dependent	Independent of cycle
Female-female association	Infrequent	Frequent
Mother-son association	Through adolescence	Throughout life
Male bonding	Primary	Very limited
Female bonding	Very limited	Primary
Heterosexual pair-bonds	No	No
Aggressive pattern	Females submit to males	Males submit to females
Male to female contact aggression	Yes	No
Female to male contact aggression	No	Yes
Infanticide	Observed	Unobserved
Warfare	Yes	No
Reconciliation	Common	More common
Grooming	Mostly males	Mostly females
Hunting (actor)	Males	Females
Food sharing (from and to)	Mostly males	Mostly females
Food control	Mostly males	Mostly females
Promiscuous matings	Within group	Within and between groups
Extra-group copulations	Secret	Public
Testes size	Large	Large
Concealed ovulation	No	Yes
Continuous receptivity	Some	Extensive
Genital swelling	At ovulation	Extended
Elaborate sexual repertoire	No	Yes
Sexual partner	Mainly heterosexual	All combinations
Genital contact (among females)	Absent	Common
Rump contact (among males)	Absent	Occurs
Submissive greeting	Pant grunt	No equivalent
Gestation length	About 8 months	About 8.5 months

Finally, whether differences exist may depend, in some instances, on the level of analysis: chimpanzees and bonobos are similar in that they both display large genital swellings, and they are different in that a chimpanzee will spend approximately 5 percent of her adult life in a swollen state versus 50 percent for a bonobo female.[91] Likewise, both species eat meat. However, while chimpanzees in several populations have been observed to eat monkey meat,[92] bonobos do not seem to eat other primates, even when they accidentally kill them.[38,93]

Differences unrelated to ecological constraint or opportunity can be assessed when environment is controlled, as in captivity. Parish[25] conducted a study in which chimpanzees and bonobos were observed in identical enclosures. The apes were identical in adult group composition for much of the study, were fed the same diet, cared for by the same keepers, and were subject to the same regime. Yet significant differences emerged between the two groups. Female bonobos, for instance, had sex in more than half of the episodes in which they fed from a simulated termite fishing mound. The chimpanzees never had sex in the context of fishing. While among chimpanzees it was the adult male who displaced others most often, it was the adult females who did so in bonobos. While bonobos used a strategy of co-feeding in two-thirds of their fishing episodes (particularly the most dominant individuals—the females), the chimpanzees were much less likely to feed (on average in only one-fifth of all bouts) at the same time as others (again, this was particularly true of the most dominant individual—the male).

It would be simplistic and unrealistic to attribute differences in the social behavior and dominance patterns of bonobos and chimpanzees merely to the differential effects of captivity on the two species. The behavior of the bonobos observed in the Stuttgart Zoo was consistent with the behavior of bonobos not only in all other captive situations, but also with the data thus far reported on wild-living populations. We must therefore ask what advantages might have selected for the behavioral divergence we do see between these two species (explored in Refs. 26 and 27).

Selection for Female Strategies

The advantages of greater female autonomy, whether through female dominance in the case of bonobos, secretive circumvention of chimpanzee male mate-guarding and territorial behavior, or non-dispersal in female chimpanzees, are manifold. The immediate advantages of high rank for bonobo females include control over food (upon which their reproductive success depends), as well as reduction in other costs such as male agonism and sexual coercion.[26] Opportunities for males to commit infanticide may be reduced.[27,94] The ultimate advantage to female dominance/high rank may be an earlier age at first reproduction than might otherwise be possible (as evidenced by a comparison with chimpanzee females living in male-dominated societies)[27] or perhaps shortened interbirth intervals in which females support multiple dependent offspring.[28]

Chimpanzee females also benefit from their strategies: where they are female philopatric, they tend to inherit good territories and experience higher rates of infant survival and more rapid production of offspring; they also have daughters that mature more quickly.[59] Finally, the power of females to drastically alter a social system cannot be denied: in the case of chimpanzees, female extra group paternity strategies negate one of the most salient benefits of male-philopatry—the benefit of living with relatives.

TABLE 3. Social organization of human ancestors: a comparison between chimpanzees and bonobos[a]

	Chimpanzees	Bonobos
1. Closed social network	No	No
2. Party composition	Unstable	Unstable
3. Females sometimes alone	Yes	No
4. Males sometimes alone	No (?)	Yes
5. Female exogamy	Yes[b]	Yes
6. Female alliances	No	Yes
7. Males have single mates	No	No
8. Duration of sexual partnerships	Short	Short
9. Hostile relations between groups	Yes	No
10. Males active in inter-group encounters	Yes	No
11. Stalking and attacking by males	Yes	No
12. Territorial defense	Yes	No

[a]Modeled on Wrangham.[56]
[b]Gombe may be an exception, but it may be a recent phenomenon.[61]

The Last Common Ancestor

Models of hominid evolution have historically focused on two variables of relevance to the arguments advanced here: the referents have been, and largely continue to be, male and chimpanzee-like.[95] In the 1960s early hominids were assumed to resemble savannah baboons in that both social systems were supposedly driven by male competition and male dominance.[96,97] Recent studies of human evolution continue the trend: "[M]ost Darwinian models of human origins incorporate females only as passive objects of male competition"[95] (p. 59) or dismiss female influence as a politically driven illusion engendered by feminism.[98] (p. 213)

Many strategies of female chimpanzees and bonobos reviewed here thus threaten or absolutely contradict models of hominid evolution. When a compilation of traits commonly used to reconstruct social organization of human ancestors[56] is applied instead to chimpanzee and bonobo social systems (TABLE 3), the dilemma is clear. Eight of fourteen traits differ between the two species. These differences complicate any characterization of "humanity's closest relative" as well as the last common ancestor. Any ancestor which may or may not display female or male alliances, which may or may not engage in female exogamy and male endogamy, which may characteristically respond peacefully or aggressively to inter-community encounters (or not participate at all), and which may or may not even live in a "community" (in the sense that it would correspond to the reproductive unit)[36,63] creates more questions than it answers.

Modelers of hominid evolution simply must reformulate their variables such that they also accommodate: real and meaningful female bonds; the possibility of systematic female dominance over males; female mating strategies that encompass extra-group paternities; hunting and meat distribution by females; the importance of the sharing of plant foods; affinitive inter-community interactions; males that do not stalk and attack and are not territorial; and flexible social relationships in which philopatry does not necessarily predict bonding pattern.

REFERENCES

1. WRANGHAM, R.W., F.B.M. DE WAAL & W.C. MCGREW. 1994. The challenge of behavioral diversity. *In* Chimpanzee Cultures. R. W. Wrangham, W. C. McGrew, F. B. M. de Waal & P. G. Heltne, Eds.Harvard University Press. Cambridge, MA.
2. WRANGHAM, R.W., W.C. MCGREW, F.B.M. DE WAAL & P.G. HELTNE. 1994. Chimpanzee Cultures. Harvard University Press. Cambridge, MA.
3. BOESCH, C. 1998. Review of *Bonobo: The Forgotten Ape* (by F.B.M. de Waal, 1997). Ethology **104(5):** 361–456.
4. CACCONE, C. & J. R. POWELL. 1989. DNA divergence among hominoids. Evolution **43:** 925–942.
5. RUVOLO, M., T.R. DISOTELL, M.W. ALLARD, W.M. BROWN & R.L. HONEYCUTT. 1991. Resolution of the African hominoid trichotomy by use of a mitochondrial gene sequence. Proc. Natl. Acad. Sci. USA **88:** 1570–1574.
6. TUTIN, C.E.G. 1996. Ranging and social structure of lowland gorillas in the Lopé Reserve, Gabon. *In* Great Ape Societies. W. C. McGrew, L. F. Marchant & T. Nishida, Eds.: 58–70. Cambridge University Press. Cambridge, England.
7. PALOMBIT, R.A. 1994. Extra-pair copulations in a monogamous ape. Anim. Behav. **47:** 721–723.
8. REICHARD, U. 1995. Extra-pair copulations in a monogamous gibbon (*Hylobates lar*). Ethology **100:** 99–112.
9. BROCKELMAN, W.Y., U. REICHARD, U. TREESUCON & J.J. RAEMAKERS. 1998. Dispersal, pair formation and social structure in gibbons (*Hylobates lar*). Behav. Ecol. Sociobiol. **42:** 329–339.
10. SOMMER, V. & U. REICHARD. 1999. Rethinking monogamy: the gibbon case. *In* Primate Socioecology—Causes and Consequences of Variation in the Number of Males. P. Kappeler, Ed. Cambridge University Press. Cambridge, England.
11. KNOTT, C.D. 1998. Social system dynamics, ranging patterns, and male and female strategies in wild Bornean orangutans (*Pongo pgymaeus*). Am. J. Phys. Anthropol. Suppl. **26:** 140 [abstract].
12. KNOTT, C. 1999. Orangutan behavior and ecology. *In* The Nonhuman Primates. P. Dolhinow & A. Fuentes, Eds.: 50–57. Mayfield Press. Mountain View, CA.
13. MCGREW, W.C. 1992. Chimpanzee Material Culture. Cambridge University Press. Cambridge, England.
14. BOESCH, C. 1994. Cooperative hunting in wild chimpanzees. Anim. Behav. **48:** 653–667.
15. ZIHLMAN, A.L., J.B. CRONIN, D.L. CRAMER & V.M. SARICH. 1978. Pygmy chimpanzees as a possible prototype for the common ancestor of humans, chimpanzees, and gorillas. Nature **275:** 744–746.
16. ZIHLMAN, A.L. 1996. Reconstructions reconsidered: chimpanzee models and human evolution. *In* Great Ape Societies. W. C. McGrew, L. F. Marchant & T. Nishida, Eds.: 293-304. Cambridge University Press. Cambridge, England.
17. WRANGHAM, R.W. & D. PETERSON. 1997. Demonic Males. Bloomsbury. London, England.
18. STANFORD, C.B. 1998. The social behavior of chimpanzees and bonobos: Empirical evidence and shifting assumptions. Curr. Anthropol. **39(4):** 399–420.
19. BOESCH, C. 1991. The effect of leopard predation on grouping patterns in forest chimpanzees. Behaviour **117:** 220–242.
20. BOESCH, C. 1996. Social grouping in Taï chimpanzees. *In* Great Ape Societies. W. C. McGrew, L.F. Marchant & T. Nishida, Eds.: 101–113. Cambridge University Press. Cambridge, England.
21. KUMMER, H. 1968. Social Organization of Hamadryas Baboons. University of Chicago Press. Chicago, IL.

22. KUMMER, H. 1975. "Adaptation of Female Anubis Baboons to Social System of Hamadryas Baboons," H. Kummer, Director. Film available through University Park, Pennsylvania. Pennsylvania State University, Audio Visual Services.
23. DE WAAL, F.B.M. 1989. Peacemaking Among Primates. Harvard University Press. Cambridge, MA.
24. JANSON, C.H. 1986. The mating system as a determinant of social evolution in capuchin monkeys (*Cebus*). *In* Primate Ecology and Conservation. J. G. Else & P. C. Lee, Eds.: 169–179. Cambridge University Press. Cambridge, England.
25. PARISH, A.R. 1994. Sex and food control in the "uncommon chimpanzee": how bonobo females overcome a phylogenetic legacy of male dominance. Ethol. Sociobiol. **15:** 157–179.
26. PARISH, A.R. 1996. Female relationships in bonobos (*Pan paniscus*): evidence for bonding, cooperation, and female dominance in a male-philopatric species. Hum. Nature **7:** 61–96.
27. PARISH, A.R. 1996b. Female relationships in bonobos (*Pan paniscus*): implications for development, reproduction, and life histories. Ph.D. thesis, University of California, Davis.
28. KANO, T. 1996. Male rank order and copulation rate in a unit-group of bonobos at Wamba, Zaïre. *In* Great Ape Societies. W. C. McGrew, L. F. Marchant & T. Nishida, Eds.: 135–145. Cambridge University Press. Cambridge, England.
29. KANO, T. 1992. The Last Ape: Pygmy Chimpanzee Behavior and Ecology. Stanford University Press. Stanford, CA.
30. FURUICHI, T. 1989. Social interactions and the life history of female *Pan paniscus* in Wamba, Zaire. Int. J. Primatol. **10(3):** 173–197.
31. HASHIMOTO, C. 1997. Context and development of sexual behavior of wild bonobos (*Pan paniscus*) at Wamba, Zaire. Int. J. Primatol. **18:** 1–21.
32. WHITE, F.J., K.D. WOOD & M.Y. MERRILL. 1998. Comment on C. B. Stanford: "The social behavior of chimpanzees and bonobos: empirical evidence and shifting assumptions." Curr. Anthropol. **39(4):** 399–420 [pp. 414–415].
33. KANO, T. 1990. The bonobos' peaceable kingdom. Natural History [November] **11:** 62–70.
34. WOOD, K.D. & F.J. WHITE. 1996. Female feeding priority without female dominance in wild pygmy chimpanzees [abstract]. Am. J. Phys. Anthropol. Suppl. **22:** 247.
35. FRUTH, B. 1995. Nests and nest groups in wild bonobos (*Pan paniscus*): ecological and behavioural correlates. Ph.D. thesis. Shaker. Aachen, Germany.
36. IDANI, G. 1990. Relations between unit-groups of bonobos at Wamba, Zaire: encounters and temporary fusions. African Study Monogr. **11:** 153–186.
37. IDANI, G. 1991. Social relationships between immigrant and resident bonobo (*Pan paniscus*) females at Wamba. Fol. Primatol. **57:** 83–95.
38. IHOBE, H. 1990. Interspecific interactions between wild pygmy chimpanzees (*Pan paniscus*) and red colobus (*Colobus badius*). Primates **31(1):** 109–112.
39. IHOBE, H. 1992. Male–male relationships among wild bonobos (*Pan paniscus*) at Wamba, Republic of Zaire. Primates **33:** 163–179.
40. FRUTH, B. 1998. Comment on Stanford, C.B. 1998: "The social behavior of chimpanzees and bonobos: empirical evidence and shifting assumptions." Curr. Anthropol. **39(4):** 399–420.
41. INGMANSON, E.J. 1998. Comment on Stanford, C.B. 1998: "The social behavior of chimpanzees and bonobos: empirical evidence and shifting assumptions." Curr. Anthropol. **39(4):** 399–420.
42. KANO, T. 1998. Comment on Stanford, C.B. 1998. "The social behavior of chimpanzees and bonobos: empirical evidence and shifting assumptions." Curr. Anthropol. **39(4):** 399-420.
43. VAN SCHAIK, C.P. & J.A.R.A.M. VAN HOOF. 1996. Toward an understanding of the orangutan's social system. *In* Great Ape Societies. W. C. McGrew, L. F. Marchant & T. Nishida, Eds.: 3–15. Cambridge University Press. Cambridge, England.
44. WRANGHAM, R.W. 1980. An ecological model of female-bonded primate groups. Behaviour **75:** 262–300.
45. RODSETH, L.R., R.W. WRANGHAM, A.M. HARRIGAN & B.B. SMUTS. 1991. The human community as a primate society. Curr. Anthropol. **323:** 221–251.

46. GOODALL, J. 1968. The behaviour of free-living chimpanzees in the Gombe Stream Reserve. Anim. Behav. Monogr. **1:** 165–311.
47. GOODALL, J. 1986. The Chimpanzees of Gombe: Patterns of Behavior. Harvard University Press: Cambridge, MA.
48. NISHIDA, T. 1979. The social structure of chimpanzees of the Mahale Mountains. In The Great Apes. D. A. Hamburg & E. R. McCown, Eds. Benjamin/Cummings. Menlo Park, CA.
49. NISHIDA, T. Ed. 1990. The Chimpanzees of the Mahale Mountains: Sexual and Life History Strategies. University of Tokyo Press. Tokyo, Japan.
50. SUGIYAMA, Y. 1988. Grooming interactions among adult chimpanzees at Bossou, Guinea, with special reference to social structure. Int. J. Primatol. **9:** 393–408.
51. LOVEJOY, C. O. 1981. The origin of man. Science **211:** 341–350.
52. FISHER, H. 1983. The Sex Contract: The Evolution of Human Behavior. Quill. New York, NY.
53. MORRIS, D. 1967. The Naked Ape. Jonathan Cape. London.
54. ALEXANDER, R.D. & K.M. NOONAN. 1979. Concealment of ovulation, parental care, and human social evolution. *In* Evolutionary Biology and Human Social Behavior. N.A. Chagnon & W. Irons, Eds.: 436–453. Duxbury, Scituate, MA.
55. MOORE, J. J. 1996. Savanna chimpanzees, referential models and the last common ancestor. *In* Great Ape Societies. W. C. McGrew, L. F. Marchant & T. Nishida, Eds.: 275–292. Cambridge University Press. Cambridge, England.
56. WRANGHAM, R.W. 1986. The significance of African apes for reconstructing human social evolution. *In* The Evolution of Human Behavior: Primate Models. W. G. KINZEY, Ed.: 51–71. SUNY Press. New York.
57. MURDOCK, G. P. 1957. World ethnographic sample. Am. Anthropol. **59:** 664–687.
58. MORIN, P.A., J.J. MOORE, R. CHAKRABORTY, L. JIN, J. GOODALL & D.S. WOODRUFF. 1994. Kin selection, social structure, gene flow, and the evolution of chimpanzees. Science **265:** 1193–1201.
59. PUSEY, A., J. WILLIAMS & J. GOODALL. 1997. The influence of dominance rank on the reproductive success of female chimpanzees. Science **277:** 828–831.
60. GAGNEUX, P., D. S. WOODRUFF & C. BOESCH. 1997. Furtive mating by female chimpanzees. Nature **387:** 327–328.
61. MORIN, P.A., J. WALLIS, J.J. MOORE & D.S. WOODRUFF. 1994. Paternity exclusion in a community of wild chimpanzees using hypervariable simple sequence repeats. Molecular Ecol. **3:** 469–478.
62. SUGIYAMA, Y., S. KAWAMOTO, O. TAKENAKA, K. KUMAZAKI & N. MIWA. 1993. Paternity discrimination and inter-group relationships of chimpanzees at Bossou. Primates **34:** 545–552.
63. GAGNEUX, P., C. BOESCH & D.S. WOODRUFF. 1999. Female reproductive strategies, paternity and community structure in wild West African chimpanzees. Anim. Behav. **57:** 19–32.
64. DORAN, D. 1997. Influence of seasonality on activity patterns, feeding behavior, ranging, and grouping patterns in Taï chimpanzees. Int. J. Primatol. **18:** 183–206.
65. GERLOFF, U., B. FRUTH, G. HOHMANN & D. TAUTZ. 1997. Community structure in bonobos (*Pan paniscus*)—Molecular analysis. Abstract in Program of the 1. Göttinger Freilandtage, Göttingen, Germany, December 9–12, 1997. Primate Report **48(2):** 1–42.
66. BADRIAN, A. & N. BADRIAN. 1984. Social organization of *Pan paniscus* in the Lomako Forest, Zaire. *In* The Pygmy Chimpanzee: Evolutionary Biology and Behavior. R. L. Susman, Ed.: 325–346. Plenum. New York.
67. KANO, T. 1980. Social behavior of wild pygmy chimpanzees *Pan paniscus* of Wamba: a preliminary report. J. Hum. Evol. **57:** 83–95.
68. KURODA, S. 1980. Social behavior of the pygmy chimpanzees. Primates **21:** 181-197.
69. WHITE, F. J. 1992. Pygmy chimpanzee social organization: Variation with party size and between study sites. Am. J. Primatol. **26:** 203-214.
70. PARISH, A.R. & F.B.M. DE WAAL 2000. Social relationships in bonobos (*Pan paniscus*) redefined: evidence for female-bonding in a "non-female-bonded" primate. Behaviour. In press.

71. FRANZ, C. 1999. "Die Struktur Soziale Beziehungen im Zusammenhang mit Weibliche Dominanz bei Bonobos" [abstract], unpublished Ph.D. thesis, Graz, Austria). 24th GSP Rundbrief. :36.
72. WRANGHAM, R.W. 1986. Ecology and social relationships in two species of chimpanzee. In Ecology and Social Evolution: Birds and Mammals. D. I. Rubenstein & R. W. Wrangham, Eds.: 353–378. Princeton University Press. Princeton, NJ.
73. EMBER, C. 1975. Residential variation among hunter-gatherers. Behav. Sci. Res. **3:** 199–227.
74. HRDY, S.B. 1999. Mother Nature: A History of Mothers, Infants and Natural Selection. Pantheon. New York.
75. SMUTS, B.B. 1995. The evolutionary origins of patriarchy. Hum. Nature **6:** 1–32.
76. BARNARD, A. 1983. Contemporary hunter-gatherers: current issues in ecology and social organization. Annu. Rev. Anthropol. **12:** 193–214.
77. KNAUFT, B.M. 1991. Violence and sociality in human evolution. Curr. Anthropol. **32:** 391–428.
78. RODSETH, L.R. 1991. Comment on Bruce M. Knauft: "Violence and sociality in human evolution." Curr. Anthropol. **32:** 414–416.
79. VIGILANT, L., R. PENNINGTON, H. HARPENDING, T.D. KOCHER & A.C. WILSON. 1989. Mitochondrial DNA sequences in single hairs from a southern African population. Proc. Natl. Acad. Sci. USA **86:** 9350–9354.
80. MELNICK, D.J. & G.A. HOELZER. 1993. What is mtDNA good for in the study of primate evolution? Evol. Anthropol. **2:** 2–10.
81. DE WAAL, F.B.M. 1988. The communicative repertoire of captive bonobos (*Pan paniscus*) compared to that of chimpanzees. Behaviour **106:** 183–251.
82. DE WAAL, F.B.M. 1989. Behavioral contrasts between bonobo and chimpanzee. *In* Understanding Chimpanzees. P. G. Heltne & L. A. Marquardt, Eds.: 154–175. Harvard University Press. Cambridge, MA.
83. NISHIDA, T. & M. HIRAIWA-HASEGAWA. 1987. Chimpanzees and bonobos: cooperative relationships among males. *In* Primate Societies. B. B. Smuts, D. L. Cheney, R. M. Seyfarth, R. W. Wrangham & T. T. Struhsaker, Eds.: 165–177. University of Chicago Press. Chicago, IL.
84. KANO, T. & M. MULAVWA. 1984. Feeding ecology of the pygmy chimpanzee (*Pan paniscus*) of Wamba, Zaïre. Am. J. Phys. Anthropol. **63:** 1–11.
85. DE WAAL, F.B.M. 1987. Tension regulation and non-reproductive functions of sex among captive bonobos (Pan paniscus). National Geogr. Res. **3:** 318–335.
86. VERVAECKE, H. & L. VAN ELSACKER. 1992. Hybrids between common chimpanzees (*Pan troglodytes*) and pygmy chimpanzees (*Pan paniscus*) in captivity. Mammalia **56:** 667–669.
87. HRDY, S.B. 1977. The Langurs of Abu: Female and Male Strategies of Reproduction. Harvard University Press. Cambridge, MA.
88. HRDY, S.B. 1979. Infanticide among animals: a review, classification, and examination of the implications for the reproductive strategies of females. Ethol. Sociobiol. **1:** 13–40.
89. HRDY, S.B. 1981. The Woman That Never Evolved. Harvard University Press. Cambridge, MA.
90. MOORE, J.J. 1998. Comment on Stanford, C. B. 1998: "The social behavior of chimpanzees and bonobos: empirical evidence and shifting assumptions." Curr. Anthropol. **39(4):** 399–420.
91. WRANGHAM, R.W. 1993. The evolution of sexuality in chimpanzees and bonobos. Hum. Biol. **4:** 47–79.
92. STANFORD, C.B. 1998. Chimpanzee and Red Colobus: The Ecology of Predator and Prey. Harvard University Press. Cambridge, MA.
93. SABATER, P., J.M. BERMEJO, G. ILLERA & J.J. VEA. 1993. Behavior of bonobos (*Pan paniscus*) following their capture of monkeys in Zaire. Int. J. Primatol. **14(5):** 797–804.
94. DE WAAL, F.B.M. 1997. Bonobo: The Forgotten Ape. University of California Press. Berkeley, CA.
95. STANFORD, C.B. & J.S. ALLEN. 1991. On strategic storytelling: current models of human behavioral evolution. Curr. Anthropol. **32(1):** 59–60.

96. DEVORE, I. & S.L. WASHBURN. 1963. Baboon ecology and human evolution. *In* African Ecology and Human Evolution. F.C. Howell & F. Bourliere, Eds.: 335–367. Aldine. New York.
97. WASHBURN, S.L. & J. LANCASTER. 1968. The evolution of hunting. *In* Man the Hunter. R. Lee & R. Devore, Eds.: 293–303. Aldine. Chicago, IL.
98. TOOBY, J. & I. DEVORE. 1987. The reconstruction of hominid behavioral evolution through strategic modeling. *In* The Evolution of Human Behavior: Primate Models. W. G. Kinzey, Ed.: 183–238. State University of New York Press. Albany, NY.

The Elements of a Scientific Theory of Self-Deception

ROBERT TRIVERS

Department of Anthropology, Rutgers University, 131 George Street, New Brunswick, New Jersey 08901-1414, USA

ABSTRACT: An evolutionary theory of self-deception—the active misrepresentation of reality to the conscious mind—suggests that there may be multiple sources of self-deception in our own species, with important interactions between them. Self-deception (along with internal conflict and fragmentation) may serve to improve deception of others; this may include denial of ongoing deception, self-inflation, ego-biased social theory, false narratives of intention, and a conscious mind that operates via denial and projection to create a self-serving world. Self-deception may also result from internal representations of the voices of significant others, including parents, and may come from internal genetic conflict, the most important for our species arising from differentially imprinted maternal and paternal genes. Selection also favors suppressing negative phenotypic traits. Finally, a positive form of self-deception may serve to orient the organism favorably toward the future. Self-deception can be analyzed in groups and is done so here with special attention to its costs.

INTRODUCTION

An important component of a mature system of social theory is a sub-theory concerning self-deception (lying to oneself, or biased information flow within an individual, analogous to deception between individuals). This sub-theory can always be turned back on the main theory itself. There can be little doubt about the need for such a theory where our own species is concerned—and of the need for solid, scientific facts which bear on the theory. Whether through a study of one's own behavior and mentation (e.g., for a novelist's treatment[1]) or of societal disasters (e.g., in aviation[2,3] or misguided wars[4,5]), or a review of findings from psychology,[6–13] we know that processes of self-deception—active misrepresentation of reality to the conscious mind—are an everyday human occurrence, that struggling with one's own tendencies toward self-deception is usually a life-long enterprise, and that at the level of societies (as well as individuals) such tendencies can help produce major disasters (e.g., the U.S. war on Viet Nam). With potential costs so great, the question naturally arises: what evolutionary forces *favor* mechanisms of self-deception?

A theory of self-deception based on evolutionary biology requires that we explain how forces of natural selection working on individuals—and the genes within them—may have favored individual (and group) self-deception, where natural selection is understood to favor high inclusive fitness, roughly speaking, an individual's (or gene's) reproductive success (RS = number of surviving offspring) plus effects on the RS of relatives, devalued by the degrees of relatedness between actor and relatives.[14] There is ample evidence that this simple principle provides a firm foundation for a general theory of social interactions.[15] Deception between individuals who are imperfectly related may often be favored when this gives an advantage in RS to the deceiver (see Refs. 15 and 16 for some examples) but the argument for *self*-deception is not so obvious.

For a solitary organism, the prospects seem difficult, if not hopeless. In trying to deal effectively with a complex, changing world, where is the benefit in misrepresenting reality to oneself? Only in interactions with other organisms, especially conspecifics, would several benefits seem to arise. Because deception is easily selected between individuals, it may also generate *self*-deception, the better to hide ongoing deception from detection by others.[2,15,17] In this view, the conscious mind is, in part, a social front, maintained to deceive others—who more readily attend to its manifestations than to those of the actor's unconscious mind. At the same time, social processes, such as parent-offspring conflict[18] in a species with a long period of juvenile dependency—or, a more general group-individual conflict–may generate conflicting internal voices, representing parental and own self-interests (or group and self), with consequent reality-distortion within the individual.[18] For example, the parental view may be overstated internally (for example, via parental manipulation), requiring careful devaluation or counter-assertion.

A stronger force may arise from the fact that different sections of our genome (mtDNA, sex chromosomes, autosomes and, separately, the maternal and paternal chromosomes) often enjoy differing degrees of relatedness to others, with consequent internal conflict between the sections potentially generating deception within the individual, a kind of "selves-deception."[19] Internal conflict may occur for other reasons, as well, and may or may not involve biased information flow. For example, it is certain that all of us possess disadvantageous traits, both genetic and developmental, and, thus, natural selection may have favored super-ordinate mechanisms for spotting negative traits in the phenotype (perhaps especially behavioral ones) and then attempting to suppress them. This may be experienced sometimes as internal psychological conflict and may or may not involve biased information flow. Finally, a positive stance toward life may have intrinsic benefits (and not only for social species). A concentration on the future—and positive outcomes therein—may benefit from seeing past setbacks as blessings in disguise and the current path chosen as the best available option. In short, positive illusions may give intrinsic benefit.[8,9] Is this self-deception or merely optimism in the service of reproductive success?[21]

SELF-DECEPTION IN THE SERVICE OF DECEIT

One model for internal fragmentation and conflict is represented in FIGURE 1. True and false information is simultaneously stored in an organism with a bias towards the true information's being stored in the unconscious mind, the false in the conscious. And, it is argued, this way of organizing knowledge is oriented towards an outside observer, who sees first the conscious mind and its productions and only later spots true information hidden in the other's unconscious. This is self-deception in the service of deception of others. It may be expected to flourish in at least the following five kinds of situations.

1. Denial of ongoing deception. Being unconscious of ongoing deception may more deeply hide the deception. Conscious deceivers will often be under the stress

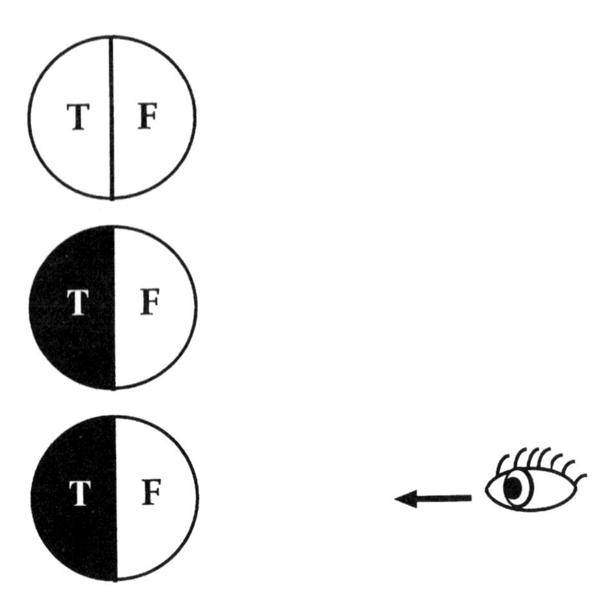

FIGURE 1. True (T) and false (F) information is simultaneously stored within an organism, but with a bias: the true is stored in the *unconscious* mind (shaded section), the better to deceive an on-looker (eye).

that accompanies attempted deception. Evidence from other animals suggests that, as in humans, deception, when detected, may often be met with hostile and aggressive actions by others.[22–25] Thus, if I were in front of you now, lying to you about something you actually care about, you might pay attention to my eye movements, the quality of my voice, and the sweat on the palms of my hands (if you can reach them) as a means of detecting the stress accompanying deception, but if I am unconscious of the deception being perpetrated all these avenues will be unavailable to you.

2. Unconscious modules involving deception. In the above example, the main activity—verbal persuasion directed at others—is deceptive, but there are also situations in which your dominant activity (say, lecturing) is honest, but a minor activity is deceitful (stealing the chalk). These can be thought of as directed by unconscious modules favored by selection so as to allow us to pursue surreptitiously strategies we would wish to deny to others. Naturally these will often remain unconscious to us. I will shortly describe in detail a deceitful little module in my own life which I have discovered primarily because my pockets fill up with contraband: hard, concrete objects that others may soon miss. What is the chance that I perform numerous unconscious selfish modules whose social benefits do not pile up in one place, where I can notice them (and others confirm them), e.g., ploys of unconscious manipulation of others (including, of course, as an academic, expropriating their *ideas*)?

I have discovered over the years that I am an unconscious petty thief. I steal small, useful objects: pencils, pens, matches, lighters and other useful objects easy to pocket. I am completely unconscious of this activity while it is happening. I am, of course, now richly aware of it in retrospect, but after at least 40 years of performing the behavior I am still unconscious ahead of time, during the action, and immediately afterwards. Perhaps because the trait is so unconscious, it appears now to have a life of its own and often seems to act directly against even my narrow interests. For example, I steal chalk from myself while lecturing and am left with no chalk with which to lecture (nor do I have a blackboard at home). I steal pencils and pens from my office and, in turn, from my home, so if I download my pockets at either destination, as I commonly do, I risk being without writing implements at the other end. Recently I stole the complete set of keys of a Jamaican school principal off of his desk between us. And so on.

In summary, noteworthy features of this module are that: (1) it is little changed over the course of my life; (2) increasing consciousness of the behavior *after* the behavior has done little or nothing to increase consciousness during or in advance of the behavior; and (3) the behavior seems increasingly to misfire, that is, to fail to steal *useful* objects.

What is the benefit of keeping this petty thievery unconscious? On the one hand, if challenged, I can act surprised and be confident in my assertion that nothing like this was ever my conscious intention (see below). On the other hand, unconsciousness ensures that my thievery will not interfere with ongoing behavior, while the piece of brain devoted to stealing can concentrate on the problem at hand, i.e., snatching the desired item undetected. Part of its consciousness has to be devoted to studying my *own* behavior since integrating its thievery into my other behavior will presumably make this harder to detect by others, including myself.

Incidentally, I believe I never, or almost never, pilfer from someone's office when it is empty. I have seen a choice pen and have seen my hand move toward it but I immediately stop myself and say, "but, Bob, that would be stealing," and I stop. Perhaps if I steal from you in front of your face I unconsciously imagine you have provided some acquiescence, if not actual approval. When I stole the principal's keys, I believe I was simultaneously handing him repayment of a small amount and wondering if I were slightly overpaying. Perhaps I reasoned to myself, "Well, this is for you, so *this* must be for me."

3. Self-deception as self-promotion. Another major source of self-deception has to do with self-promotion, self-exaggeration on the positive side, denial on the negative, all in the name of producing an image that we are "beneffective," to use Anthony Greenwald's[7] apt term, toward others. That is, we benefit others and are effective when we do it. If you ask high school seniors in the United States to rank themselves on leadership ability, fully 80% say they have better than average abilities, but for true feats of self-deception you can hardly beat the academic profession. When you ask professors to rate themselves, an almost unanimous 94% say they are in the top half of the profession![26] For many other examples, see Refs. 7 and 13. Tricks of the trade are biased memory, biased computation, changing from active to passive voice when changing from describing positive to negative outcomes, and so on.

4. The construction of biased social theory. We all have social theories. We have a theory of our marriages. Husband and wife, for example, may agree that one party is a long-suffering altruist, while the other is hopelessly selfish, but they may disagree over which is which.[15] We each tend to have a theory regarding our employment. Are we an exploited worker, underpaid and underappreciated for value given (and fully justified in minimizing output and stealing company property)? We usually have a theory regarding our larger society as well. Are the wealthy unfairly increasing their own resources at the expense of the rest of us? Does democracy permit us to reassert our power at regular intervals? Is the judicial system systematically biased against our kind of people (African-Americans for example)? The capacity for these kinds of theories presumably evolved in part to detect cheating in our relationships and in the larger system of reciprocal altruism.

Social theory is easily expected to be biased in favor of the speaker. Social theory inevitably embraces a complex array of facts and these may be very partially remembered and very poorly organized, the better to construct a consistent self-serving body of social theory. Contradictions may be far afield and difficult to detect. When Republicans in the House of Representatives bemoaned what the Founding Fathers would have thought had they known that a successor President was having sex with an intern, the Black American comedian Chris Rock replied that the Founding Fathers were not having intercourse with their interns, they were having intercourse with their *slaves*! This kind of undercuts the moral force of the argument given (for recent evidence supporting his assertion, see Ref. 27).

Alexander[17] was, I think, the first person to point out that group selection thinking—the mistaken belief that natural selection favors things that are good for the group or the species—is just the kind of social theory you would expect to be promulgated in a group-living species whose members are concerned to increase each other's group orientation.

5. *Fictitious narratives of intention.* Just as we can misremember the past in a self-serving way, so we can be unconscious of ongoing motivation, instead experiencing a conscious stream of thoughts which may act, in part, as rationalizations for what we are doing, all of which is immediately available verbally should we be challenged by others: "But I wasn't thinking that at all, I was thinking such-and-such." A common form in myself is that I wish to go to point C, but can not justify the expense and time. I leap, however, at a chance to go to point B, which brings me close enough to point C so that, when there, I can easily justify the extra distance to C, but I do not think of C until I reach B. We may have much deeper patterns of motivation which may remain unconscious, or nearly so, for much longer periods of time, unconscious patterns of motivation in relationships, for example.

In summary, the hallmark of self-deception in the service of deceit is the denial of deception, the unconscious running of selfish and deceitful ploys, the creation of a public persona as an altruist and a person beneffective in the lives of others, the creation of self-serving social theories and biased internal narratives of ongoing behavior which hide true intention. The symptom is a biased system of information flow, with the conscious mind devoted, in part, to constructing a false image and at the same time being unaware of contravening behavior and evidence. The general cost of self-deception, then, is misapprehension of reality, especially social, and an inefficient, fragmented mental system. For a deeper view of these processes we must remember that the mind is not divided into conscious and unconscious, but into differing degrees of consciousness. We can deny reality and then deny the denial, and so on, *ad infinitum*. Consciousness comes in many, many degrees and forms. We can feel anxious and not know why. We can be aware that someone in a group means us no good, but not know who. We can know who, but not why, and so on.

The examples in this article are all taken from human life. While language greatly increases the possibilities for deceit and self-deception in our species, selection probably favored deception in social species for hundreds of millions of years and

TABLE 1. Consciousness (neuronal times)[a]

			Time
Finger	⇒	Brain	20 ms
Round trip			50 ms
Sensation	⇒	Consciousness	500 ms
Round trip	+	Cognitive processing	100–200 ms
Neuronal start of act	⇒	Conscious "intention"	350 ms
"Intention"	⇒	Action	200 ms

this may have selected for some mechanisms of self-deception. Two animals evaluating each other in an aggressive encounter (or even in courtship) will be selected to pay close attention to the other individual's apparent self-evaluation and level of motivation, both of which can be boosted by selective forgetting, as in humans.[28] In humans the major sex hormones (e.g., testosterone and estradiol) seem to be positively associated with degree of self-inflation.[28] Since testosterone is sometimes positively associated with aggression and aggression with self-deception (see below) such connection may make functional sense in both humans and other animals[5] (where it could easily be pursued experimentally).

NEURONAL TIMES IN CONSCIOUSNESS

It is common to imagine that our conscious mind occupies a central place in our life, where apprehension of reality and subsequent decision-making is concerned. It is easy to imagine that information reaching our brain is immediately registered in consciousness and likewise that signals to initiate activity originate in the conscious mind. Of course, unconscious processes go on at the same time and unconscious processes may affect the conscious mind but there is not a great deal of time, for example, for something like denial to operate, certainly not if this requires spotting a signal and then, before it can reach consciousness, shunting it aside. And, voluntary activity, of which we are conscious as we act, may be affected by unconscious factors, but nevertheless plays the overriding role in directing activity. This is the conventional (pre-Freudian) view.

Thirty years of accumulating evidence from neurophysiology suggests that this is an illusion (TABLE 1). The first and, perhaps, most startling fact is that while it takes a nervous signal only about 20 ms to reach the brain, it requires a full 500 ms for a signal reaching the brain to register in consciousness! This is all the time in the world, so to speak, for emendations, changes, deletions, and enhancements to occur. Indeed, neurophysiologists have shown that stimuli, at least as late as 100 ms before an occurrence reaches consciousness, can affect the content of the experience.[29] Some additional times are the following.

It takes only 50 ms for a signal from the finger to cause, via a round-trip to the brain stem, the finger to be moved. Additional cognitive processing may require another 150 ms, but all of this is achieved without consciousness. Finally, what do we make of the following fact? 350 ms *before* we consciously intend to do something the relevant neuronal activity begins and there is a further 200 ms delay after we "intend" to do something before we actually do it. It seems as if our conscious mind is more of an on-looker than a decision-maker.

THE LOGIC OF DENIAL AND PROJECTION

Denial and projection are basic psychological processes serving self-deception, though in slightly different ways. Sometimes we will wish to deny something, usually negative (e.g., that we have caused harm to others or "incriminating" personal facts regarding adultery, robbery or something shameful). At other times we may wish to project something onto others which is true of ourselves. In simple voice-recognition choice experiments (see below) denying one variable means choosing (or projecting) the other, and *vice versa,* but the two are distinguished by relevance to self (own voice more important than other). Projection and denial are likely to have different dynamics. Denial will easily engender denial of denial, the deeper to bury the falsehood. Denial may plausibly require a heightened level of arousal, the better to attend quickly to the facts needing denial and shunt them from consciousness. Projection, by contrast, may often be a more relaxed operation: it would be nice if the facts were true, but not critical if they are not.

These speculations are supported by the classic voice-recognition experiments of Gur and Sackeim,[6] where unconscious self-recognition is measured by a relatively large jump in galvanic skin response (GSR). Some people deny their own voices some of the time, while others project their voice some of the time. In each case, the skin (GSR) has it right. Furthermore, when interviewed afterwards, almost all deniers deny their denial, while half of those projecting their voices are conscious after the fact that they sometimes made mistakes of exactly this sort. A comparison of the overall levels of GSRs shows that deniers exhibit the greatest GSRs to all stimuli, while projectors show the more relaxed profile typical of those who make no mistakes, as well as the hopelessly confused (those who both deny and project, sometimes fooling their own skin). Finally, Gur and Sackeim showed that denial and projection were motivated in a logical fashion: individuals made to feel bad about themselves started denying their own voices, while people made to feel better about themselves started projecting their own voices—as if self-presentation was being contracted or expanded according to relevant facts.

A student could go a long way by devising a series of follow-up experiments requiring only a tape recorder and a machine for reading the galvanic skin response. Is denial really associated with greater arousal than projection or correct apprehension of reality? What is happening with those individuals who make both kinds of mistakes—are they really completely confused some of the time? And if so, why? What kinds of voices of yourself do you deny after failure and which kinds do you project when you succeed (or believe you have)? If it is really true, as Douglas and Gibbins[30,31] seem to show, that voices of familiar others evoke a GSR stronger than unfamiliar others, then what kinds of events cause us to deny familiar others? Is denial or projection more likely with increasing testosterone? And so on. Note that there is a large industry in the U.S. devoted to the use of lie-detector tests (which employ GSR as one if their measures), largely in the world of job interviews and job-related thefts. There is a parallel academic literature investigating the lie detector

TABLE 2. Homophobia scale: sample questions[32]

1.	I would feel comfortable working closely with a male homosexual
4.	If a member of my sex made a sexual advance toward me, I would feel angry.
5.	I would feel comfortable knowing that I was attractive to members of my own sex.
12.	I would deny to members of my peer group that I had friends who were homosexual.
14.	If I saw two men holding hands in public I would feel disgusted.
17.	I would feel uncomforable if I learned that my spouse or partner was attracted to members of his or her own sex.

methodology in various settings. It should be easy to integrate the study of self-deception into these studies. Indeed, it may be possible to see under what conditions self-deception decreases detection by others, both those using a lie-detector machine and those not. It would also be possible, in principle, to adapt their methodology to the study of self-deception in animals: birds, for example, may also show greater physiological arousal to their own or close relative's voice than to others and they could be trained to peck when they "thought" they heard their own voice instead of another's.[25]

Denial of personal malfeasance may often strongly necessitate its projection onto others. Once years ago while driving, I took a corner too sharply and my one-year-old baby fell over in the back seat and started to cry. I heard myself harshly berating her nine-year-old sister (my stepdaughter)—as if she should know by now that I like to take my corners on two wheels, and brace the baby accordingly. But the very harshness of my voice served to warn me that something was amiss. Surely the child's responsibility in this matter was, at best, 10%. The remaining 90% belonged to me, but by denying my own role, someone else had to bear a greater burden. That is, denial of my own responsibility required that responsibility be strongly projected onto someone else, to balance the "responsibility equation."

In a somewhat similar fashion, it has been argued that denying one's own homosexual tendencies will cause one to project these sexual tendencies onto others. It is as if we are aware that there is some homosexual content in the immediate neighborhood and, denying our own portion, we go looking for the missing homosexuality in others. Some striking experimental work has recently been produced in support of this possibility.[12] Fully heterosexual men (no homosexual behavior, no homosexual fantasies) are divided into those that are relatively homophobic and those who are not. Homophobic men are defined as those who are uncomfortable with, fearful of, and hostile toward homosexual men. Homophobia is measured by a series of 25 questions (TABLE 2). A rough analogue with the GSR was provided by a plethysmograph attached to the base of the penis which measures changes in circumference, while interviews provided information on conscious perception of tumescence and arousal. Of course, we are unconscious of our GSRs, but conscious of changes in penile circumference, at least beyond some threshold, so the analogy is not precise, but the methodology provides results of parallel interest to those of Gur and Sackeim.[6]

When the two groups of men are exposed to four-minute sexual videos (heterosexual, lesbian, and male homosexual), the plethysmograph shows that both sets of men respond with similar levels of arousal to the heterosexual and lesbian videos but that only the *homophobic* men show a significant response to the male homosexual video. Interviews afterwards show that both categories of men give accurate estimates of their degree of tumescence and arousal to all stimuli with one exception: the homophobic men deny their response to the male homosexual video!

The results make a certain kind of superficial sense. Those heterosexual males who are, according to their own account, fully heterosexual in behavior and in fantasy yet who will actually experience arousal to the sight of two men making love would be expected to be more uncomfortable in the vicinity of homosexual men. These men, after all, represent continual possible sources of arousal for the man's latent homosexual affect. Discomfort around homosexuals and disgust and anger at them may be expected to be larger where homosexual threat is greater. Note again a dynamic between denial and projection. Denying their own homosexual feelings may force the individual to project a greater danger of those same tendencies onto others.

Ramachandran[10,11] has recently produced very striking evidence that processes of denial—and subsequent rationalization—appear to reside preferentially in the left brain. People with a stroke on the right side of the body (damage to the left brain) never or very rarely deny their condition, while a certain, small percentage of those with left-side paralysis deny their stroke and, when confronted with strong counter-evidence, indulge in a remarkable array of rationalizations denying the *cause* of their inability to move (arthritis, a general lethargy, etc.). This is consistent with other evidence that the right hemisphere is more emotionally honest, while the left hemisphere is actively engaged in self-promotion. It goes without saying that we need much more evidence on the underlying physiology, neurobiology and anatomy of mechanisms of self-deception.

INTERACTION WITH OTHER BIOLOGICAL SYSTEMS

Internal conflict and biased information flow within the individual probably have multiple biological sources, self-deception evolving in the service of deceit being only one. The alternative sources are taken up here with particular attention to their interactions.

1. Parent-offspring conflict. As is now well recognized, parents and offspring are expected to be in conflict in any outbred species since each will be related to self by 1 but to the other by only 1/2. This 1/2 degree of relatedness leads to a strong overlap in self-interest, but also an imperfect one, giving scope to various kinds of conflict.[18] Especially important in our own species is the fact that parent-offspring conflict extends to the behavioral tendencies of the offspring with the parent being selected to mold a more altruistic and less selfish offspring–at least as these behaviors affect other relatives—than the offspring is expected to act on its own. On the assumption that an internal representation of the parental voice is valuable to the child when their interests overlap closely, it can easily be imagined that selection has accentuated the parental voice in the offspring to benefit the parent and that some conflict is expected within an individual between its own self-interest and the internal representation of its parents' view of its self-interest.

It is easy to imagine that mechanisms of deceit and self-deception could be parasitized in this interaction. For example, low parental investment may coexist with exaggerated displays of parental affections, the latter serving as cover for the former.

The offspring may be tempted to go along with the parental show since resistance and malaffection may lead to even less investment. Yes, mommy loves you and you love mommy too. But one can easily imagine that having to adopt this self-deception as one's own may have long-term negative consequences and may lead to later internal psychological conflict when you are no longer under your parent's immediate control (via investment).

A good clinical example of this is provided by Dori LeCroy.[33] A thirty-year-old woman arrived for therapy appointments in a hesitant and apprehensive manner which (when challenged) she explained by her desire to avoid intruding on another's "personal space." In a wispy, vacant style she described herself as a loving and "spiritual" person who put special value on kindness, tolerance, and forgiveness. She related events in her life with an emphasis on ill-treatment by friends and relatives, including physical abuse as a child from her alcoholic mother, but the complaints were accompanied by rationalizations which absolved others of blame (her mother was really "a beautiful person" with troubles of her own, for example). Most notably, she displayed no anger, no outrage, no desire for revenge. Instead, she worried about the well-being of the perpetrators! LeCroy speculates that abuse suffered as a child led to overidentification with the abuser: "Self-deception of this kind would have enabled her to behave devotedly as abused children frequently do, and thereby solicit nurture."[33] It is important to note that the woman had not forgotten the facts regarding the past, indeed she volunteered them, but she had apparently transmuted her anger and resentment into oversolicitous indulgence, first for her mother and then for others. To reconcile the facts of the matter—that the maternal abuse was just fine—she had to agree to a negative self-image: she became bad and her mother good. Recently her mother has come around and now provides some real investment, but the patient herself still seems saddled with an imposed self-deception going to the heart of her identity. We are not attracted to people with a negative self-image, too timid to intrude and displaying an otherworldly attachment to altruism, even in the face of mistreatment!

2. Internal genetic conflict. A stronger potential source of internal conflict and biased information flow within the individual is internal *genetic* conflict, due to differing degrees of relatedness to others enjoyed by different parts of an individual's genome; these in turn are due to different rules of inheritance. For example, mitochondrial DNA (mtDNA) is passed only mother to offspring, while, of course, the autosomes are passed from each parent. One kind of conflict this can set up is over inbreeding. Autosomes enjoy an increased relatedness to offspring when they practice inbreeding, but this is not true for mtDNA, which is always related to progeny on the maternal side by 1. Put another way, since the mtDNA in any given individual is only coming from one parent, it does not increase relatedness for that parent to be related to the second parent. An autosome deciding whether inbreeding would be advantageous has to set against the increase in relatedness a decrease in quality of the offspring due to inbreeding depression. But the mtDNA will only see the inbreeding depression; thus as long as there is any inbreeding depression (and there often is), mtDNA will oppose inbreeding that the autosomes may favor.

There is no evidence regarding such interactions in animals, but there is striking evidence of exactly this kind of conflict in plants (for a good review of the relevant theory, see Ref. 34). Since most plants are hermaphrodites they can, in principle, practice "selfing" where the pollen and the ovules come from the same plant: this raises degree of relatedness to offspring from 1/2 to 1. About a 1/2 to 3/4 of all flowering plants are capable of selfing and in these species (but only rarely in obligately non-selfing species) one finds a most interesting conflict: mtDNA causes abortion of the male function or sterile pollen (cytoplasmic male sterility), while the nuclear DNA often acts to re-establish male function. This is exactly consistent with mtDNA's always opposing inbreeding when there is an outbred alternative.

The kind of conflict I have been describing pits a small part of the genotype against almost all the other genes: for this reason, such conflict is expected to be infrequent and resolved usually in favor of the dominant set of genes. A more important kind of internal genetic conflict for our own species pits one-half of the genotype against the other half. I refer to the phenomenon of genomic imprinting or parent-specific-gene expression (reviewed in Ref. 35). A small number of genes in us have the property that they are expressed only when inherited from one sex, the copy inherited from the opposite sex being silenced (or sometimes there is only a quantitative difference in gene expression depending on parent-of-origin).

The importance of genomic imprinting is that it allows imprinted genes to act on the basis of exact degrees of relatedness to each parent. This inevitably leads to conflict between paternal and maternal genes.[36] Possible psychological conflicts arising from imprinting are easy to describe.[37] Consider, for example, a contemplated act of inbreeding with your mother's sister's offspring. You are related on the maternal side and will thus enjoy an increase in relatedness to any resulting offspring by inbreeding on the maternal side, but the paternal genes will enjoy no increase in relatedness though they will suffer any inbreeding depression associated with the inbreeding. We can imagine your maternally active genes urging you to consider the inbreeding while your paternally active genes might take a moralistic posture and emphasize the biological defects thereby generated. Whether mtDNA has also been selected to decrease inbreeding, as in plants, is as yet unknown.

There is very intriguing indirect evidence suggesting that parts of the body may differ in the degree to which they express maternally active versus paternally active genes (reviewed in Ref. 19). In mice chimeras which consist of a mixture of normal cells with cells that have either a double dose of maternal genes (and no paternal ones) or a double dose of paternal genes (and no maternal ones), it turns out that the two added kinds of cells survive and proliferate differentially according to tissue: thus, doubly maternal cells do well in the neocortex of the brain but do not survive and proliferate in the hypothalamus and vice versa for doubly paternal cells. By similar logic the tissue producing dentin appears to be more maternally active, while the tissue producing enamel is more paternally active. Thus, it is possible that there are conflicts at the level of tissues in which one can also imagine *selves*-deception, that is, deceitful signals sent out from one tissue, overemphasizing one parent's interests whose signals are devalued by another tissue, overemphasizing the opposite sexed parent's interests. Where maternal kin are much more frequent in the social group than paternal kin, maternally active tissue in the neocortex may say, in effect, "Family is important, I like family, I believe in investing in family" while the hypothalamus may reply, "I'm hungry!"[37]

We can imagine interactions between genomic imprinting and other systems we have been discussing. For example, parental indoctrination will work better when it interacts with the appropriate imprinted genes: maternal manipulation with maternally active genes in the progeny and paternal manipulation with paternally active genes.[19] At the same time it is easy to imagine that mechanisms useful in self-deception to deceive others may prove useful in within-individual conflict. If selfish impulses are kept unconscious, the better to hide them from others, and they may also stay unconscious, the better not to be spotted by oppositely imprinted genes.

3. Selection to suppress negative traits. Everyone can expect to have some negative traits that are stuck in the phenotype either through misdevelopment or through genetic defect, and these are likely to have been such a regular part of our existence for so long that we may well wonder whether selection has not favored a mechanism which searches for such negative traits and attempts to suppress them. All genes in the individual would be in agreement with such a program, including the defective gene. Mutation will inevitably supply some negative traits,[38] but it is well to be aware of the fact that even in the absence of such a supply some selective factors by themselves generate some negative traits. For example, sex antagonistic genes are those that have opposite effects on reproductive success when found in the two sexes. As long as the net effect is positive, the gene will be favored, even though, when found in the opposite sex, it has negative effects on lifetime reproductive success.

William Rice's[39–41] beautiful experiments on *Drosophila* demonstrate clearly that sex antagonistic genes are a regular part of the *Drosophila* genome and by extension are expected in all sexually reproducing species that are not perfectly, lifelong monogamous. This means that each sex is a partial compromise between the two sexes and contains numerous traits disadvantageous to that sex (but advantageous in the opposite sex).

Naturally, if a mechanism for suppressing negative traits does exist, one may well expect internal conflict, forces acting to maintain the negative trait being opposed by efforts at suppression. There is no selection to increase the resistance, but as suppression is selected to become more effective, more negative genes will remain in the genotype because the suppression has reduced or eliminated the cost. It is easy to imagine an interaction between this mechanism and parent-offspring conflict, since parents may help you locate—and encourage you to suppress—such negative traits, but due to imperfect overlap in self-interest, they may encourage you to think a trait negative to yourself when it is in reality only negative to themselves. Similarly, it is conceivable that paternally active genes (for example) may attempt to suppress maternally active ones (or vice versa) by pretending that it is an organism-wide negative phenotypic trait that needs to be suppressed.

Prayer and meditation are two widespread examples of people wrestling with their phenotypes, some of which may have been favored by selection to suppress negative phenotypic traits, including the negative phenotypic trait of self-deception! Many famous passages from the world's great religions, as well as rituals of prayer and meditation, are directed against self-deception, as in this loose translation of Matthew 7:1–5 in the New Testament of the Bible: "Judge not that ye be not judged, for you are projecting your faults onto others; get rid of your own self-deception first, then you will have a chance of seeing others objectively."

4. Positive illusions? Another important possibility is that self-deception has intrinsic benefit for the organism performing it, quite independent of any improved ability to fool others. In the past twenty years an important literature has grown up[8,9] which appears to demonstrate that there are intrinsic benefits to having a higher perceived ability to affect an outcome, a higher self-perception, and a more optimistic view of the future than facts would seem to justify. It has been known for some time that depressed individuals tend not to go in for the routine kinds of self-inflation that we have described above. This is sometimes interpreted to mean that we would all be depressed if we viewed reality accurately, while it seems more likely that the depressed state may be a time of personal re-evaluation, where self-inflation would serve no useful purpose. While considering alternative actions, people evaluate them more rationally than when they have settled on one option, at which time they practice a mild form of self-deception in which they rationalize their choice as the best possible, imagine themselves to have more control over future events than they do, and see more positive outcomes than seem justified. What seems clear is that they gain direct benefits of functioning from these actions.[42] Life is intrinsically future-oriented and mental operations that keep a positive future orientation at the forefront result in better future outcomes (though perhaps not as good as those projected). The existence of the placebo effect is another example of this principle (though it requires the cooperation of another person ostensibly dispensing medicine). It would be very valuable to integrate our understanding of this kind of positive self-deception into the larger framework of self-deceptions we have been describing.

SELF-DECEPTION AND HUMAN DISASTERS

There can be little doubt that self-deception makes a disproportionate contribution to human disasters, especially in the form of misguided social policies, wars being perhaps the most costly example. This is part of the large downside to human self-deception. Since the general cost of self-deception is the misapprehension of reality, especially social reality, self-deception may easily generate large social costs (everyone on the airplane dies, the entire nation is devastated by a war some of its members started).

Disasters are, of course, studied in retrospect so the evidence is not yet scientific for the connection to self-deception, but it is certainly suggestive. In the following examples, we also see how analysis of individual self-deception can easily be extended to groups: pairs of individuals, an organization and an entire society.

Two-party self-deception. Trivers and Newton's[2] analysis of the crash of Air Florida's Flight 90 suggests that the pilot was practicing self-deception and the co-pilot acquiesced. The first clue comes from the cockpit conversation during take-off (TABLE 3). The co-pilot was flying the airplane, yet it was he who noticed contradictory information from the instrument panel and repeatedly spoke while it mattered (i.e., while they could still safely abort the flight). The pilot spoke only once, offering a false rationalization for the disturbing instrument readings. Only when it was too late—they were in the air—did the pilot start talking, while the co-pilot fell silent. An analysis of their conversation prior to take-off showed a consistent pattern of reality denial by the pilot (TABLE 4). His casual approach to reality, coupled with overconfidence, may have served him well in many minor situations, but proved fatal when real danger required close attention to reality, including the psychological state of his co-pilot.

When an organization practices deception toward the larger society, this may induce organizational self-deception. Richard Feynman[3] analyzed the cause of the Challenger disaster and concluded that NASA's deceptive posture toward U.S. soci-

TABLE 3. Crash of Air Florida flight 90[2]

	Co-pilot	Pilot
During take-off	Speaks	Silent[a]
After lift-off	Silent	Speaks

[a]Except for one rationalization.

TABLE 4. Conversations during taxiing prior to take-off[2]

Co-pilot	Pilot
• Detailed description of snow on wings	• Diminutive description of snow on wings
• Calls attention to danger they face (too long since de-icing)	• Deflects attention to ideal world (de-icing machine on runway)
• Asks for advice on take-off	• Tells him to do what he wants

TABLE 5. Feynman's analysis of NASA's shift to self-deception[3]

1960s	Aim:	• Go to moon
		• No conflict with larger society
		• No internal conflict re facts
		• Built from bottom up
	Result:	• Success
1970s	Aim:	• Emply a $5 billion bureaucracy
		• Need to convince larger society — repeated manned flight via shuttle
		• Bottom splits from top, which does not wish to know true facts re safety
		• Built from top down
	Result:	• Challenger disaster

ety had bred organizational self-deception. When NASA was given the assignment and the funds to travel to the moon in the 1960s, the society, for better or worse, gave full support to the project: Beat the Soviets to the moon (TABLE 5). As a result, NASA could design the moon vehicle in a rational way. The vehicle was designed from the bottom up, with multiple alternatives tried at each step, permitting maximum flexibility as the spacecraft was developed. Once the U.S. reached the moon, NASA was a five-billion-dollar bureaucracy with no work to do. Its subsequent history, Feynman argued, was dominated by a need to generate funds, and critical design features, such as manned flight versus unmanned flight, were chosen precisely because they were costly. In addition, manned flight had glamour appeal, which would generate enthusiasm for the funding. At the same time it was necessary to sell this project to Congress and the American people. The very concept of a reusable vehicle—the so-called Shuttle—was designed to appear inexpensive, while in fact it was very costly (more expensive, it turned out, than using brand new devices each time).

Means and concepts were chosen for their ability to generate cash-flow and the apparatus was then designed top-down. This had the unfortunate effect that when a problem surfaced, such as had with the O-rings, there was little parallel exploration or knowledge to solve the problem. Thus NASA chose to minimize the problem and the unit within NASA that was consigned to deal with safety became an agent of rationalization and denial, instead of one of rational study of safety factors.

Some of the most extraordinary mental gyrations in service of institutional self-deception occurred within the Safety Unit. Seven of twenty-four Challenger flights had shown O-ring damage. Feynman showed that if you merely plotted chance of damage as a function of temperature at time of take-off you got a significant negative relationship: lower temperature meant a higher chance of O-ring damage. To prevent themselves from seeing this, the Safety Unit performed the following mental operation. They said that seventeen flights showed no damage and were thus irrelevant and could be excluded from further analysis. Since some of the cases of damage occurred during high-temperature take-offs, temperature at take-off could be ruled out as a causative agent. One of the O-rings had been eaten 1/3 of the way through. Had it been eaten all the way through, the flight would have blown up, as did the Challenger. But NASA cited this case of 1/3 damage as a virtue. They claimed to have built in a "threefold safety factor"! This is a very unconventional use of language. By law you must build an elevator strong enough so that the cable can support a full load with no damage. Then you must make it eleven times stronger. This is called an eleven-fold safety factor. NASA has the elevator hanging by a thread and calls it a virtue. They even used circular argumentation with a remarkably short radius: since manned flight had to be much safer than unmanned flight, it perforce was. In short, in service of the larger institutional deceit and self-deception, the Safety Unit was thoroughly corrupted to serve propaganda ends, that is, to create the appearance of safety where there was none.

There is thus a close analogy between self-deception within an individual and self-deception within an organization, both serving to deceive others. In neither case is information completely destroyed (all 12 engineers at Thiokol, which built the O-ring, voted against flight that morning). It is merely relegated to portions of the person or the organization that are inaccessible to consciousness (we can think of the people running NASA as the conscious part of the organization). In both cases the entity's relationship to others determines its internal structure of information. In a non-deceitful relationship information can be stored logically and coherently. In a deceitful relationship information will be stored in a biased manner the better to deceive others—but with serious potential costs. Note, however, that it is the astronauts who suffered the ultimate cost, while the upper echelons of NASA—indeed, the entire organization minus the dead—may have enjoyed a net benefit (in employment, for example) from their casual and self-deceived approach to safety.

Self-deception is especially likely in warfare. Richard Wrangham has recently extended the analysis of self-deception to human warfare in a most revealing way.[5] Evolutionary logic suggests that self-deception is apt to be especially costly in interactions with outsiders, members of another group. In interactions with group members, self-deception will be inhibited by two forces: a partial overlap in self-interest gives greater weight to the opinion of others and within-group feedback provides a partial corrective to personal self-deception. In interactions between groups, everyday processes of self-enhancement are uninhibited by negative feedback from others, nor by concern for their welfare, while derogation of the outsiders' moral worth, physical strength, and bravery is likewise unchecked by feedback and shared self-interest. These result in faulty mechanisms of assessment, and aggression will be more likely where each partner is biased in an unrealistic direction in self- and other-assessment, making conflicts more likely to occur and contests therefore more costly, on average, without any average gain in benefits.[5] Derogation of the moral status of your enemies only makes you underestimate their motivation (consider U.S. assessment of the Vietnamese). For an excellent analysis of this phenomenon, as applied to the Old Testament of the Bible, see Hartung.[43]

Processes of group self-deception only make matters worse: Within each group individuals are misoriented in the same direction, easily reinforcing each other and absence of contrary views is taken as confirming evidence (even silence is misinterpreted as support).[5] Tuchman[4] has frightening stories to tell of an individual leader and his cohorts whipping themselves into a frenzy of self-deception prior to launching an ill-advised, indeed disastrous, attack on neighbors.

Military incompetence—losing while expecting to win—is accompanied by four common symptoms: overconfidence, underestimation of the neighbor, ignoring intelligence reports, and wastage of manpower.[5] The latter two are noteworthy. The logic of self-deception preserves conscious illusion by becoming unconscious of contrary evidence, even when provided by one's own agents, whose very purpose it is to provide accurate information. Note in the Challenger disaster how the unit assigned to consider safety ended up being subverted to rationalize unsafety, even though its ostensible purpose was to view the matter objectively.[3] Wastage of manpower is a direct cost of self-deception since forces are deployed along illusory lines of attack, instead of rationally calibrated toward the real situation.

Wrangham makes an important distinction between raids and battles.[5] Lethal raids are attacks on a few neighbors, with numerical superiority being a key stimulus to attack. Raids have a long evolutionary history (chimpanzee males practice lethal raids)[44] and opportunities for self-deception are minimized by the ease of rational assessment (e.g., evidence of numerical superiority). Battles are set pieces between large opposing armies. They are a recent invention (within historical times, more or less), rational assessment is much more difficult, and a long evolutionary history of derogating others[13] makes misassessments especially likely. In short, we should be especially vigilant in guarding against self-deception when contemplating warfare.

CONCLUSION

Self-deception appears to be a universal human trait which touches our lives at all levels—from our innermost thoughts to the chance that we will be annihilated together in warfare. It affects the relative development of intellectual disciplines (the more social the content, the less developed the discipline: contrast physics and sociology) as well as the relative degree of consciousness of individuals (generally, more self-deceived, less conscious). An evolutionary analysis suggests that the root cause is social, including selection to deceive others, selection on others to manipulate and deceive oneself, and selection on competing sections of one's own genotype. There are undoubtedly complex and important interactions between these (and other) kinds of self-deception. The relevant evidence stretches from personal anecdote to historical analysis, but we especially need more biological evidence on the genetics, endocrinology, physiology and neuroanatomy of self-deception and we need to integrate very disparate findings from experimental, social and clinical psychology into the evolutionary analysis. We also need a detailed theory for the evolution of deception (many elements exist already) and a theory of consciousness based on our understanding of self-deception. Evolutionary theory promises to provide a firm foundation for a science of self-deception, which should eventually be able to predict both the circumstances expected to induce greater self-deception and the particular forms of self-deception being induced.

ACKNOWLEDGMENTS

I am grateful to Drs. Helena Cronin, Dori LeCroy, and Peter Moller for encouraging me to publish this article, to Mr. John Martin (Rockford, Illinois), and to the Ann and Gordon Getty Foundation for generous financial support. I am also thankful to Drs. David Haig, Dori LeCroy, David Smith, and especially Richard Wrangham for a series of detailed and valuable comments on the manuscript.

REFERENCES

1. McEwan, I. 1997. Enduring Love. Jonathan Cape. London.
2. Trivers, R.L. & H.P. Newton. 1982. The crash of Flight 90: doomed by self-deception? Science Digest (November) : 66, 67 and 111.
3. Feynman, R. 1988. What Do You Care What Other People Think? Further Adventures of a Curious Character. Norton. New York.
4. Tuchman, B. 1988. The March of Folly: From Troy to Viet Nam.
5. Wrangham, R. 1999. Is military incompetence adaptive? Evol. Hum. Behav. **20:** 3–12.
6. Gur, R. & H.. A. Sackeim. 1979. Self-deception: a concept in search of a phenomenon. J. Pers. Soc. Psychol. **37:** 147–169.
7. Greenwald, A.G. 1980. The totalitarian ego: fabrication and revision of personal history. Am. Psychol. **35:** 603–618.
8. Taylor, S.E. & D.A. Armor. 1996. Positive illusions and coping with adversity. J. Pers. **64:** 873–898.
9. Taylor, S.E. 1998. Positive illusions. *In* Encyclopedia of Mental Health, Vol. 3. H.S. Friedman, Ed.: 199–208. Academic Press, San Diego, CA.
10. Ramachandran, V. & D. Rogers-Ramachandran. 1996. Denial of disabilities in anosognosia. Nature **382:** 501.
11. Ramachandran, V. 1997. The evolutionary biology of self-deception, laughter, dreaming and depression: some clues from anosognosia. Med. Hypotheses **47:** 347–362.
12. Adams, H.E., L. W. Wright, Jr & B.A. Lohr. 1996. Is homophobia associated with homosexual arousal? J. Abnorm. Psychol. **105:** 440–445.
13. Krebs, D.L &. Denton, K. 1997. Social illusions and self-deception: the evolution of biases in person perception. *In* Evolutionary Social Psychology. J. A. Simpson & D.T. Kenrick, Eds: 21-48. Erlbaum Associates. Mahwah, NJ.
14. Hamilton, W. D. 1994. The genetical evolution of social behaviour. I, II. J. Theor. Biol. **7:** 1–52.
15. Trivers, R. 1985. Social Evolution. Benjamin/Cummings. Menlo Park, CA.
16. Krebs, J.R. & R. Dawkins. 1984. Animal signals: mindreading and manipulation. *In* Behavioural Ecology, 2nd ed. J.R. Krebs & N.B. Davies, Eds.: 380–402. Sinauer. Sunderland, MA.

17. ALEXANDER, R.D. 1979. Darwinism and Human Affairs. University of Washington Press: Seattle, WA.
18. TRIVERS, R.L. 1974. Parent-offspring conflict. Am. Zool. **14:** 249–264.
19. TRIVERS, R. & A. BURT. 1999. Kinship and genomic imprinting. *In* Genomic Imprinting. An Interdisciplinary Approach. R. Ohlsson, Ed.: 1–23. Springer. Heidelberg, Germany.
20. LEWIS, M. 1997. Altering Fate: Why the Past Does Not Predict the Future. Guilford Press. New York, NY.
21. TIGER, L. 1979. Optimism: The Biology of Hope. Simon and Schuster. New York.
22. ROHWER, S. 1977. Status signalling in Harris sparrows: some experiments in deception. Behaviour **61:** 107–129.
23. ROHWER, S & F.A. ROHWER. 1978. Status signalling in Harris sparrows: experimental deception achieved. Anim. Behav. **26:** 1012–1022.
24. MØLLER, A.P. & J.P. SWADDLE. 1987. Social control of deception among status signalling house sparrows *Passer domesticus*. Behav. Ecol. Sociobio. **20:** 307–311.
25. TRIVERS, R. 1991. Deceit and self-deception: the relationship between communication and consciousness. *In*: Man and Beast Revisited. M. Robinson&L.Tiger, Eds.: 175–191. Smithsonian. Washington, DC.
26. MELE, D. 1997. Real self-deception. Behav. Brain Sci. **20:** 91–136.
27. FOSTER E, M. JOBLING, P. TAYLOR, P. DONNELLY, P. DE KNIJFF, R. MIEREMET, T. ZERJAL & C. TYLER-SMITH. 1998. Jefferson fathered slave's last child. Nature **396:** 27–28.
28. CASHDAN, E. 1995. Hormones, sex and status in women. Horm. Behav. **29:** 354–366.
29. LIBET, B. 1996. Neuronal time factors in conscious and unconscious mental functions. *In* Toward a Science of Consciousness: The First Tucson Discussion and Debates. S. R. Hameroff, A.W. Kaszniak & A. Scott, Eds.: 337–347. MIT Press. Cambridge, MA.
30. DOUGLAS, W. & K. GIBBINS. 1983. Inadequacy of voice recognition as a demonstration of self-deception. J. Pers. Soc. Psychol. **44:** 589–592.
31. SACKEIM, H.A. & R.C. GUR. 1985. Voice recognition and the ontological stuatus of self-deception. J. Pers. Soc. Psychol. **48:** 213–215.
32. HUDSON, W.W. & W.A. RICKETTS. 1980. A strategy for the measurement of homophobia. J. Homosexuality **5:** 356–371.
33. LECROY, D. 1998. Darwin in the clinic: an evolutionary perspective on psychodynamics found in a single case study. ASCAP **11:** 6–12.
34. FRANK, S. 1989. The evolutionary dynamics of cytoplasmic male sterility. Am. Naturalist. **133:** 345–376.
35. OHLSSON, R. Ed. 1999. Genomic Imprinting. An Interdisciplinary Approach. Springer. Heidelberg.
36. HAIG, D. 1997. Parental antagonism, relatedness asymmetries, and genomic imprinting. Proc. Roy. Soc. Lond. B. **264:** 1657–1662.
37. TRIVERS, R. 1997. Genetic Basis of intra-psychic conflict. *In* Uniting Psychology and Biology: Integrative Perspectives on Human Development. N. Segal, G.E. Weisfeld & C.C. Weisfeld, Eds.: 385–395. Am. Psychol. Assoc. Washington, DC.
38. EYRE-WALKER, A. & P.D. KEIGHTLEY. 1999. High genomic deleterious mutation rates in hominids. Nature **397:** 344–347.
39. RICE, W. 1992. Sexually antagonistic genes: experimental evidence. Science **256:** 1436–1439.
40. RICE, W. 1998. Male fitness increases when females are eliminated from gene pool: implications for the Y chromosome. Proc. Natl. Acad. Sci. USA **95:** 6217–6221.
41. HOLLAND, B. & W.R. RICE. 1999. Experimental removal of sexual selection reverses intersexual antagonistic coevolution and removes a reproductive load. Proc. Natl. Acad. Sci. USA **96:** 5083–5088.
42. KREBS, D., K. DENTON & N.C. HIGGINS. 1988. On the evolution of self-knowledge and self-deception. *In* Sociobiological Perspectives on Human Development. K. B. MacDonald, Ed. Springer. New York.
43. HARTUNG, J. 1995. Love thy neighbor: the evolution of in-group morality. Skeptic **3:** 86–99.
44. WRANGHAM, R. & D. PETERSON. 1996. Demonic Males: Apes and the Origins of Human Violence. Houghton Mifflin. Boston, MA.

The Evolution of Moral Dispositions in the Human Species

DENNIS L. KREBS

Psychology Department, Simon Fraser University, Burnaby, British Columbia, V5A 1S6, Canada

ABSTRACT: Kohlberg's model of moral development is viewed from the perspective of evolutionary biology. Moral judgments defining Kohlberg's stages of moral development are seen as manifestations of structures evolved to uphold systems of cooperation. Game theory research on adaptive strategies of cooperation supports the conclusion that humans inherit dispositions to uphold the systems of cooperation implicit in the first three stages in Kohlberg's sequence, but not the systems of cooperation implicit in the highest stages. The empirical evidence on real-life morality is more consistent with a biological model of ontogenesis than is the model espoused by Kohlbergians. Although people occasionally make moral judgments in their everyday lives to reveal their solutions to moral dilemmas, as Kohlberg's model assumes, they more often make moral decisions that advance their adaptive interests.

THE EVOLUTION OF MORAL DISPOSITIONS IN THE HUMAN SPECIES

In a sense, I began working on this paper thirty years ago, while I was a graduate student, though I didn't know it at the time. One of the most inspiring experiences I had in graduate school was to take a seminar from the eminent developmental psychologist, Lawrence Kohlberg. Kohlberg was a kind of creative genius, and I was intrigued by his model of moral development.[1] In Kohlberg's model, the moral aspect of human nature resides in the ability to reason: the better people's ability to figure out the solutions to moral dilemmas, the more moral they are. In graduate school, I was pretty good at pure reason, and I liked the idea that this could make me moral. I can remember seizing every opportunity to espouse what I believed were Stage 6 principles. But that was the 1960s.

During this era, while drafting a review of the psychological literature on altruism,[2] I was approached by a graduate student from the Biology Department, who was writing a paper on reciprocal altruism in nonhuman animals. We traded drafts, talked about altruism, and eventually became friends. This student was Robert Trivers.

I can remember sitting in Trivers' flat, listening to him talk about strange things like why male lizards were larger than female lizards and why birds emitted alarm calls. The more I thought about the questions he asked, the more fascinated I became with the theoretical perspective from which he derived them. Trivers looked at humans as just another species. Why are men bigger than women? Why do people from all cultures practice reciprocity?

After I graduated, I pursued two interests, one stemming from my experiences with Kohlberg; the other stemming from my experiences with Trivers. I launched a research program aimed at evaluating Kohlberg's model of morality and I wrote theoretical papers on the evolution of altruism. I kept these two interests separate until a few years ago, when, after reviewing Richard Alexander's book on the biology of morality,[3] it occurred to me that evolutionary theory might be better equipped to account for the results of my research on Kohlberg's model than Kohlberg's theory was.

My goal in this paper is to describe Kohlberg's model of morality, to identify what I see to be its main limitations, and then to demonstrate how looking at Kohlberg's model through the eyes of an evolutionary psychologist produces a picture of human morality that is significantly more valid, though less pretty, than the picture painted by Kohlberg.

KOHLBERG'S MODEL OF MORALIZATION

Kohlberg derived his model primarily from data he obtained from a longitudinal study he launched in the late 1950s.[4] In this study, Kohlberg gave a sample of boys a set of nine hypothetical moral dilemmas, asked them what the characters in the dilemmas should do, and then probed extensively to get at the underlying structure of the moral reasoning from which these boys derived their decisions. The actual decisions the boys made about what the characters should do did not matter much to Kohlberg; what mattered was the reasons they gave to justify their decisions. Eventually, Kohlberg developed a scoring manual based on the reasons these boys gave, containing what he called criterion judgments diagnostic of structures of moral reasoning.

Kohlberg's longitudinal study produced four main conclusions. First, as people develop morally, they acquire up to six increasingly sophisticated structures of moral reasoning in an invariant sequence. These structures define stages of moral development. Second, these structures are "structures of the whole" that organize the ways in which those who have acquired them think about all moral issues. Third, new structures of moral reasoning transform and displace old structures. For example, once people acquire the Stage 3 idea that "it is right to do unto others as you would have them do unto you," they will abandon the Stage 2 idea that it is right to do to others as they do to you. Finally, the more sophisticated a person's understanding of why a course of action is right—i.e., the higher her or his stage of moral development—the more likely the person is to behave accordingly.

In Kohlberg's early writings,[1] he argued that the sixth stage in his developmental progression was the pinnacle of morality. After considering the data from his longitudinal study and the complaints of philosophers, he came to decide that after Stage 4, people might adopt several equally moral structures. The structures that define Stage 5 uphold utilitarian principles that maximize good or welfare. The structures that define Stage 6 uphold the means or processes through which people should achieve the ends prescribed by Stage 5 judgments. These processes involve adopting what Colby and Kohlberg[4] characterize as a "moral point of view," defined as "a point of view that ideally all human beings should take toward one another as free and equal autonomous persons. This means equal consideration of the claims or points of view of each person affected by the moral decision to be made."

EVALUATION OF KOHLBERG'S MODEL OF MORALITY

Over the years, with the help of many students, I have pursued a program of empirical research aimed at evaluating Kohlberg's model of moral development.[5–15] The main goals of this program were (*a*) to determine the extent to which Kohlberg's model could account for the types of moral judgment people make in their everyday lives, and (*b*) to examine the relation between moral judgment and moral behavior.

In the end, we were forced to conclude that Kohlberg's model of morality does not account well for the empirical data on real-life morality, and that the ways in which people reason about Kohlberg's hypothetical dilemmas bear little relation to their tendency to behave in moral ways. More specifically, we reached the following conclusions. First, moral reasoning is structurally flexible. People do not derive all their moral judgments from the structures that define their latest stage of development. People who make relatively high-stage moral judgments in response to Kohlberg's dilemmas often make low-stage moral judgments about their real-life moral conflicts. Second, old structures are not transformed and displaced when new structures are acquired. Third, there are significant differences between moral judgments about hypothetical dilemmas and moral judgments about dilemmas involving real people and real consequences. Fourth, the relation between the author and object of a moral judgment may affect the form of the judgment. In particular, moral judgments about oneself tend to differ from moral judgments about others. And, finally, people virtually never make Stage 5 or 6 moral judgments in their everyday lives.

When the empirical findings from our research did not fit with Kohlberg's model, we revised Kohlberg's model accordingly, then conducted research on the revised model, and so on. Slowly but surely I putted toward the conclusion that our efforts were not best invested in repairing the Kohlbergian craft. Better to abandon ship, salvage what we could, and build a new vessel. I examined the models developed by psychologists of various persuasions, but none seemed to hold more promise than Kohlberg's model. Eventually, it occurred to me to book passage on a biological boat, and see where it would go.

LOOKING AT KOHLBERG'S MODEL THROUGH A BIOLOGICAL LENS

TABLE 1 summarizes the types of moral judgment that form the foundation of Kohlberg's model. Like Kohlberg, an evolutionary psychologist would view these judgments as manifestations of, or output from, internal psychological structures whose function is to solve moral problems, and, like Kohlberg, an evolutionary psychologist would be interested in mapping the design of these structures or "mental organs." However, unlike Kohlberg, an evolutionary psychologist would expect the structures to have been shaped by the adaptive functions they served in ancestral environments, especially with respect to real-life problems pertaining to survival, resource accumulation, reproduction, and care of offspring.

We can take a second look at the stage-typed judgments in TABLE 1 and ask what function is implicit in their design? My answer to this question is: upholding systems of cooperation. Moral judgments classified at different Kohlbergian stages uphold different systems of cooperation. I believe the essence of morality lies in the idea that people have a duty to uphold the systems of cooperative exchange that have evolved

TABLE 1. Stage-typed criterion judgments

Stage	Criterion judgments
1	Avoid getting beaten up, spanked, hit, put in jail, or punished Obey powerful authorities
2	Pay people back • Return favors, show appreciation • Get even
3	Promote the welfare, strength, and harmony of one's family and friends Set a good example for others to be kind, generous, compassionate Leave a good impression on the community
4	Uphold the orderly and smooth functioning of society so society can be productive
5	Evaluate proposed action in terms of its consequences for all the people involved and long-term consequences for social norms and cultural standards

in the groups to which they belong. I feel secure in this belief because it is consistent with virtually all conceptions of morality with which I am familiar and it is shared by eminent scholars from an array of academic areas.[3,16–18] Quoting Jim Rest,[19] many scholars regard morality "as standards or guidelines that govern human cooperation—in particular how rights, duties, and benefits are to be allocated.... Moralities are proposals for a system of mutual coordination of activities and cooperation among people."

THE EVOLUTION OF COOPERATION

To understand the evolution of morality, we must understand the evolution of cooperation. I believe the nature of cooperation has been captured best by Axelrod and Hamilton[20] and Axelrod,[21] so I will draw on their research to describe the principles underlying the evolution of cooperation. I am aware that the conclusions of these collaborators are limited by the parameters of their research, but I don't believe these limitations compromise the validity of the basic principles they have identified.

Axelrod and Hamilton created computer contests based on Prisoner's Dilemma paradigms, pitting various strategies against each another. In their model, each strategy is equivalent to an allele in an ancestral environment; each contest is a generation; points gained in exchanges equate to the propagation of alleles. The main question these investigators asked is which alleles (i.e., strategies) will be selected (that is to say *win*) in competitions against other alleles. A related question was whether an evolutionarily stable strategy would emerge, that is, a strategy that could not be defeated by any other strategy.

Selfish Individualism

Consider first a strategy Axelrod and Hamilton call defection, which I will call selfish individualism. Alleles for selfish individualism induce individuals to behave in a way that give them the best chance of maximizing their immediate gain from specific incidents of exchange—to take whatever others offer and give nothing in return. Selfish individualism is a powerful strategy. Often overlooked in the implications of Axelrod and Hamilton's research is the finding that selfish individualism cannot be bettered by any strategy competing against it on a one-on-one basis. If it competes against a cooperative strategy—defined as giving in order to get—it reaps what the cooperator gives without suffering the costs of reciprocation. If it competes against a selfish strategy, it "draws," thus evading the costs of exploitation. Note that Axelrod and Hamilton did not find that a cooperative strategy interacting with a cooperative strategy (a giver interacting with a giver) reaped fewer benefits than a selfish strategy interacting with a selfish strategy (a taker interacting with a taker). They found only that no strategy can beat selfish individualism one on one.

Once selfishly individualistic alleles go to work in a population defeating cooperative alleles, they flood the population. Ironically, the success of selfishly individualistic alleles vastly reduces the pay-offs from the strategy, because the victorious takers end up interacting with other victorious takers, leaving no givers to exploit.

Indiscriminate Altruism in a Population of Indiscriminate Altruists

Now consider the following scenario: A group of individuals all inherit alleles to engage in indiscriminate altruism, defined as giving to or helping any member of their group who needs help. In the parameters of the computer contests created by Axelrod and Hamilton, every single member of this group would come out ahead of every single member of a group of selfish individualists. It is plausible to assume that groups of indiscriminate altruists would out-compete groups of selfish individualists in many circumstances. For example, Alexander[3] has suggested that the most significant selective pressure in our ancestral environment was hostile groups of hominids, and that cooperative groups would have prevailed over uncooperative groups in inter-tribal wars.

The potential benefits of alleles for indiscriminate altruism notwithstanding, the evolution of indiscriminate altruism faces a huge obstacle: altruistic alleles lose in every exchange with selfishly individualistic alleles. If somehow a group of indiscriminate altruists did evolve, it would be vulnerable to invasion by selfishly individualistic alleles, which, of course, is the central obstacle to group selection.

Tit for Tat

The most widely discussed finding from the iterated computer contests sponsored by Axelrod[21] is that a cooperative strategy called "tit for tat" prevailed over selfish individualism. Tit for tat involves cooperating on the first move, then copying the choice made by one's partner on the previous move. Although tit for tat loses against selfish individualism on the first move, it cuts its losses quickly by behaving selfishly toward selfish individualists on subsequent moves. In effect, selfish individualism transforms tit for tat into itself, minimizing losses from the interaction, but producing minimal gains. However, when tit for tat encounters cooperative strategies, it behaves in a cooperative way, thus reaping the benefits of cooperation. Note that the most significant payoff from tit for tat stems from cooperative exchanges, and just as selfishness begets selfishness, cooperation begets cooperation, maximizing cooperators' gains. In a population containing a sufficient number of tit-for-tat strategies, tit for tat can defeat selfish individualism because it reaps as many benefits as the selfish alleles it encounters except on the first move, plus all the benefits of cooperating with "tit for tatters" and other cooperators, without suffering the costs of unprotected cooperation. An added bonus of tit for tat is that if it floods a population, it creates an environment in which pure cooperation may thrive. Indeed, in a completely tit-for-tat environment you could not tell the difference between tit for tat and pure cooperation because everyone would be cooperating.

Following the publication of Axelrod's[21] and Axelrod and Hamilton's[20] findings, a spate of investigators conducted computer contests in which they introduced other strategies and changed the parameters of Axelrod and Hamilton's research. The upshot of these studies was to demonstrate that other strategies can defeat tit for tat in some circumstances. Interestingly, most of these winning strategies were more cooperative than tit for tat (e.g., "tit for two tats" or "generous tit for tat"). The following findings are relevant to the conclusions I will reach in this paper. First, sets of different strategies may evolve in a population, and, because the viability of these strategies is frequency-dependent, they may fluctuate in proportion.[22] I will argue that humans inherit dispositions to uphold several systems of cooperation. Second, strategies that "learn" may defeat strategies that do not learn, and reputation plays an important role in learning.[23] Third, ostracism favors cooperation.[24] I will argue that reputation and ostracism are instrumental in the evolution of indirect reciprocity. Fourth, punishing defectors and establishing norms may contribute to the spread of cooperation.[25] I will argue that societal systems of indirect reciprocity cannot evolve without appropriate rules and sanctions. And, finally, mistakes may hinder the evolution of cooperative strategies and reduce the effectiveness of the tit-for-tat strategy, because a selfish mistake from a tit-for-tat cooperator can launch an unbroken string of selfish exchanges.[26]

The Adaptiveness of Kohlbergian Structures of Cooperation

With this analysis of the evolution of cooperation, let's return to the cooperative strategies upheld by Kohlbergian criterion judgments and ask which structures could have evolved. I believe the evidence supporting the evolution of Stage 1 and 2 structures is strong and clear, so I will not invest much time on supporting arguments. I have reviewed the evidence more fully in a chapter I contributed to the *Handbook of Evolutionary Psychology.*[27]

Stage 1 Structures

Stage 1 judgments uphold selfishly individualistic strategies directing individuals to maximize their immediate somatic benefits and minimize their immediate somatic losses. One limitation of the Prisoner's Dilemma is it presumes equality among participants. However, many exchanges take place between people of unequal power, defined as the ability to reward and punish those with whom they exchange resources. Kohlberg's Stage 1 strategy is sensitive to power differentials, directing individuals to defer to those who are more powerful than they are, making the best of a bad situation and living to fight another day. There is plenty of evidence for the evolution of dominance-deference structures in nonhuman species.[27,28]

Stage 2 Structures

Stage 2 structures uphold systems of direct reciprocity: you scratch my back and I'll scratch yours. Axelrod's tit for tat is one such strategy, and as we have seen, it is powerful. Indeed, direct reciprocity is even more powerful in many real-life contexts than it is in Prisoner's Dilemma paradigms. In Prisoner's Dilemma contests, the value of items exchanged—i.e., points in the game—are fixed and invariant across exchange partners. In contrast, in real-life exchanges, people may exchange items of relatively little value to them, but great value to the recipient, in return for items of relatively little value to their partners and great value to them—a phenomenon economists call "gains in trade." The more I think of gains in trade, the more convinced I become that they are one the great wonders of the social world.

Systems of direct reciprocity have evolved among many non-human animals.[27-29] The system of nutrient exchange in the vampire bats studied by Wilkinson,[30] which clearly demonstrates the power of gains in trade, is probably best known.

Stage 3 Structures

If you look at Kohlberg's Stage 3 criterion judgments, you will find many that uphold relationships between mates and among relatives. Elsewhere,[27] I have argued that dispositions to assist mates and relatives probably evolved through sexual selection and kin selection, and that judgments upholding pair-bonded and kin-based relationships tend to be more care-oriented than other types of moral judgment. Here, I will focus on the adaptive value of reciprocity among members of in-groups.

Many of the moral judgments classified in Kohlberg's system as Stage 3 uphold systems of indirect reciprocity. Indirect reciprocity may take two forms. First, person A gives to person B, who gives to person C, who gives to person A: "What goes around comes around." Second, all members of a group may give to a central distributor that redistributes the resources to those who have contributed. Note that you need at least three individuals—or a group—for indirect reciprocity. The question is: could systems of indirect reciprocity have evolved through natural selection? In terms of payoffs, indirect reciprocity has the potential to generate more benefits than direct reciprocity does through increasingly efficient gains in trade. Person B may be able to give person C more valuable benefits at less cost than person A could have, and ditto with respect to exchanges between C and A.

The potential gains from indirect reciprocity notwithstanding, it could not evolve without a mechanism to protect it from invasion by selfish individualism. In essence, this means that it must contain a way of preventing cheaters from prospering. Clearly, it is more difficult to detect defections in indirect reciprocity than it is to detect them in more direct exchanges—who is to know whether you have paid back the benefits I bestowed on you to some third party? Who could keep track of all exchanges among members of large groups? The best we can do is to observe members of the groups to which we belong to see whether, in general, they help other members, and allocate our assistance to them accordingly. Well, actually, we can do a little better. We can compare notes with other members of our group. Therefore, we would expect gossip and reputation to play important roles in systems of indirect reciprocity. Cooperators should be praised, admired, and popular; and cheaters should be blamed, shunned, and ostracized.

According to the evolutionary biologist, Richard Alexander,[3] systems of indirect reciprocity have evolved in the human species, and perhaps in other species. Alexander argues that "moral systems are systems of indirect reciprocity." Alexander believes that in groups of repeatedly interacting individuals, indirect reciprocity will pay off because (*a*) individuals will admire and select as partners those who behave beneficently, (*b*) groups will reward altruists and their relatives directly by endowing them with enhanced status, medals for heroism, etc., and (*c*) "the beneficent individual may be rewarded by simply having the success of the group within which he behaved beneficently contribute to the success of his own descendants and collateral relatives." Those who cheat will be punished through losses in status, rejection as partners, ostracism from the group, and negative effects on the group that filter back to the cheater and his or her relatives. It follows that members of groups practicing indirect reciprocity should be vigilant for selfishness.

In recent computer simulations, Nowak and Sigmund[31] supported the idea that indirect reciprocity could evolve through the mechanisms identified by Alexander. Nowak and Sigmund made the assumption that pairs of interactants are unlikely to meet again, minimizing the opportunity for direct reciprocity. Behaving altruistically enhanced an individual's reputation or "image," and behaving selfishly degraded it. Nowak and Sigmund found that if altruists discriminated in favor of those with a good reputation, altruism could evolve and become evolutionarily stable. The logic underlying the adaptive value of indirect reciprocity is similar to the logic underlying tit for tat—selfishness begets selfishness and cooperation begets cooperation—except, in indirect reciprocity, through third parties.

It is important to note that systems of direct and indirect reciprocity are not mutually exclusive; the latter could be embedded in the former. We can help those who help us as well as giving help to, and receiving help from, third parties. In sufficient quantity, tit for tat has the capacity to support other systems of cooperation by punishing selfish individualists. Indeed, as mentioned earlier, if everyone inherited tit-for-tat structures, and if everyone interacted with everyone else, everyone would cooperate, rendering direct reciprocity, indirect reciprocity, and indiscriminate altruism indistinguishable. In Axelrod's computer contests, after tit for tat defeats selfish individualism, virtually all nice strategies reaped approximately the same gains.

Stage 4 Structures

The system of cooperation upheld by Kohlberg's Stage 4 structure is an expansion of indirect reciprocity from relatively small in-groups containing individuals who, at least, know other members of their group by reputation, to complex social systems based on divisions of labor. In such systems indirect reciprocity is institutionalized. Individuals give to and receive from a central distributor. A common currency such as money enhances the efficiency of such systems.

It is easy to see that Stage 4 systems of indirect reciprocity contain the potential to maximize the benefits of those who participate in them, but it is equally easy to see that such systems could not evolve without antidotes to cheating. Without the antidotes inherent in tit for tat and indirect reciprocity, Stage 4 systems of cooperation need institutions devoted to detecting cheating, and punishing cheaters—police and legal sanctions. The group, or society, becomes the agent of reward and punishment in Stage 4 systems of indirect reciprocity.

Could structures supporting Stage 4 systems of cooperation have evolved in ancestral environments through natural selection? If we assume that our ancestors evolved in relatively small groups, probably not exceeding 150 members,[32] and that their social systems were relatively simple, the answer implied is no. I do not believe the evidence supports the contention that we are evolved to uphold Stage 4 systems on their own terms. I believe the motivational impetus to uphold Stage 4 systems derives from lower-stage values and sanctions. Thus, people obey the law and fulfill their social duties to avoid punishment (Stage 1), to maximize their individual returns (Stage 2), and to cultivate a good reputation (Stage 3). This is one of the senses in which the cooperative strategies of lower-stages are embedded in, and support, the cooperative strategies of higher stages.

Summary of Evidence that Stages 1-3 Are Evolved Structures

To summarize, I have argued that structures inducing people to practice the systems of cooperation upheld by Kohlberg's Stages 1, 2 and 3 moral judgments have evolved in the human species. In addition to the evidence I have adduced, I offer the following support. First, these forms of reciprocity would be expected to be adaptive in the relatively small groups in which most experts believe our ancestors lived. Second, cross-cultural research on humans indicates that all people everywhere practice these forms of cooperation. To quote a classic review of the evidence by Gouldner[33]: "A norm of reciprocity is, I suspect, no less universal and important ... than the incest taboo." Finally, if you examine the criterion judgments from Kohlberg's scoring manual, you will find significantly more frequent allusions to affective correlates in Stages 1–3 moral judgments than in higher-stage moral judgments. In particular, Stage 1 judgments are based in needs-based and fear-based emotions; Stage 2 in gratitude and retribution; and Stage 3 in solidarity, loyalty, and approbation and disapprobation.

ONTOGENETIC STAGE ACQUISITION FROM A PHYLOGENETIC PERSPECTIVE

I have been looking at the structures of moral judgment identified by Kohlberg from a phylogenetic perspective. Can this perspective account for the ontogenetic sequence of stage-acquisition observed by Kohlberg and other psychologists?

From a biological perspective, we would expect individuals to acquire structures in a sequence governed by the adaptive tasks or problems they face at different phases in their lives. Psychologists such as Aronfreed,[34] Bronfenbrenner,[35] and Higgins and Eccles-Parsons[36] have advanced models of social development based on this expectation. Children begin their lives interacting mainly with adults. As they grow older, they interact with peers. Developmental psychologists such as Damon and Hart[37] have suggested that children's relations with adults and peers constitute two social worlds. Piaget's early book is full of observations of children practicing what he called the "morality of constraint" in their relations with adults (comparable to Kohlberg's Stage 1) and the "morality of cooperation" in their relations with peers (comparable to Kohlberg's Stage 2). Recent research has supported Piaget's observations.[38]

If young children's social worlds are dominated by adults, we would expect Stage 1 structures to emerge before Stage 2 structures. However, in contrast to Kohlberg's assumption that the former structure is transformed and displaced by the latter, we would expect Stage 1 structures to coexist with Stage 2 structures inasmuch as children participate in the types of social relation organized by these structures. As documented by Krebs and Van Hesteren,[9] the empirical evidence supports this "additive-inclusive" assumption.

During adolescence, children enter additional social worlds. They form cliques and gangs, and they begin to date. Reproductive effort tends to gain sway over the somatic effort that dominates earlier phases of development. As children approach adolescence, they "become increasingly concerned about their appearance and their reference groups' opinion of them".[9] During adolescence, social image, reputation, and fear of ostracism become salient.[39]

As adolescents grow into adults, they participate in other social worlds, governed by other "moral orders."[40] With respect to Stage 4, the evidence supports the contention that adults who have invested in the social system and who stand to gain from it make Stage 4 judgments, and those who have not and do not make lower-stage (and sometimes higher-stage) judgments upholding their own interests and the interests of their in-groups.[41]

Additive Stage Acquisition

If structures upholding particular systems of cooperation evolved because they were adaptive with respect to particular types of social relation, we would expect children and adults to retain the structures as long as they engaged in the social relations. Therefore, as implied earlier, in place of Kohlberg's assumption that new stage-structures transform and displace old stage-structures, we would expect new stage-structures to be added to older stage-structures, and older stage-structures to be retained and activated in the types of context in which they were selected in ancestral environments.[44] (p. 25)

Our research and the research of other social scientists support this expectation (see Ref. 9 for a review). Adults who display the ability to make high-stage moral judgments on Kohlberg's test may make Stage 1 judgments in real-life contexts involving relations with powerful authorities.[42] Milgram's classic study[43] on obedience demonstrates that such judgments parallel behavioral dispositions. I would expect Stage 1 types of cooperation to be prevalent in cults led by charismatic and dominant leaders and in military contexts. Adults engage in Stage 2 forms of cooperation in contexts involving business transactions and material exchanges,[8] Stage 3 forms of cooperation in their family and other in-groups,[9] and Stage 4 forms of cooperation when upholding the rules, regulations, and laws of their societies.[9]

These findings demonstrate that the moral judgments people make and the moral behaviors they display in their everyday lives are the product of an interaction between the structures of morality they have acquired ontogenetically and the environmental, situational, or contextual factors that govern the activation of these structures. People are not "in" a stage of moral development; rather, they acquire an increasingly broad range of strategies that enable them to adapt to an increasingly broad range of social contexts. People do not develop general "structures of the whole"; they acquire domain-specific structures that evolved in ancestral environments.[44] Indeed, as suggested by Damon,[45] people may develop structures significantly more domain-specific than the structures that define Kohlbergian stages—for example, structures dealing with relations with authorities, distributive justice, corrective justice, and prosocial behavior.

Inclusiveness

Kohlberg[4] has argued that his stage-structures are increasingly inclusive in the sense that new stage-structures contain or incorporate transformed older stage-structures within them. The moral judgments that define Kohlberg's stages pertain to an increasingly broad array of social relations, with new stage-structures containing an increasingly inclusive set of principles to organize them. As suggested earlier, we would not be surprised to find structures upholding selfish individualism, direct reciprocity, and indirect reciprocity within the same social system (and within the same individual). A biological perspective makes it clear how and why different systems of social exchange can be embedded in each other—why indirect reciprocity is more general and more inclusive than direct reciprocity, and why direct reciprocity is more general and inclusive than selfish individualism. An evolutionary perspective also offers a clear and simple explanation for why high-stage structures are "better" than low-stage structures: the adaptive benefits are greatest to those who practice the forms of cooperation they support.

COULD STRUCTURES MEDIATING STAGE 5–6 STRATEGIES HAVE EVOLVED?

As implied earlier, virtually all ultimate moral principles espoused by philosophers of ethics, including those that define Kohlberg's Stages 5 and 6, are based on two prescriptions: (*a*) maximize benefits to humankind and (*b*) allocate these benefits in a non-discriminatory way. Indiscriminate cooperation and indiscriminate altruism meet these criteria within the types of computer simulations sponsored by Axelrod. Computer simulations clearly establish that although such unconditional strategies could maximize the benefits for everyone if everyone practiced them, they could not evolve because they are vulnerable to selfish individualism (and nepotism, and discrimination against out-groups).

I feel secure in concluding that structures supporting the types of behavior prescribed by lofty principles of morality could not have evolved through natural selection because all eminent biologists who have examined the issue (e.g., Darwin,[46] Williams,[47] and Wright[48]) have reached the same conclusion. Although Alexander[3] concluded that a "modicum" of indiscriminate beneficence could have evolved through indirect reciprocity, his evidence supports only the evolution of Stage 3 in-group and Stage 4 national systems of indirect reciprocity, with no extension to out-groups or all of humanity.

Kohlberg's Stages 5 and 6 are different from his first four stages. They are much "colder" and more logical; there is virtually no mention of affect in any of Kohlberg's Stage 5 criterion judgments. At least one of Kohlberg's collaborators, John Gibbs,[49] has argued that Stages 5 and 6 are "metatheoretical" forms of reasoning, quite different from the forms of reasoning in Kohlberg's earlier stages. We have yet to observe any Stage 5–6 moral judgments about real-life consequential moral conflicts. Such forms of reasoning have not been observed cross-culturally, and it is difficult to imagine how they could have evolved in the environments of our ancestors.

THE MORAL TRAGEDY OF HUMAN NATURE

The story that unfolds from an evolutionary analysis of morality reads like a Greek tragedy. If everyone were to uphold Stage 5–6 systems of cooperation based on moral principles such as "give to everyone according to his need," "do unto others as you would have them do unto you," "behave in a way that maximizes the greatest good for the greatest number," everyone would come out ahead. This, in effect, is what philosophers of ethics exhort us to do. If we all upheld such systems, the world would be a wonderful place. Social relations would be harmonious; everyone would help and support each other, regardless of race, creed, or color. We wouldn't have to worry about war or crime. We could invest all the money we could save from the arms race, police, and jails in enhancing the quality of our lives. But, because Stage 5–6 systems of cooperation are unconditional, they contain no antidotes to selfish and other discriminatory strategies, and thus are destined to fail. At best, we are evolved to uphold systems of indirect reciprocity practiced in relatively small groups of people who know one another by reputation. In such groups, it is possible that tit-for-tat strategies could support some indiscriminate altruism on a frequency-dependent basis, but the greater the proportion of indiscriminate altruists, the greater the vulnerability of this strategy to more selfish and discriminatory strategies.

MAKING MORAL JUDGMENTS

But wait! Kohlberg has found that people make Stage 5–6 moral judgments in response to his moral dilemmas. Doesn't this indicate that Stage 5–6 structures have evolved? My answer to this question is that the capacity to engage in the type of reasoning that gives rise to Stage 5–6 moral judgments has evolved, but not the disposition to engage in Stage 5 or 6 forms of behavior. It is important to note that the Stage 5–6 moral judgments Kohlberg has observed were made by a small sample of highly educated people; that they prescribe how story-book characters—not real people or the person making the judgment—ought to solve hypothetical, nonconsequential moral dilemmas; and that they consist of words, not deeds.

Prescriptive Moral Judgments as a Form of Social Influence

It is instructive to compare the ways in which cognitive-developmental and biological theorists view moral judgments. When people express moral judgments to others, they are engaging in a form of communication. From Kohlberg's perspective, the purpose of such communication is to express one's solution to a moral problem. In contrast, from a biological perspective the purpose of such communication is more social, to influence the behavior of others in ways designed to enhanced the inclusive fitness of the communicator.

Human and nonhuman animals communicate with their conspecifics in order to manipulate them. From a biological perspective, we would expect people to make moral judgments that (*a*) induce others to give more than their share to, and take less than their share from, systems of cooperative exchange, and (*b*) enable them to take more and give less. An important implication of these expectations is that, in contrast to Kohlberg's assumption, moral judgments about oneself should differ from moral judgments about others in rough proportion to the extent to which one's genetic interests conflict with those of others.

When, in our research program, we stepped out of the Kohlbergian fold of hypothetical moral dilemmas and began to observe people making moral judgments in their everyday lives, we found that although people occasionally made moral judgments to convey their solutions to hypothetical moral dilemmas, such as those raised by capital punishment and euthanasia, such judgments were rare. When people make prescriptive moral judgments in their everyday lives, they usually direct them toward people whose behavior they are trying to influence. In effect, people exhort others to uphold the systems of cooperation from which they stand to benefit. From this perspective, people who preach Stage 5–6 principles—Martin Luther King Jr., for example—are, in effect, preaching that others ought not discriminate against them and those like them. When people preach altruism, they are exhorting others to overcontribute. When people condemn selfishness, they are attempting to persuade others not to cheat.

Passing Judgment on Others

Kohlberg's model is based exclusively on prescriptive moral judgments about what people ought and ought not do, but many, if not most, of the moral judgments people make in their everyday lives are not prescriptive in nature. They are judgments about the goodness or badness of people, judgments philosophers of ethics call *aretaic*. When I imagine what the first moral judgment made by one of our hominid ancestors was like, I picture a primate-like creature approvingly praising or angrily blaming another primate-like creature for behaving in a cooperative or uncooperative way. Cosmides[50] has demonstrated that humans inherit structures designed to detect cheating. Darwin[46] believed approbation and disapprobation played a significant role in the evolution of morality. The obvious function of such judgments is to induce others to uphold systems of cooperation, to overcontribute, and to refrain from cheating.

Also prevalent among real-life moral judgments are judgments made about others to third parties, that is, *gossip*. Gossip is a powerful form of social control.[51] Social psychologists have found that gossip constitutes a high proportion of social talk. A primary function of gossip is to spread the word about cheaters—to identify, condemn, and ultimately punish those who exploit cooperative systems of social exchange. Through gossip, people also may identify and praise altruists and make informed decisions about whether they will cooperate with others.

Passing Judgment on Oneself

We would expect the moral judgments people pass on themselves and those whose interests they share to be significantly more praising and less blaming than the moral judgments they pass on others, and there is plenty of research to support this expectation. We observed an interesting example in some of our early research on Kohlberg's model. When we asked people to rate how morally they had behaved or how moral they were, all of our participants rated themselves well above average, a phenomenon we called the self-righteous bias.[5] In another study,[14] Phil Laird and I found that participants made significantly more external and exculpatory attributions about their own real-life transgressions than they did about transgressions committed by others. The less closely identified participants were with those who committed transgressions against them, the less exculpatory their judgments. Bandura[52] has described a variety of other mechanisms people invoke to justify their reprehensible deeds.

Moral Judgment as Impression Management

Earlier, I discussed the importance of reputation in systems of indirect reciprocity. When people talk about themselves and others, they induce their audiences to form cognitive representations of the realities they are attempting to convey. It is in people's interest to induce others to form representations of reality—images of themselves and others—that are in their own interest. In contrast to the Kohlbergian interpretation, we would expect people to preach lofty moral principles in order to induce others to form representations of them as highly moral people, with concomitant benefits.

CONCLUSION

The portrait of human nature that has flowed from the biological brush I used in this paper is much grayer than the portrait painted by Kohlberg and his colleagues, but it has not been my goal to paint a rosy picture. My goal has been to paint an accurate picture, and I feel confident the biological picture I have painted corresponds more closely to the empirical evidence my colleagues and I have collected than Kohlberg's model does. I should, however, make it clear that the evidence I have presented does not warrant the conclusion that humans are immoral by nature. Far from it. The conclusion warranted by the arguments I have presented is that humans are evolved to behave morally and immorally—to uphold at least three systems of cooperation, but to fudge on them when they have reason to believe they can get away with it, or more exactly, when they got away with it in ancestral environments. The trick—and this is the main practical implication of the biological model I have sketched—is to build into systems of cooperation constraints on cheating that are sufficiently powerful to insure that cheaters do not prosper.

There is plenty of room in biological models for a substantial amount of moral behavior. There is nothing wrong with Stage 1, 2, and 3 systems of cooperation. Virtually all the moral behaviors in which people engage in their everyday lives involve deference to authority, instrumental exchange, and in-group cooperation. In addition, some of the fitness-enhancing mechanisms I have discussed would be expected to increase the incidence of morality. For example, the disposition to obey rules backed by authorities, to imitate, and to conform would be expected to mediate moral behaviors.[53] Cultivating a reputation for morality requires that one behave morally most of the time. Kin-recognition mechanisms would be expected to mediate altruistic overtures to kin-like members of in-groups.[54] One's genetic self contains others, and so also may one's psychological self. Perspective-taking mechanisms designed to enhance our ability to predict the reactions of others may give rise to empathic reactions that mediate altruistic behaviors.[54] And, the well-documented need for people to maintain cognitive consistency may, as the philosopher Peter Singer[55] has argued, induce people to behave in ways they prescribe others ought to behave. People are, in a phrase, as moral as they have to be, and perhaps, a little more.

ACKNOWLEDGMENTS

I would like to acknowledge the ideas and inspiration conveyed by students in my 1999 Psychology 461 and 960 seminars.

REFERENCES

1. KOHLBERG, L. 1969. Stage and sequence: the cognitive-developmental approach to socialization. *In* Handbook of Socialization: Theory and Research. D. Goslin, Ed. Rand McNally. Chicago, IL.
2. KREBS, D.L. 1970. Altruism—an examination of the concept and a review of the literature. Psychol. Bull. **73:** 258–302.
3. ALEXANDER, R. D. 1987. The biology of moral systems. Aldine de Gruyter. New York.
4. COLBY, A. & L. KOHLBERG. 1987. The Measurement of Moral Judgment (Vols. 1-2). :30. Cambridge University Press. Cambridge, England.
5. DENTON, K. & D.L. KREBS. 1990. From the scene to the crime: The effect of alcohol and social context on moral judgment. J. Pers. Soc. Psychol. **59:** 242–248.
6. KREBS, D. L., S.C. VERMEULEN, J.I. CARPENDALE & K. DENTON. 1991. Structural and situational influences on moral judgment: The interaction between stage and dilemma. *In* Handbook of moral behavior and development: Theory, research, and application. W. Kurtines & J. Gewirtz, Eds.: 139–169. Erlbaum Associates. Hillsdale, NJ.
7. KREBS, D.L., K. DENTON, S.C. VERMEULEN, J. CARPENDALE & A. BUSH. 1991. The structural flexibility of moral judgment. J. Pers. Soc. Psychol. **61:** 1012–1023.
8. CARPENDALE, J. & D. KREBS. 1992. Situational variation in moral judgment: in a stage or on a stage? J. Youth Adolesc. **21:** 203–224.
9. KREBS, D.L. & F. VAN HESTEREN. 1994. The development of altruism: toward an integrative model. Dev. Rev. **14:** 1–56.
10. CARPENDALE, J. & D.L. KREBS. 1995. Variations in moral judgment as a function of type of dilemma and moral choice. J. Pers. **63:** 289–313.
11. KREBS, D.L., G. WARK & D.L. KREBS. 1995. Lessons from life: toward a functional model of morality. Moral Educ. Forum **20:** 22–29.
12. KREBS, D.L., K. DENTON & G. WARK. 1997. The forms and functions of real-life moral decision-making. J. Moral Educ. **20:** 131–145.
13. WARK, G. & D.L. KREBS. 1997. Sources of variation in real-life moral judgment: Toward a model of real-life morality. J. Adult Dev. **4:** 163–178.
14. KREBS, D. & P. LAIRD. 1998. Judging yourself as you judge others: perspective-taking, moral development, and exculpation. J. Adult Dev. **5:** 1–12.
15. KREBS, D.L. & K. DENTON. 1999. On the relations between moral judgment and moral behavior. *In* The Context of Morality. D. Garz, F. Oser & W. Althof, Eds. M. Suhrkamp. Frankfurt, Germany.
16. PIAGET, J. 1932. The Moral Judgment of the Child. Routledge & Kegan Paul. London, England.
17. RAWLS, J. 1971. A Theory of Justice. Harvard University Press. Cambridge, MA:
18. DURKHEIM, E. 1961. Moral Education: A Study in the Theory and Application in the Sociology of Education. Free Press. New York.
19. REST, J.F. 1983. Morality. *In* Handbook of Child Psychology, Vol. 3: Cognitive Development, 4th ed. J.H. Flavell & E.M. Markman, Eds.: 556–629. Wiley. New York.
20. AXELROD, R. & W.D. HAMILTON. 1981. The evolution of cooperation. Science **211:** 1390–1396.
21. AXELROD, R. 1984. The Evolution of Cooperation. Basic Books. New York.

22. BENDOR, J. & P. SWISTAK. 1995. Types of evolutionary stability and the problem of cooperation. Proc. Natl Acad. Sci. USA **69:** 3596–3600.
23. POLLOCK, G. & L.A. DUGATIKIN. 1992. Reciprocity and the evolution of reputation. J. Theor. Biol. **159:** 25–37.
24. HIRSHLEIFER, D. & E. RASMUSSEN. 1989. Cooperation in a repeated prisoner's dilemma game with ostracism. J. Econ. Behav. Org. **12:** 87–106.
25. AXELROD, R. 1986. An evolutionary approach to norms. Am. Pol. Sci. Rev. **80:** 1101–1111.
26. STEPHENS, D.W., K. NISHIMURA & K.B. TOYER. 1996. Error discounting in the iterated Prisoner's Dilemma. J. Theor. Biol. **167:** 457–469.
27. KREBS, D.L. 1998. The evolution of moral behavior. *In* Handbook of Evolutionary Psychology: Ideas, Issues, and Applications. C. Crawford & D. L. Krebs, Eds.: 337–368. Erlbaum Associates. Hillsdale, NJ.
28. TRIVERS, R. 1985. Social Evolution. Benjamin Cummings. Menlo Park, CA.
29. DUGATKIN, L.A. 1997. Cooperation Among Animals: An Evolutionary Perspective. Oxford University Press. New York.
30. WILKINSON, G.S. 1990. Food sharing in vampire bats. Sci. Am. Feb.: 76–82.
31. NOWAK, M.A. & K. SIGMUND. 1998. Evolution of indirect reciprocity by image scoring. Nature **393:** 573–577.
32. DUNBAR, R. 1966. Grooming, Gossip, and the Evolution of Language. Faber and Faber. London.
33. GOULDNER, A.W. 1960. The norm of reciprocity: a preliminary statement. Am. Sociol. Rev. **25:** 161–178.
34. ARONFREED, J. 1968. Conduct and conscience. Academic Press. New York.
35. BRONFENBRENNER, U. 1979. The Ecology of Human Development. Harvard University Press. Cambridge, MA.
36. HIGGINS, A. & J.E. ECCLES-PARSON. 1983. Social cognition and the social life of the child: stages as subcultures. *In* Social Cognition and Social Development: A Sociocultural Perspective. E.T. Higgins, D.N. Ruble and W.W. Hartup, Eds.: 137–151. Cambridge University Press. New York.
37. DAMON, W. & D. HART. 1992. Self understanding and its role in social and moral development. *In* Developmental Psychology: An Advanced Textbook, 2nd ed. M. H. Bornstein & E. M. Lamb, Eds.: 421–465. Erlbaum Associates. Hillsdale, NJ.
38. YOUNISS, J. 1986. Development in reciprocity through friendship. *In* Altruism and Aggression: Biological and Social Origins. C. Zahn-Waxler, M. Cummings & R. Ianottie, Eds.: 88–106. Cambridge University Press. Cambridge, England.
39. BROWN. B.B., M.J. LOHR & E.L. MCCLENAHAN. 1986. Early adolescents' perceptions of peer pressure. J. Early Adolesc. **6:** 139–154.
40. HARRE, R. 1984. Personal Being: A Theory for Individual Psychology. Harvard University Press. Cambridge MA.
41. REST, J. 1986. Moral development in young adults. *In* Adult Cognitive Development: Methods and Models. R.A. Mines & K.S. Kitchener, Eds.: 92–111. Praeger. New York.
42. NEWITT, C & KREBS, D.L. 1999. Structural and contextual sources of moral judgment. In preparation.
43. MILGRAM, S. 1974. Obedience to Authority. Harper. New York.
44. TOOBY, J. & L. COSMIDES. 1990. The past explains the present: emotional adaptions and the structure of ancestral environments. Ethol. Sociobiol. **11(4/5):** 375–424.
45. DAMON, W. 1977. The Social World of the Child. Jossey-Bass. San Francisco, CA.
46. DARWIN, C. 1871. The Descent of Man and Selection in Relation to Sex. Appleton. New York.
47. WILLIAMS, G. 1966. Adaptation and Natural Selection. Princeton University Press. Princeton, NJ.
48. WRIGHT, R. 1994. The Moral Animal. Pantheon Books. New York.
49. GIBBS, J., K.S. BASINGER & D. FULLER. 1992. Moral maturity: measuring the development of sociomoral reasoning. Erlbaum Associates. Hillsdale NJ.
50. COSMIDES, L. 1989. The logic of social exchange: Has natural selection shaped how humans reason? Studies with the Wason selection task. Cognition **31:** 187–276.

51. GOODMAN, R.F. & A. Ben-ZE'EV. 1994. Good Gossip. University of Kansas Press. Lawrence, KS.
52. BANDURA, A. 1991. Social cognitive theory of moral thought and action. *In* Handbook of Moral Behavior and Development, Vol 1. W. M. Kurtines & J. L. Gewirtz, Eds.: 54–104. Erlbaum Associates. Hillsdale NJ.
53. SIMON, H. 1990. A mechanism for social selection of successful altruism. Science **250:** 1665–1668.
54. KREBS, D. 1988. The challenge of altruism in biology and psychology. *In* Sociobiology and Psychology: Ideas, Issues and Applications. C. Crawford, M. Smith & D. Krebs Eds.: 81–118. Erlbaum Associates. Hillsdale, N.J.
55. SINGER, P. 1981. The Expanding Circle: Ethics and Sociobiology. Farrar, Straus & Giroux. New York.

Genomic Imprinting, Sex-Biased Dispersal, and Social Behavior

DAVID HAIG

Department of Organismic and Evolutionary Biology, Harvard University, 26 Oxford Street, Cambridge Massachusetts 02138, USA

ABSTRACT: Some genes carry a record of the sex of the gene's carrier in the previous generation that influences the gene's expression in this generation. This additional information can result in intragenomic conflicts between an individual's maternally and paternally derived alleles over behaviors that affect relatives with whom the individual has different degrees of maternal and paternal relatedness. Asymmetries of relatedness can arise because of sex-biased dispersal. For example, if females remain in their natal group and males disperse, female members of a group will all be matrilineal relatives, but may have unrelated fathers. Sex-linked inheritance creates an evolutionary bias in favor of social groups that trace descent through the homogametic sex. This bias has a positive and negative aspect. The positive aspect is increased relatedness among siblings of the homogametic sex. The negative aspect is the lack of sex-linked relatedness between parents and offspring of the heterogametic sex.

INTRODUCTION

In classical Mendelian genetics, a gene's effects were assumed to be independent of its parental origin, but recent research has shown that some genes have different effects depending on whether the gene was inherited via a sperm or an egg. This phenomenon is known as genomic imprinting.[1–3] There is now substantial evidence that imprinted genes may influence human behavior. For example, children who inherit a chromosomal deletion of 15q11–q13 from their father have a behavioral phenotype that differs from that of children who inherit a similar deletion from their mother.[4] Similarly, girls with Turner's syndrome who inherit their single X chromosome from their mother score higher on a scale of social dysfunction than do those who inherit their X from their father.[5] Other evidence suggests an important role for imprinted genes in neural development. For example, cells that lack paternally derived genes contribute disproportionately to the neocortex of the developing brains of experimental mouse chimeras, whereas cells that lack maternally derived genes are excluded from the neocortex, but make a substantial contribution to the hypothalamus.[6,7]

At first sight, what is good for an individual's maternally derived genes should also be good for the individual's paternally derived genes, because both sets of genes have the same chance of being transmitted to each of the individual's offspring and thus have a common interest in promoting the individual's survival and reproduction. However, this symmetry of interests may be broken when the individual's behavior affects relatives that are kin on the maternal side, but not on the paternal side, or the reverse.[8] W. D. Hamilton's concept of inclusive fitness[9] has been widely employed to explicate the action of natural selection on behaviors that affect relatives. This paper will discuss simple modifications to the theory of inclusive fitness that take account of genomic imprinting; will illustrate the modified theory by exploring the consequences of sex-biased dispersal for patterns of relatedness within social groups; and will attempt to identify implications for the evolution of social behavior.

RELATEDNESS AND IMPRINTING

In a simple version of Hamilton's rule, an individual's inclusive fitness is increased by performing an action that confers a benefit B on the fitness of another individual at cost C to the actor's own fitness if

$$r > \frac{C}{B} \tag{1}$$

where r is a measure of the degree of relationship of the beneficiary to the actor.[10] This coefficient of relatedness has been defined in various ways, but can be thought of as the probability that a gene present in the actor is also present in the beneficiary because of recent common descent. For example, if an action of a mother confers a benefit B on an offspring at cost C to herself, $r = 1/2$ because the two alleles at a diploid locus in the mother have equal chances of being transmitted to her offspring.

The appropriate coefficient of relatedness when an outbred offspring confers a benefit B on its mother at cost C to itself has also been considered to be a half. But, in this case, $r = 1/2$ reflects uncertainty about the parental origin of an allele chosen at random from the offspring's genome rather than uncertainty about which allele was present in a gamete. This is because a maternally derived allele is necessarily present in the offspring's mother, whereas a paternally derived allele is necessarily absent. Thus, $\bar{r} = 1/2$ can be seen to be an average of $r = 1$ (for a maternally derived allele) and $r = 0$ (for a paternally derived allele). By similar reasoning, the conventional coefficient of relatedness for half-sibs ($\bar{r} = 1/4$) can be seen to be an average of $r = 1/2$ for alleles derived from the shared parent and $r = 0$ for alleles derived from the unshared parent.

Thus, two different factors of one-half have entered into traditional calculations of relatedness. The first arises when calculating the probability that an allele is transmitted from parent to offspring and reflects the random nature of meiotic segregation: each successful gamete has an equal chance of carrying either one of the two alleles at a locus in the parent (in the absence of meiotic drive or gametic selection). The second arises when calculating backwards from offspring to parent and reflects uncertainty about whether a particular allele entered a zygote in an egg or sperm. This uncertainty depends on the absence of information about parental origin. When such information is present, the probability of one-half that a gene in the offspring entered via an egg decomposes into probabilities of one for maternally derived alleles and zero for paternally derived alleles (and the reverse for a gene that entered via a sperm). The probability that a randomly chosen allele of the actor is present in the beneficiary ($\bar{r}$) is the appropriate measure of relatedness if a gene's expression is unaffected by whether it entered the zygote in an egg or a sperm. However, such a measure is inappropriate if the gene's expression depends on its parental origin.

When one individual is related to another via a grandparent or more distant ancestor, two or more links from offspring to parent enter into calculations of relatedness. At each link a question arises whether an allele's parental origin is known or unknown. One can therefore imagine a hierarchy of degrees of imprinting. A gene could be said to carry a zero-order imprint (or be unimprinted) if it carried no information about its parental origin; a first-order imprint if it carried information about its parental origin, but not about whether it entered the parent in an egg or a sperm; a second-order imprint if it carried information about its parental and grandparental origin; and so on. For example, the probability that one of an individual's genes has been inherited from a maternal grandmother would be calculated as one-quarter for a gene with a zero-order imprint; one-half or zero for a gene with a first-order imprint; and one or zero for a gene with a second-order imprint. So far, evidence is lacking for genes with second-order imprints or higher and this paper will assume first-order imprinting only.

A Note Concerning Kin Recognition

It is a wise child who knows his father and an even wiser child who knows her paternal first half-cousins. So far, the discussion has proceeded as if actors knew their "true" degree of relatedness to beneficiaries. However, from the perspective of natural selection, a class of beneficiaries corresponds to all individuals that are treated in the same manner by a class of actors, and need not correspond precisely to any of the kinship categories of an omniscient geneticist. Uncertainty of paternity and cognitive limitations are important reasons why actors may treat individuals with different degrees of "true" relatedness as belonging to a single class of beneficiaries. Litters, for example, will sometimes contain a mixture of full-sibs and maternal half-sibs, but if actors are unable to discriminate between these two types of siblings, "littermate" would comprise a single class of beneficiaries. Members of this class would have a coefficient of relatedness equal to one-half for maternally derived alleles, but the corresponding coefficient for paternally derived alleles would reflect the long-term average probability that littermates share the same father.

Hamilton[11] concluded, "The situations in which a species discriminates in its social behavior tend to evolve and multiply in such a way that the coefficients of relationship involved in each situation become more nearly determinate." In other words, natural selection will tend to favor actors who are able to subdivide potential beneficiaries into classes with a lower variance of "true" relatedness. But this conclusion should be qualified by the observation that an individual may benefit from being classified by an actor as belonging to a class that has an average coefficient of relatedness greater than the individual's "true" relatedness. Thus, natural selection on actors to make ever-finer discriminations of kinship may be opposed by natural selection on recipients of lower-than-average relatedness to confound such discrimination.[12–14]

GENOMIC IMPRINTING AND THE NUCLEAR FAMILY

Haig and Westoby[15] proposed that imprinting has evolved when a gene's expression in one individual has fitness implications for other individuals towards whom the first has different degrees of maternal and paternal relatedness. Suppose that an action confers a benefit B on a member of a class of individuals at cost C to the actor. If all alleles were unimprinted, natural selection would favor autosomal alleles that caused the action to be performed when

$$r = \frac{m+p}{2} > \frac{C}{B} \quad \textbf{(2a)}$$

where m is the probability that a member of the class of potential beneficiaries carries a maternally derived allele of the actor and p is the corresponding probability for a paternally derived allele. But, given a source of imprinted alleles, natural selection would favor maternally derived alleles that caused the action to be performed when

$$m > \frac{C}{B} \quad \textbf{(2b)}$$

but would favor paternally derived alleles that caused the action to be performed when

$$p > \frac{C}{B} \quad \textbf{(2c)}$$

Thus, maternally derived alleles would be selected to counter the effects of paternally derived alleles if (2b) were satisfied but not (2c), or (2c) but not (2b).[16]

Consider the case of an action by an offspring that confers a benefit B on the offspring's mother at cost C to the offspring. A maternally derived allele that caused such an action would be selectively favored if the benefit to the mother exceeded the cost to the offspring. By contrast, no benefit to the mother (no matter how great) could compensate a paternally derived allele for a fitness cost to the offspring (no matter how small). Therefore, whenever $B > C$, natural selection would favor alleles that conferred benefits on mothers when an allele had spent the previous generation in a female body, but not when it had spent the previous generation in a male body.

Paternally derived alleles are indifferent to costs and benefits experienced by an offspring's mother, but not to costs and benefits experienced by the offspring's father. Therefore, the conclusion that paternally derived genes will maximize an offspring's individual fitness without regard to costs to the mother's residual reproductive value is predicated on the assumption that the mother's and father's residual reproductive values are uncorrelated. This would be the case if each of a mother's offspring had a different father. By contrast, there would be a perfect correlation if parents paired for life and never took additional or substitute partners.[17] In this case, a benefit to the mother's fitness would always be associated with an equal benefit to the father. Put in other words, benefits (or costs) imposed on a parent translate into extra (or fewer) surviving siblings. An offspring's maternally derived and paternally derived alleles will benefit equally if these are full-sibs but not if they are half-sibs. Long-term fidelity of sexual partners thus mitigates conflicts between the maternally derived and paternally derived alleles of their offspring over actions that affect parents and siblings.

Monogamy does not eliminate all conflicts, however. An offspring's mother and father will usually have different sets of collateral kin. The mother's inclusive fitness is increased via benefits conferred on her kin but not via benefits conferred on the father's kin, and vice versa. Moreover, this system of conflicting allegiances splits the genomes of each of their offspring down the middle with the offspring's maternally derived alleles favoring her kin and the offspring's paternally derived alleles favoring his.

SEX-BIASED DISPERSAL

The genetic-conflict hypothesis has so far largely been applied to interactions between parents and offspring—and to interactions between half-sibs—because it is in these interactions that differences between m and p are large, and selective forces correspondingly strong.[18–20] However, the hypothesis also applies to actions that affect more-distant relatives. In general, natural selection can favor imprinted expression of genes determining an altruistic action if members of the class of potential beneficiaries have different probabilities of carrying the actor's maternally derived and paternally derived alleles.[8] One of the simplest ways that such asymmetries of relatedness can arise is via sex-biased dispersal.

Every social group has its own web of relatedness, but an example can illustrate how sex-biased dispersal and mating system may interact to determine complex, interlocking patterns of matrilineal and patrilineal relatedness. FIGURE 1 presents the hypothetical pedigree of a social group of six females from a species in which males disperse, but females remain in their natal group. At any particular time, offspring are fathered by one or more males who have entered the group from elsewhere, but these males are periodically replaced by a new group of unrelated males. All offspring conceived during the tenure of a group of males will be called a cohort, with all members of a cohort assumed to be conceived by independent sampling from a large well-mixed sperm pool into which each male has made a contribution proportional to his chances of paternity. The six females belong to three cohorts: female 1 is the only member of the first cohort; females 2 and 3 belong to the second cohort; and females 4, 5 and 6 belong to the third.

The probability that two individuals share the same paternally derived allele is s among members of a cohort, but zero for members of different cohorts. In other words, s is the probability that a gene in the sperm that fathers one member of a cohort will also be present in the sperm that fathers another member of the cohort. Therefore, $s = 1/2$ if all members of a cohort have the same father, but $s < 1/2$ if there is some degree of multiple paternity within cohorts.

Autosomal Loci

The pattern of relatedness for maternally derived autosomal alleles can be represented by a matrix **M,** whose elements m_{ij} are the probabilities that the maternally derived allele at an autosomal locus in individual$_i$ (*rows*) is also present in individual$_j$ (*columns*) because of recent common descent (the dotted lines group together coefficients of relatedness for members of the same cohort).

All six females are matrilineal relatives ($m_{ij} > 0$ for all i,j). Of particular interest, a maternally derived allele of a daughter is equally likely to be transmitted to one of her mother's gametes as to one of her own gametes. The matrix **M** is asymmetric be-

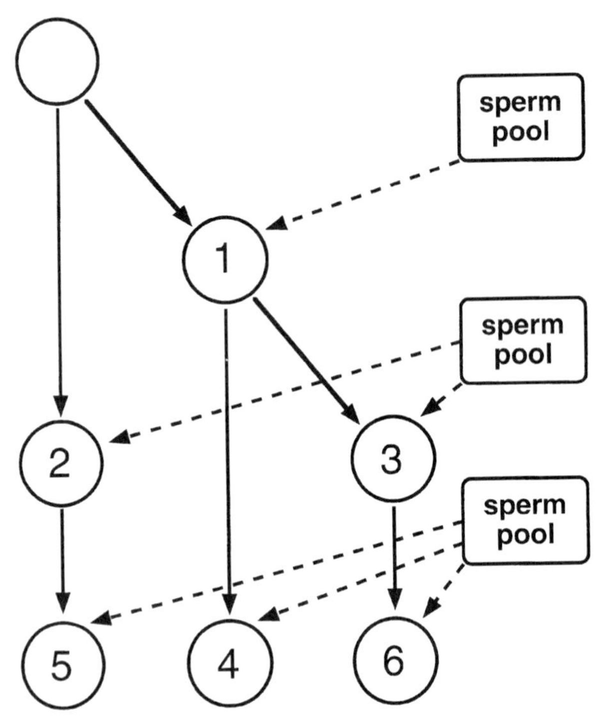

FIGURE 1. Hypothetical pedigree of a social group in a species with female philopatry and periodic turnover of breeding males. The six female group members (*numbered circles*) belong to three different paternity cohorts (represented by three different sperm pools).

$$\mathbf{M} = \left[\begin{array}{c|cc|ccc} 1 & \frac{1}{2} & \frac{1}{2} & \frac{1}{2} & \frac{1}{4} & \frac{1}{4} \\ \hline \frac{1}{2} & 1 & \frac{1}{4} & \frac{1}{4} & \frac{1}{2} & \frac{1}{8} \\ 1 & \frac{1}{4} & 1 & \frac{1}{2} & \frac{1}{8} & \frac{1}{2} \\ \hline 1 & \frac{1}{4} & \frac{1}{2} & 1 & \frac{1}{8} & \frac{1}{4} \\ \frac{1}{4} & 1 & \frac{1+4s}{8} & \frac{1}{8} & 1 & \frac{1+4s}{16} \\ \frac{1}{2} & \frac{1+4s}{8} & 1 & \frac{1}{4} & \frac{1+4s}{16} & 1 \end{array}\right]$$

cause the probability that a maternally derived allele of a daughter is present in her mother is one, but the probability that a maternally derived allele of a mother is present in her daughter is one-half. The degree of multiple paternity within cohorts affects the probability that one female is related to another via her maternal grandfather. In this manner, the sharing of male partners by female group-members strengthens bonds of kinship between matrilines.

The pattern of relatedness for paternally derived autosomal alleles can similarly be represented by a matrix **P,** whose elements p_{ij} are the probabilities that the paternally derived allele at an autosomal locus in individual$_i$ (*rows*) is also present in individual$_j$ (*columns*) because of recent common descent

$$\mathbf{P} = \left[\begin{array}{c:cc:ccc} 1 & 0 & \frac{1}{2} & \frac{1}{2} & 0 & \frac{1}{4} \\ \hdashline 0 & 1 & s & 0 & \frac{1}{2} & \frac{s}{2} \\ 0 & s & 1 & 0 & \frac{s}{2} & \frac{1}{2} \\ \hdashline 0 & 0 & 0 & 1 & s & s \\ 0 & 0 & 0 & s & 1 & s \\ 0 & 0 & 0 & s & s & 1 \end{array}\right]$$

All p_{ij} are zero if j belongs to an older cohort than i (or is related to i solely via a member of an older cohort). As the number of males contributing to each sperm pool increases (i.e., as s decreases), all p_{ij} approach zero except for a female's relatedness to herself and her direct descendants.

In summary, male-biased dispersal creates groups that are bound together by bonds of matrilineal kinship. The degree to which groups are also bound together by patrilineal kinship depends on the mating system; in particular, the degree to which females share sperm donors and the rate at which sperm donors are replaced. In the pedigree of FIGURE 1, an individual is related to members of older cohorts maternally but not paternally. By contrast, degrees of paternal relatedness among members of the same cohort may exceed degrees of maternal relatedness if the number of donors to the sperm pool is small and/or the sperm donors are closely related. Therefore, whether it is an individual's maternally or paternally derived alleles that are more strongly represented in younger cohorts will depend on relatedness within the individual's own cohort and on the proportion of the members of younger cohorts that are descendants of the individual's own cohort. Thus, asymmetries of maternal and paternal relatedness within social groups may be strongly influenced by the relative ages of the individuals being compared.

Sex-Linked Loci

In species with male dispersal and female philopatry, autosomal alleles of either parent (and X-linked alleles of mothers) have a 50% chance of being transmitted to a son who will leave the group. By contrast, an X-linked allele of a father is always transmitted to daughters and stays within the group for the next generation. Therefore, coefficients of X-linked relatedness between group members are always greater than or equal to the corresponding coefficients of autosomal relatedness. Matrices of X-linked relatedness for FIGURE 1 can be derived by replacing s with $2s$ wherever s occurs in **M** and **P**.

If females rather than males were the heterogametic sex (ZW females, ZZ males), Z-linked genes of mothers would be transmitted to sons who depart the group, whereas daughters who remain within the group would receive their Z-linked genes from their fathers. As a consequence, members of successive cohorts would be unrelated for Z-linked genes. For the pedigree of FIGURE 1, the probability that the paternally derived allele at a Z-linked locus in individual$_i$ would also be present in individual$_j$ can be represented by the matrix

$$\mathbf{Z} = \left[\begin{array}{c|cc|ccc} 1 & 0 & 0 & 0 & 0 & 0 \\ \hline 0 & 1 & s & 0 & 0 & 0 \\ 0 & s & 1 & 0 & 0 & 0 \\ \hline 0 & 0 & 0 & 1 & s & s \\ 0 & 0 & 0 & s & 1 & s \\ 0 & 0 & 0 & s & s & 1 \end{array}\right]$$

By contrast to Z-linked genes, W-linked genes are transmitted from a mother to all of her daughters. Therefore, all females in the social group of FIGURE 1 would carry an identical W chromosome and all coefficients of W-linked relatedness would be one ($w_{ij} = 1$ for all i,j). The same would be true for any other heritable unit that is transmitted with high fidelity from mother to daughter (including mitochondrial genes and stories mothers tell their daughters).

Implications

What then does theory predict about the behavioral effects of imprinted genes in a species with female philopatry and male-biased dispersal? The evolutionary prediction is simplest when all members of a social group are matrilineal relatives but have unrelated fathers. In this case, maternally expressed imprinted alleles would be predicted to promote behaviors that benefit other group members, whereas paternally expressed imprinted alleles would be predicted to promote an individual's own fitness at the expense of other group members. Predictions are more complex if paternity within a cohort is dominated by one or a few related males. In this case, relatedness among members of a cohort may be higher for paternally derived alleles (especially for paternally-derived X-linked alleles) than for maternally derived alleles.[21] Paternally expressed imprinted alleles might favor altruistic behaviors directed to members of the same cohort, but oppose similar behaviors directed to members of older cohorts, with maternally expressed imprinted alleles having reciprocal effects. Predictions would be more complex still if individuals maintained social ties to both their mother's and their father's family.

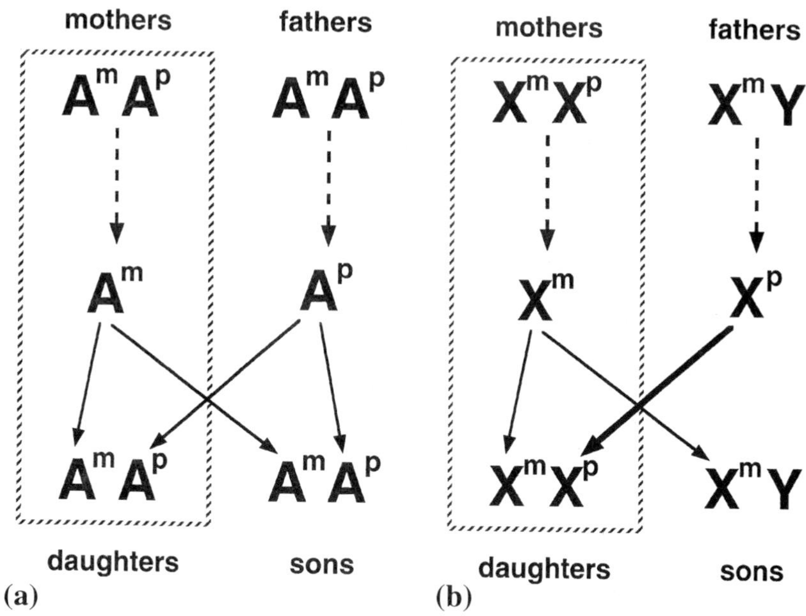

FIGURE 2. Patterns of transmission of autosomal and X-linked genes. Female philopatry is represented by the box that links together mothers and daughters. Imprints are reset during gametogenesis (*dashed arrows*). **(a)** Both males and females have a maternal and paternal set of autosomes. Maternal autosomes (A^m) and paternal autosomes (A^p) are equally likely to be transmitted to sons or daughters. **(b)** Females have a maternal X chromosome (X^m) and a paternal X chromosome (X^m); males have a maternal X chromosome only. Therefore, fathers and sons are unrelated for X-linked genes, and paternally derived X-linked genes are always transmitted to daughters who remain within the group (*bold arrow*).

HETEROGAMETY AND PHILOPATRY

Autosomal alleles of either parental origin, carried by either sex, have a 50% chance of being transmitted to the dispersing sex in the next generation, whether this sex is male or female (FIGURE 2a). Therefore, patterns of autosomal relatedness will be broadly similar in social groups based on male and on female philopatry, because fathers have the same degree of relatedness to sons as mothers have to daughters. Despite this symmetry, average degrees of relatedness would tend to be higher when females remain within their natal group and males disperse because two females will usually have greater confidence that they are mother and daughter than two males will have that they are father and son. Uncertainty of paternity therefore becomes one factor that may favor social systems based on matrilineal descent.

X-linked alleles of females are equally likely to be transmitted to male or female offspring (like the autosomal alleles of either sex), but X-linked alleles of males are always transmitted to daughters (FIGURE 2b). The effect on patterns of X-linked relatedness—both between and within generations—provides another bias in favor of female philopatry and matrilineal kin groups.

Between generations: Fathers are unrelated to their sons, and sons are unrelated to their fathers, with respect to X-linked genes ($m = 0$). By contrast, each of a mother's X-linked alleles has a 50% chance of being transmitted to a daughter ($m = p = 1/2$), and a daughter's maternally derived X-linked alleles are necessarily present in her mother ($m = 1$). Therefore, natural selection on X-linked genes will oppose altruistic sacrifices by fathers to enhance their sons' fitness and altruistic sacrifices by sons to enhance their fathers' fitness (tempered by the degree to which a father's other offspring are matrilineal kin of the son), but may favor analogous sacrifices by mothers for the benefit of daughters or by daughters for the benefit of mothers. Male heterogamety thus provides a selective bias in favor of greater cooperation among females of successive generations than among males of successive generations. X-linked inheritance similarly provides a bias in favor of paternal care directed towards daughters ($m = 1$) rather than sons ($m = 0$).

Within generations: All of a father's daughters are genetically identical with respect to their paternal X chromosome ($p = 1$). If common paternity were assured, natural selection on paternally derived X-linked alleles would favor altruistic sacrifices by females for the benefit of a paternal half-sister (or full-sister) provided that the benefit to the sister exceeded the cost to self. By contrast, maternal half-brothers (or full-brothers) are no more closely related to each other for maternally derived X-linked alleles than for maternally derived autosomal alleles ($m = 1/2$). Male heterogamety thus provides a selective bias in favor of greater cooperation among female siblings than among male siblings.

By a complementary argument, natural selection on Z-linked genes in species with female heterogamety favors male philopatry and patrilineal kin groups.

Between generations: Daughters are unrelated to mothers, and mothers are unrelated to daughters, with respect to Z-linked genes. By contrast, each of a father's Z-linked alleles has a 50% chance of being transmitted to a son ($m = p = 1/2$), and a son's paternally derived Z-linked alleles are necessarily present in his father ($p = 1$). The bias in favor of greater cooperation among males of successive generations weakens as uncertainty of paternity increases.

Within generations: All of a mother's sons are genetically identical with respect to their maternal Z chromosome. The Z-linked boost to relatedness among homogametic siblings is unaffected by uncertainty of paternity (unlike the X-linked boost to relatedness in taxa with male heterogamety).

The invocation of a selective bias favoring greater cooperation among individuals of the homogametic sex, and greater dispersal of members of the heterogametic sex, presupposes that X-linked genes have greater power than Y-linked genes to influence behavior in species with male heterogamety (and that Z-linked genes have greater power than W-linked genes in species with female heterogamety). It should be emphasized that the hypothesis invokes a selective bias based on the system of genetic inheritance, but does not exclude an important, or even dominant, role for ecological factors in determining patterns of sex-biased dispersal and sociality.

A Brief History

X-linked genes have haplodiploid inheritance. Therefore, the arguments of the previous section can be considered a simple extension of Hamilton's hypothesis that haplodiploidy predisposed the Hymenoptera to the evolution of cooperation among female kin.[11] Hamilton himself conjectured that the "XX" genotype of male birds would favor cooperation among brothers, but immediately dismissed the idea as "rather unlikely" because sex-linked loci are a minority in the genome.[22] Whitney revived the idea that haplodiploid inheritance of sex chromosomes would favor greater cooperation among adults of the homogametic sex, and predicted that female (XX) mammals would show more social cohesiveness than conspecific males (XY), but that male (ZZ) birds would be more socially cohesive than females (ZW).[23]

In a review of the ethological literature, Greenwood[24] found a bias towards greater male dispersal in mammals and greater female dispersal in birds, but dismissed Whitney's hypothesis on the basis of criticisms by Kurland. Greenwood's citation was to a book chapter (in press) in a volume that was never published.[25] Kurland's critique appeared in a little-cited paper which argued that "sex-linked altruism" would be negated by the evolution of autosomal suppressors.[26] Subsequent discussions of the evolution of sex-biased dispersal[27–30] have cited Greenwood's dismissal of Whitney, apparently without having read Kurland.

Trivers also noted the association between female heterogamety and male helpers in birds and, like Kurland, postulated intragenomic conflict between autosomal and sex-linked loci.[31] Following Trivers' suggestion, Kawecki investigated the conflict between sex chromosomes and autosomes with respect to sib-altruism.[32] In his simulations, X-linked genes that caused altruistic behavior simultaneously selected for autosomal suppressors and for autosomal or sex-linked modifiers that increased the benefit-to-cost ratio of altruistic behavior. Because such modifiers would sometimes spread to fixation before autosomal suppressors could block the behavior, Kawecki argued that the haplodiploid inheritance of sex chromosomes could facilitate the evolution of cooperation among homogametic siblings, even though most of their genome is located on autosomes.

The hypothesis that sex-linked loci are predisposed to favor greater dispersal of the heterogametic sex and stronger social ties among relatives of the homogametic sex deserves reappraisal for at least two reasons. First, previous discussions have emphasized the sex-linked boost to relatedness among homogametic siblings, but have neglected the sex-linked lack of relatedness between heterogametic parents and offspring. Second, the average coefficient of relatedness between homogametic full-siblings ($\bar{r}$ = 3/4) can be seen to be an average of m = 1/2 and p = 1 for X-linked genes (and the reverse for Z-linked genes).[33] Thus, the fact that homogametic offspring of a heterogametic parent share an entire sex chromosome, together with the prospect that this chromosome may be subject to genomic imprinting, raises the possibility that sex-linkage provides a stronger predisposition to cooperative behaviors than had previously been recognized. (For an alternative hypothesis making similar predictions about the relationship between sex chromosomes and social behavior see Reeve and Shellman-Reeve.[34])

Phylogenetic Comparisons

The previous section reviewed arguments that the difference between male and female heterogamety may have contributed to the tendency for male-biased dispersal (and female philopatry) in mammals but the opposite tendency in birds. However, the coincidence of the heterogametic sex with the sex that usually disperses in two taxa will remain only circumstantial evidence in support of the hypothesis unless similar tendencies are found in other taxa with independently evolved sex chromosomes or until the extent of social cooperation among individuals of the homogametic sex is shown to increase as the degree of sex-linkage increases within taxa with a common origin of heterogamety.

The ratio of autosomal to sex-linked loci varies greatly among taxa, and this variation might allow phylogenetic correlations between the extent of sex-linkage and the expression of various social traits. All loci are autosomal in species without sex chromosomes, whereas the entire genome is effectively X-linked in haplodiploid taxa. Between these extremes, there is considerable variation in the proportion of the genome that resides on sex chromosomes. In well-studied taxa, the eutherian X chromosome comprises 5% of the genome; the marsupial X chromosome 3% of the genome,[35] and the avian Z chromosome 10% of the genome.[36]

An alternative means of probing the role of sex-linked inheritance in social evolution would be to generate and test additional predictions about differences in social organization between birds and mammals. For example, male and female heterogamety differ in the effects of polyandry on patterns of sex-linked relatedness. Uncertainty of paternity in mammals does not affect the absence of X-linked relatedness between fathers and sons nor the degree of X-linked relatedness between mothers and daughters, but does reduce the high relatedness among female members of the same cohort for paternally derived X-linked alleles. By contrast, uncertainty of paternity in birds reduces Z-linked relatedness between father and sons, but does not affect the identity between a mother's Z chromosome and the maternally derived Z chromosomes of her sons. For these reasons, one might predict greater generational depth in matrilineal kin groups of mammals than in patrilineal kin groups of birds, but a stronger tendency for male birds (rather than female mammals) to postpone reproduction and help parents raise siblings.

The distinct method of X inactivation in marsupials may have partially negated the selective bias favoring cooperation among homogametic siblings with the same father. Somatic tissues of female eutherians are a mosaic of cells; some with an inactive paternal X, others with an inactive maternal X,[37] whereas it is always the paternal X that is inactive in female marsupials (inactivation is sometimes incomplete).[38] Therefore, natural selection acting on marsupial social behavior should be relatively blind to the high relatedness for paternally derived X-linked genes of paternal half-sisters and full-sisters (because alleles at a paternally inactive locus are subject to natural selection solely on their effects when maternally derived). If so, matrilineal social groups should have arisen more frequently in eutherians than marsupials. Indeed, complex societies, comparable to those found in social eutherians, have not been reported from marsupials.[39,40]

Perhaps the strongest test of the hypothesis will come when imprinted genes have been identified on the mammalian X chromosome. Differences in the expression and phenotypic effects of such genes could then be phylogenetically mapped onto evolutionary changes in social organization. For example, humans and chimps appear to have a history of female-biased dispersal[41,42] (but see also Hrdy's paper in this volume, p. 75) unlike the typical eutherian pattern of male-biased dispersal. One could then ask whether the resulting differences in asymmetries of patrilineal and matrilineal relatedness have left a trace in the evolution of X-linked imprinted genes.

RECIPROCITY AND RELATEDNESS

Kinship is not necessary for the evolution of cooperative behaviors: unrelated individuals may gain mutual benefits via reciprocal altruism, as may close relatives.[43] The interaction between reciprocity and kinship is a large and complex topic, but here I will merely sketch two interesting questions raised by genomic imprinting. First, does kinship between the related parts of two individuals' genomes facilitate cooperation between the unrelated parts? For example, consider interactions between two maternal half-sibs ($m = 1/2, p = 0$). The paternally derived alleles of sib_1 would not profit from an unreciprocated benefit conferred on sib_2 (at a lesser cost to sib_1), but would profit if the action were reciprocated.

Second, can different elements within an individual practice reciprocity? For example, an individual's maternally derived alleles would gain no benefit from an unreciprocated altruistic action conferred on the individual's father's sister ($m = 0, p = 1/2$), whereas the individual's paternally derived alleles would gain no benefit from a similar action conferred on the individual's mother's brother ($m = 1/2, p = 0$), but both sets of genes might benefit if both actions were performed. Conditions are particularly conducive for the evolution of reciprocity when two parties interact repeatedly, with an indefinite date for termination of their association, and these conditions appear to be satisfied in interactions between an individual's maternally derived and paternally derived genomes. Thus, genomic imprinting raises the intriguing possibility of reciprocal interactions between different sets of genes within an individual, and all the complexity that entails.

THE PARLIAMENT OF THE MIND

Will genomic imprinting require behavioral ecologists to change the way they investigate and interpret animal behavior? That is, would the outward behavior of an organism whose genome contained imprinted genes differ in any way from that of an otherwise identical organism whose genome contained no imprinted genes? Answers to these questions are currently unresolved. One possible resolution would be that imprinting is largely irrelevant. In this scenario, the effects of maternally expressed and paternally expressed genes would mutually cancel[44] so that old-fashioned calculations of inclusive fitness—in which the separate interests of maternally and paternally derived genomes were not considered—would give adequate predictions of behavior. Another resolution would give genomic imprinting a profound influence on how decision-making processes are organized within the brains of social organisms. In this scenario, the problems of cooperation and conflict that behavioral ecologists have studied in interactions between individuals would be internalized within individuals, and issues of reciprocity, trust, threat, and bluff would be an intrinsic part of brain function.

In our own species, one can ask similar questions about subjective experience. Is genomic imprinting irrelevant or does it have some causal relation to our perception of internal conflict? In the latter case, does the presence/absence of intragenomic conflicts explain why some minds function harmoniously whereas others are consumed in recrimination and internecine strife, or could this difference be explained by the presence/absence of reciprocity between the different stakeholders of the Self?

ACKNOWLEDGMENTS

Thanks are due to Tim Flannery for discussions of marsupial social organization. Paul Sherman and Jon Wilkins made helpful comments on the manuscript.

REFERENCES

1. Bartolomei, M.S. & S.M. Tilghman. 1997. Genomic imprinting in mammals. Annu. Rev. Genet. **31:** 493–525.
2. Constância, M., B. Pickard, G. Kelsey & W. Reik. 1998. Imprinting mechanisms. Genome Res. **8:** 881–900.
3. Morison, I.M. & A E. Reeve. 1998. A catalogue of imprinted genes and parent-of-origin effects in humans and animals. Hum. Mol. Genet. **7:** 1599–1609.
4. Hultén, M., S. Armstrong, P. Challinor *et al.* 1991. Genomic imprinting in an Angelman and Prader-Willi translocation family. Lancet **338:** 638–639.
5. Skuse, D.H., R.S. James, D.V.M. Bishop *et al.* 1997. Evidence from Turner's syndrome of an imprinted X-linked locus affecting cognitive function. Nature **387**: 705–708.
6. Allen, N.D., K. Logan, G. Lally *et al.* 1995. Distribution of parthenogenetic cells in the mouse brain and their influence on brain development and behavior. Proc. Natl Acad. Sci. USA **92:** 10782–10786.
7. Keverne, E.B., R. Fundele, M. Narasimha *et al.* 1996. Genomic imprinting and the differential roles of parental genomes in brain development. Dev. Brain Res. **92:** 91–100.
8. Haig, D. 1997. Parental antagonism, relatedness asymmetries, and genomic imprinting. Proc. Roy. Soc. Lond. B **264:** 1657–1662.
9. Hamilton, W.D. 1964. The genetical evolution of social behaviour. I. J. Theor. Biol. **7:** 1–16.
10. Hamilton, W.D. 1963. The evolution of altruistic behaviour. Am. Naturalist **97:** 354–356.
11. Hamilton, W.964. The genetical evolution of social behaviour. II. J. Theor. Biol. **7:** 17–52.
12. Beecher, M.D. 1991. Successes and failures of parent-offspring recognition in animals. *In* Kin Recognition. P. G. Hepper, Ed.: 94–124. Cambridge University Press. Cambridge, England.
13. Sherman, P.W., H.K. Reeve & D.W. Pfennig. 1997. Recognition systems. *In* Behavioural Ecology, 4th ed. J. R. Krebs & N. B. Davies, Eds.: 69–96. Blackwell Scientific Publications. Oxford, England.
14. Reeve, H.K. 1998. Game theory, reproductive skew, and nepotism. *In* Game Theory and Animal Behavior. L. A. Dugatkin & H. K. Reeve, Eds.: 118–145. Oxford University Press. Oxford, England.
15. Haig, D. & M. Westoby. 1989. Parent-specific gene expression and the triploid endosperm. Am. Naturalist. **134:** 147–155.
16. Shakespeare, W. 1623. Hamlet.
17. Burt, A. & R. Trivers. 1998. Genetic conflicts in genomic imprinting. Proc. Roy. Soc. Lond. B **265:** 2393–2397.
18. Moore, T. & D. Haig. 1991. Genomic imprinting in mammalian development: a parental tug-of-war. Trends Genet. **7:** 45–49.
19. Haig, D. & C. Graham. 1991. Genomic imprinting and the strange case of the insulin-like growth factor-II receptor. Cell **64:** 1045–1046.
20. Mochizuki, A., Y. Takeda & Y. Iwasa. 1996. The evolution of genomic imprinting. Genetics **144:** 1283–1295.
21. Altmann, J. 1979. Age cohorts as paternal sibships. Behav. Ecol. Sociobiol. **6:** 161–164.
22. Hamilton, W.D. 1972. Altruism and related phenomena, mainly in social insects. Annu. Rev. Ecol. Syst. **3:** 193–232.
23. Whitney, G. 1976. Genetic substrates for the initial evolution of human sociality. I. Sex chromosome mechanisms. Am. Naturalist **110:** 867–875.
24. Greenwood, P. J. 1980. Mating systems, philopatry and dispersal in birds and mammals. Anim. Behav. **28:** 1140–1162.

25. DEVORE, I. Personal communication.
26. KURLAND, J. . 1979. Can sociality have a favorite sex chromosome? Am. Naturalist. **114:** 810–817.
27. WOOLFENDEN, G.E. & J.W. FITZPATRICK. 1986. Sexual asymmetries in the life history of the Florida scrub jay. *In* Ecological Aspects of Social Evolution. D.I. Rubenstein & R.W. Wrangham, Eds.: 87–107. Princeton University Press. Princeton, NJ.
28. PUSEY, A.E. 1987. Sex-biased dispersal and inbreeding avoidance in birds and mammals. Trends Ecol. Evol. **2:** 295–299.
29. JOHNSON, M.L. & M.S. GAINES. 1990. Evolution of dispersal: theoretical models and empirical tests using birds and mammals. Annu. Rev. Ecol. Syst. **21:** 449–480.
30. COCKBURN, A. 1998. Evolution of helping behavior in cooperatively breeding birds. Annu. Rev. Ecol. Syst. **29:** 141–177.
31. TRIVERS, R.L. 1985. Social Evolution. 186. Benjamin/Cummings. Menlo Park, CA.
32. KAWECKI, T.J. 1991. Sex-linked altruism: a stepping-stone in the evolution of social behavior? J. Evol. Biol. **4:** 487–500.
33. HAIG, D. 1992. Intragenomic conflict and the evolution of eusociality. J. Theor. Biol. **156:** 401–403.
34. REEVE, H.K. & J.S. SHELLMAN-REEVE. 1997. The general protected invasion theory: sex biases in parental and alloparental care. Evol. Ecol. **11:** 357–370.
35. GRAVES, J.A.M. & J.W. FOSTER. 1994. Evolution of mammalian sex chromosomes and sex-determining genes. Int. Rev. Cytol. **154:** 191–259.
36. SOLARI, A.J. 1994. Sex Chromosomes and Sex Determination in Vertebrates. CRC Press. Boca Raton, FL.
37. HEARD, E., P. CLERC & P. AVNER. 1997. X-chromosome inactivation in mammals. Annu. Rev. Genet. **31:** 571–610.
38. COOPER, D.W., P.G. JOHNSTON, J.L. VANDEBERG & E.S. ROBINSON. 1990. X-chromosome inactivation in marsupials. Austr. J. Zool. **37:** 411–417.
39. RUSSELL, E.M. 1984. Social behaviour and social organization of marsupials. Mammal Rev. **14:** 101–154.
40. LEE, A.K. & A. COCKBURN. 1985. Evolutionary Ecology of Marsupials. Cambridge University Press. Cambridge, England.
41. MORIN, P.A., J.J. MOORE, R. CHAKRABORTY *et al.* 1994. Kin selection, social structure, gene flow, and the evolution of chimpanzees. Science **265:** 1193–1201.
42. SEIELSTAD, M.T., E. MINCH & L.L. CAVALLI-SFORZA. 1998. Genetic evidence for higher female migration rate in humans. Nature Genet. **20:** 278–280.
43. TRIVERS, R. L. 1971. The evolution of reciprocal altruism. Q. Rev. Biol. **46:** 35–57.
44. JAENISCH, R. 1997. DNA methylation and imprinting: why bother? Trends Genet. **13:** 323–329.

Do Extraterrestrials Have Sex (and Intelligence)?

JEROME H. BARKOW

Department of Sociology and Social Anthropology, Dalhousie University, Halifax, Nova Scotia, Canada B3H3J5

ABSTRACT: This thought experiment addresses the range of possible evolved psychologies likely to be associated with extraterrestrial (ET) intelligence. The analysis rests on: (1) a number of assumptions shared by the SETI project; (2) recent arguments concerning convergent evolution; and (3) current theories of how intelligence evolved in our own species. It concludes that, regardless of how and which cognitive abilities arise initially, extraterrestrially they can develop into intelligence only if an amplification process involving a form of predation and/or sexual selection occurs. Depending on the amplification process, ETs may be xenophobic; however, it is more probable that they will be ethnocentric. Their ideas of reciprocity and fairness are likely to at least overlap with our own. They will definitely be culture-bearing and probably have two sexes, both of which are intelligent. Regardless of the degree of physical similarity of ETs to ourselves, convergence makes it likely that we will at least find their evolved psychology similar enough to our own for comprehension.

Let us pretend that a science fiction scenario suddenly becomes real. We establish contact with extraterrestrials. Immediately, scientists, journalists, and Pentagon officials have a list of questions. The Security Council of the United Nations wants to know whether the extraterrestrials are xenophobic and interested only in destroying us, or whether they see us as potential friends and allies. Do they have hidden Machiavellian agendas? Is there a basis for diplomacy? The journalists begin by asking whether the extraterrestrials have sexes and, if so, how many. The natural scientists want to know the extraterrestrials' biology and technology, while the anthropologists are asking whether they have culture. Entrepreneurs are wondering whether we can appreciate one another's arts and crafts and entertainment. The questions are endless.

Let us conduct a thought experiment in order to narrow our questions and perhaps develop some tentative answers. Its goal will be to distinguish between the possible and the impossible, the probable and the improbable. The modus operandi will be to begin by taking a look at how our own psychology most likely evolved, then to consider variations on these scenarios, variations that could produce an evolutionary psychology different from our own. In short, in this thought experiment we are exploring alternative evolutionary routes that potentially lead to a species different from ourselves, but which we nevertheless would recognize as intelligent. To avoid disputes over the meaning of "intelligent," let us define that term operationally as "the ability to visit or otherwise contact us."

Thought experiments begin with assumptions. Our essential assumptions are that there is life on other planets, and that in some cases it will be intelligent (as defined above).

IS THERE LIFE ON OTHER PLANETS AND, IF SO, IS IT INTELLIGENT?

This issue has received considerable attention in recent years from astronomers and others. The existence of Earth-like planets elsewhere in the universe, the evolution of life on those planets, and the possibility of that life's developing intelligence have been dealt with by Carl Sagan, Francis Drake, Amir Aczel, and others.[1–7, 8] (p. 150) From 1992 to 1993 the United States financed a Search for Extraterrestrial Intelligence (SE TI). What was actually being searched for were radio transmissions from extraterrestrials. SETI continues to the present time, although since 1993 it has been privately financed. The search has now expanded to include an effort to detect flashes of laser light that could represent the attempts of extraterrestrials to communicate with us.[9]

Amir Aczel's[8] recent book typifies the optimism of SETI supporters; his title, *Probability 1*, telegraphs his conclusions:

> The probability of extraterrestrial life is 1.00, or a number that for all purposes is 1.00. We are not alone. And while we haven't seen anyone from outside our planet yet, and while the distances to the stars are so dauntingly immense, someday in the future there might be contact.[8] (p. 215)

Aczel's arguments are rooted in astronomy, physics, chemistry, and probability theory, and even summarizing his thinking would be beyond the scope of this paper (which is primarily concerned with evolutionary psychology). Nevertheless, his work and that of his predecessors certainly justifies a thought experiment based on the assumption that, yes, there is life out there on other planets.

But even if there were life, would it be intelligent life? Aczel continues to be entirely confident. "Given enough millions of years from the time the DNA molecule arrives or evolves on a planet, intelligence will inevitably be the ultimate outcome."[8] (p. 150) Here we must pause, for Aczel has now strayed into evolutionary biology, and at least one prominent evolutionist would not agree with him.

Stephen J. Gould, in his well-known study of the Burgess Shale faunas, *Wonderful Life,*[10] argues that there was nothing inevitable or even likely about the evolution of intelligence even on our own planet. For Gould, if one were to "rewind the tape of life" and replay it, we probably would have a very different evolutionary history. Gould has long argued that evolution is a matter of "contingency," and tends to deemphasize the roles of natural selection and adaptation. Ultimately, for Gould, the evolution of so unlikely a trait as "intelligence" is as much a matter of pure chance as anything else. As Simon Conway Morris[11] puts it, Gould's "argument, largely using the Burgess Shale faunas, was that the range of variation in the Cambrian was so huge and the end results in terms of the diversity of today's world so restricted that the history could be regarded as one colossal lottery."

Fortunately for our thought experiment, Morris's recent book, *The Crucible of Creation: The Burgess Shale and the Rise of Animals*, gives us strong grounds for disagreeing with Gould. Where Gould emphasizes contingency, Morris focuses on *convergence*, convergent evolution in particular: "Put simply, contingency is inevitable, but unremarkable. It need not provoke discussion, because it matters not. There are not an unlimited number of ways of doing something. For all its exuberance, the forms of life are restricted and channelled."[11] (p. 12), [13] (pp. 203–204) Morris persuasively reminds us of how frequently we find convergent evolution producing similar forms from dissimilar lineages. In part, he convinces us with examples. There is the 65-million-year-old South American marsupial strikingly similar to the much more recent—and placental—sabre-toothed tiger.[11] (pp. 203–204) There are the two varieties of moles, each a tunneling animal with short and powerful digging forelimbs and poor eyesight, but which, in spite of appearances, are related only by convergent evolution, one being a placental mammal and the other a marsupial. He discusses the similarities of the wings of birds and bats. He convinces us of his main point, that "again and again we have evidence of biological forms stumbling on the same solution to a problem."[11] (p. 204) The problems to which Morris refers are adaptive problems, reminding one of the argument of evolutionary psychology that our psychological traits evolved as solutions to adaptive problems. But before we move on to evolutionary psychology, let us first make explicit the relevance of Morris's convergence argument to the evolution of intelligence on other planets.

For Morris, if Gould's "tape of life" were to be replayed, we might well get different species from different lineages, but we would also meet with many familiar forms and behaviors. Let us move that tape to another planet, one that supports life. Here, too, the argument from convergent evolution implies that we would still meet with many familiar forms. We recall that Aczel and his predecessors conclude that there are an immense number of planets bearing life; if so, it seems inevitable that some extraterrestrial species would have faced adaptive problems similar to those faced by our own ancestors. If convergence is the rule then in some of these species evolution must have produced intelligent beings. This assumption, crucial to the present task, seems warranted. Now we are ready to return to our main question about the nature of those intelligent beings.

THE ENVIRONMENT OF EVOLUTIONARY ADAPTEDNESS

What environment gave rise to the selection pressures that produced the intelligence and cultural capacity of our own species? It was the environment of our ancestors, that is, their *environment of evolutionary adaptedness*, the EEA. To understand the evolution of extraterrestrial intelligence, therefore, we need only begin with a clear picture of our own EEA, suggest reasonable changes in that early environment, and discuss the likely evolutionary psychology of a species that evolved in this altered EEA.

Unfortunately, the EEA question is perhaps the weakest aspect of evolutionary psychology.[12] There was no single EEA—we evolved over millions of years and across much geography, so that our environment of evolutionary adaptedness would have varied across both time and place.[13] Moreover, there is a growing consensus that much of human cognitive capacity is, in fact, shared by the anthropoid apes,[14–17] and may have been shared by our common ancestors. In short, different aspects of our intelligence probably first evolved during different periods of time.

The EEA problem does not seem to have hindered the development of a robust and data-based evolutionary psychology. After all, in that field a wrong reconstruction of the EEA is likely to produce a hypothesis that is simply invalid, and careful research will presumably reveal this. If my picture of the EEA involves our having evolved primarily as hunters rather than gatherers and cultivators, but my empirical research shows that, transculturally, most children love to collect and to cultivate rather than to watch animals and play at throwing projectiles, then perhaps it is time for me to rethink my picture of the EEA.[18,a] Unfortunately for the present effort, thought experiments cannot be corrected so readily.

If there was no single EEA for our own species, presumably there was no single EEA for our extraterrestrials. However, as Charles Crawford[18] points out, we can distinguish between the EEA of a species and the EEA of a particular adaptation. William Irons[19] comes to much the same conclusion in his argument that we should replace the concept of the "environment of evolutionary adaptedness" (EEA) with that of the "adaptively relevant environment," or ARE. "Relevant" here refers to "relevant to a specific adaptation." The approach Crawford and Irons take permits us to focus not on the totality of the EEAs of a species, but on specific traits and clusters of traits. Thus, we can talk about a component or kind of intelligence and ask about the kind of environment in which this specific trait would have conferred an adaptive advantage—would have led individuals with this characteristic to have a fitness advantage over others. This approach is clearly artificial in that an adaptation exists not in isolation, but in interaction with all other existing adaptations, while the totality of adaptations themselves interact with and alter their environment in what Laland *et al.*[20] term "niche construction." The notion of an identifiable "adaptively relevant environment" clearly represents a considerable simplification, but let us accept it heuristically.

With the Irons and Crawford approach, we need not seek to recreate the entire EEA of our extraterrestrials. Rather, we can specify psychological mechanisms or traits and the AREs in which they would have been adaptive. This strategy permits us to begin.

XENOPHOBIA AND ETHNOCENTRISM

Will our extraterrestrials wish to annihilate us, or otherwise hate and fear us? That will depend on the ARE we posit. For example, Alexander and others[21–29] have suggested that our intelligence and cultural capacity evolved as the result of a self or auto-predation process. Bands of our ancestors would, in effect, have culled one another of the stupid, the slow to be able to make and use tools well, the individuals unable to grasp basic hunting/raiding/defending strategy, and the ones who failed to cooperate with other band members in the face of external threat. This culling process would have selected for individuals with more rather than less intelligence, tool (weapons)-making skills, and ability to communicate and cooperate with others.

[a]For a full discussion of the nature of evolutionary psychology hypotheses and a refutation of the argument that they are unfalsifiable, see Ketelaar, T. and B.J. Ellis. 2000. Are evolutionary explanations unfalsifiable? Evolutionary psychology and the Lakatosian philosophy of science. Psychological Inquiry **11:** 1–21.

Even as a predator may, by culling the slow-of-foot, cause its prey to evolve fleetness, we may have been our own predator, causing our species to evolve intelligence.

For our extraterrestrials, let us alter this scenario from self-predation to *co-predation* or *inter-species rivalry*. Suppose they evolved in company with a closely competing species. Each species would have culled the other of the dull, uncooperative, and uncommunicative. Each species would have supplied the environment (or at least the ARE) in which intelligence was adaptive. Each species, too, would necessarily have been selected for automatic hostility towards the other. Perhaps, in the end, only one of these antagonistic species survived.

Suppose that we now meet such an extraterrestrial species, one whose intelligence is a product of co-predation. If we in any way trigger their automatic hostility to rival species, we may find ourselves with a xenophobic and even genocidal enemy. In such a case, the only way to avoid conflict would be for us to find some way to convince the extraterrestrials that we are in some sense the same species that they are, their siblings rather than the enemy. Of course, this will not necessarily be possible. We should also ask why such a species would have a project analogous to SETI in the first place. Presumably, their SETI would be looking for external threats rather than for a cooperative exchange of information with another species. If contact comes not from radio waves or laser pulses but because either they or we actually develop some form of interstellar travel, we should expect them either to attack us or to flee from us.

Suppose, however, that the extraterrestrials evolved with self-predation, as we ourselves likely did, so that the conflict and culling that led to their intelligence was much the same as those of our own ancestors. In that case, we should expect the extraterrestrials to be not xenophobic but ethnocentric. They are therefore likely to react as we do to external threat, by increasing in-group solidarity and cooperativeness, and with a ready hostility towards other groups. They are also likely to readily assume that they are intrinsically superior to us. We ourselves would presumably react ethnocentrically to such an extraterrestrial species, suggesting that our relationship with them would potentially be tense but open to the possibilities of diplomacy and alliance.

Finally, let us suppose that the intelligence of our extraterrestrials was the product of neither predation nor self-predation but of another process entirely, such as tool-using. If so, they might exhibit neither xenophobia nor ethnocentrism. The question is: could tool use lead to intelligence? It seems unlikely that any ecological adaptation, including that of tool use, could result in intelligence without a subsequent *amplifying process*. Self-predation and co-predation are possible amplifying processes, but so is *sexual selection*. However, sexual selection can only occur in a species that has sex.

WILL EXTRATERRESTRIALS HAVE SEX?

Why Two Sexes?[b]

Why do we have two sexes? Why not none, or three? As we did with the question of whether there is life on other planets, let us rely on some of the experts in this field. This time, however, we get no single answer. The standard account of the two-sex problem (often associated with George Williams)[30] has been that having two sexes increases the efficiency of natural selection—rather like shuffling the deck frequently increases the probability of a "winning hand." In this case, a "winning hand" refers to having offspring with a set of genes well adapted to the current ecology. Because ecology continually changes, adaptation requires that genetic change track ecological change. This tracking occurs more quickly if the organism's set of genes, including new mutations, is continually "shuffled" or rearranged. However, Barton and Charlesworth,[31] in a recent review article of the two-sexes problem, find that this argument is valid only if a number of assumptions (including assumptions about mutation rates) are made, otherwise the faster adaptation is offset by the fact that the genetic recombination—the reshuffling—also breaks up winning hands, that is, already existing adaptive sets of genes.[31] (p. 1988)

A more recent answer to the two-sexes problem, also discussed by Barton and Charlesworth, has to do with the effects of parasites. Parasites tend to have a shorter life span than do their host species. With only one sex, the host's longer time between generations means that it cannot evolve defenses against the parasite as fast as the parasite can evolve advantages. When the host has two sexes, however, an offspring's defenses against parasites may differ from those of the parental generation, reducing the parasite's advantage. The result is a never-ending co-evolutionary, reciprocal positive feedback process in which the adaptations of the parasite drive selection for resistant adaptations in the host, and in which the host's resistant adaptations in turn drive selection for adaptations in the parasite. However, though they are sympathetic to this model, Barton and Charlesworth find that it rests on a crucial technical assumption that does not necessarily obtain in all cases (the assumption that "sex does increase additive fitness variance").[31] (p. 1987)

Finally, having two sexes permits a species to rid itself of deleterious mutations. With one sex, such mutations tend to accumulate because offspring are generally identical to their parents. With two sexes, offspring vary from one another and from their parents so that those individuals with a lower load of deleterious alleles outreproduce those with a larger load. Thus, the two-sexed species rids itself of harmful mutations at a higher rate than does the species with only one sex. This advantage, however, depends on assumptions about mutation rates and the proportion of existing deleterious alleles.[31,32]

Sexual reproduction with two sexes comes at a substantial cost. Whereas for an asexual species offspring have 100 percent of a parent's genes, with two sexes this proportion is halved. Presumably, this cost is more than offset by the various likely advantages already discussed. But if two sexes are good, why not three? The answer is that the more sexes, the greater the degree of dilution of the parental genes; apparently, with more than two sexes the dilution is not offset by whatever advantages multiple sexes might bring.[31]

Barton and Charlesworth[31] conclude their review of the various routes by which two sexes may originate and be maintained by pointing out that the various alternative hypotheses are not mutually exclusive, but that their relative importance remains

[b]For an excellent introduction to the problem of sex, including the "why two sexes" question, see Science **281:** 1979–2008, "The evolution of sex." Geary[32] (pp. 15–21) also provides a useful summary of the arguments about sexes, as does D. M. Buss. 1999. Evolutionary Psychology: The New Science of the Mind. : 100–103. Allyn & Bacon. Needham Heights, MA.

to be determined. This conclusion is more than adequate for present purposes: if there may be multiple routes for the evolution and maintenance of two sexes under varying circumstances, it is reasonable for us to assume that at least some extraterrestrials do have two, but most likely only two sexes. Two sexes mean that sexual selection is possible: Would sexual selection have played a role in the evolution of the intelligence of extraterrestrials?

SEXUAL SELECTION

Having two sexes means that each parent contributes a gamete. Each gamete has one half of the genes of its parent. A new organism is formed—reproduction takes place—when one gamete combines with another. Producing a gamete requires an expenditure of energy termed by Trivers[33] "parental investment." One sex will typically invest more in its gametes and subsequently in the entire reproductive process than will the other. By convention, the sex that provides the greater parental investment is called "female," while the sex that provides less investment is termed "male." Trivers argues that the sex with the greater parental investment will be more discriminating in selecting a mate than is the sex with the lesser investment, so that members of the latter sex compete with one another for access to the former. Usually, though not always, it is the female that provides the greater investment.[c]

Sexual selection, "the processes associated with mate choice and competition for mates,"[32] (p. 20) explains much of animal morphology and behavior. For example, in some species males compete for females, with the winners producing most of the next generation. In such a species whatever morphology or behavior increases a male's chance of winning will be selected for. In elephant seals, for example, it will be sheer size coupled with aggressiveness towards other males. The result is that the males are far larger than the females. In deer, where stags contest using their antlers, sexual selection favors enormous racks of antlers, despite their considerable energetic cost. In other species, sexual selection may be primarily about female choice. A female may select the male who appears to have the "best genes." If bright plumage is a sign of "good genes" (in the sense of resistance to parasites, in particular), then selection will present us with a peacock's tail feathers. "Runaway" sexual selection may hypertrophy a particular trait. But let us look at the human situation.

Discussion of sexual selection usually focuses on the sexual dimorphisms it produces. This is especially true in the case of human beings, for whom there exists a large and controversial literature on sex differences in evolved psychology.[d] However, for present purposes we need to focus not on the differences between the sexes produced by sexual selection but on the similarities.

In a 37-country survey, David Buss[34] found that both women and men, when asked to rank 13 traits for desirability in a long-term mate, ranked intelligence sec-

[c]See Trivers[32] (pp. 215-218) for examples of species in which, despite the female's initially greater investment in the gamete, it is the male that provides the greater overall proportion of parental investment. In such species it is the male and not the female that is the more discriminating in selecting a mate. For an excellent introduction to sexual selection, see Cronin, H. 1991. The Ant and The Peacock: Altruism and Sexual Selection from Darwin to Today. Press Syndicate of the University of Cambridge. Cambridge, England.

ond. (Interestingly, "kindness and understanding" were ranked first.) There is a growing consensus among evolutionists that sexual selection was a crucial process in the development of human intelligence (for examples see Refs. 13, 32, and 35). This conclusion is not surprising, as it is likely that a mate's intelligence increases the ability to provide parental investment. "Intelligent" activities likely to have increased the potential parental investment of a partner in the course of human evolution would include skill in tool- and weapon-making, skill in fire-making, in processing of foodstuffs, in locating food sources, in cooperating with others to gain food (as in a cooperative hunt), in conveying foodstuffs to a place of safety (such as a home camp), in caring for offspring, in protecting oneself and others from injury, in finding or making shelter, in learning from others, in communicating and in being sensitive to the communications of others, in paying attention to the environment, in being able to influence the behavior of others—and no doubt in many more ways. In our own species, sexual selection clearly strengthened selection for intelligence and for possible indicators of intelligence. It may well be, if Buss's respondents behave in real life the way that they rank items in a paper-and-pencil test, that sexual selection for intelligence continues today.

Both in our own species and likely for our intelligent extraterrestrials, sexual selection would have acted as an amplifier for intelligence, *regardless of the nature of the earlier selection pressures that had initially led to the relevant cognitive capacities.* In short, diverse early selection pressures for various cognitive abilities, once amplified by sexual selection, could have had a similar result: intelligence. For example, for our own species there is a body of opinion that argues that tool use, a trait we share with our close relative the chimpanzee, was one of the major selection pressures for cognitive abilities, linked both to the origins of human language and to sexual selection.[e] Tools may have been particularly useful, among early hominids, in extracting food from nuts and from bones. Even when tools are not used, primates require a considerable and varied cognitive set of abilities to obtain food.[14] (p. 179–184) Given sexual selection, from such beginnings may have come intelligence and language.[f] Our extraterrestrials, however, may owe their initial cognitive abilities to

[d] See, for example: Symons, D. 1979. The Evolution of Human Sexuality. Oxford University Press. New York; Daly, M. & M. Wilson. 1984. Sex, Evolution and Behavior, 2nd ed. Willard Grant. Boston, MA; Ellis, B. J. 1992. The evolution of sexual attraction: evaluative mechanisms in women. *In* The Adapted Mind: Evolutionary Psychology and the Generation of Culture. J.H. Barkow, L. Cosmides and J. Tooby, Eds.: 267–288. Oxford University Press. New York; Buss, D. M. 1994. The Evolution of Desire. Basic Books, New York; Symons, D. 1995. Beauty is in the adaptations of the beholder: the evolutionary psychology of human female sexual attractiveness. *In* Sexual Nature, Sexual Culture. P.R. Abramson and S.D. Pinkerton, Eds.: 80–118. University of Chicago Press. Chicago; Geary[32]; and Angier, N. 1999. Woman: An Intimate Geography. Houghton-Mifflin. Boston, MA.

[e] See, for example: Parker, S. T. & K. R. Gibson. 1979. A developmental model for the evolution of language and intelligence in early hominids. Behav. Brain Sci. **2:** 367–408; Parker, S. T. 1985. A social-technological model for the evolution of language. Curr. Anthropology **27:** 671–739; Gibson, K. R. 1986. Cognition, brain size and the extraction of embedded food resources. *In* Primate Ontogeny, Cognitive and Social Behaviour. J. G. Else and P. C. Lee, Eds.: 93–105. Cambridge University Press. Cambridge, England; Gibson, K. R. & T. Ingold. 1993. Tools, Language and Cognition in Human Evolution. Cambridge University Press. Cambridge, England; McGrew, W. C. 1995. Thumbs, tools and early humans. Science **268:** 586; Mellars, P. & K. R. Gibson. 1996. Modelling the Early Human Mind. Cambridge University Press. Cambridge, England.

an ecology entirely different from our own, such as the problems posed by a pelagic environment. In their case, too, however, sexual selection may have amplified these abilities into intelligence.

What of the dimorphisms often (though not necessarily) produced by sexual selection—the antlers, the brilliant plumage, the huge size that we see in some species? Could it happen that, on an extraterrestrial world, sexual selection has produced an intelligent species in which one sex also has, say, large tusks or bright fur? Could it be that extraterrestrial males will be much larger than their females, as with elephant seals? The fact that elephant seals are not intelligent adumbrates the answer to these rhetorical questions.

Sexual selection for two or more energetically expensive traits would presumably weaken selection for each of them. Large brains are very costly for an organism to produce and maintain: it is difficult to envisage a successful species being selected both for large brains and for another costly trait, such as the annual growth and shedding of antlers. However, energetically less costly attributes, such as bright coloration, could probably evolve along with intelligence. Alternatively, we might discover an only fairly intelligent species with only fairly large antlers. In such a case we would have to do the discovering, as presumably an only "fairly intelligent" species (one that would not actually be intelligent by the working definition of intelligence we are using) would not be capable of interstellar communication or travel.

Could sexual selection produce radically sexually dimorphic intelligence? For our own species there is considerable controversy over whether we have a slight degree of sexual dimorphism in some cognitive abilities[32] (pp. 312–313): Is it possible that, for our extraterrestrials, the dimorphism will be so great that only one sex will be intelligent? For example, let us assume that the males use their intelligence to form tool-using coalitions that compete with other coalitions in herding females: Could it be that males but not females would be sexually selected for tool use and cooperation, so that ultimately the males but not the females became intelligent? The simple answer is "no." As Miller[35] points out, linkage between the two sexes means that what is selected for in one tends to appear automatically in the other. Dimorphism in intelligence would require it to be maladaptive for one of the sexes, and it is difficult to imagine a scenario in which this would be so. Sexual dimorphism in intelligence is not the same as dimorphism in, for example, antlers. Antlers and intelligence are both very costly, but while large antlers increase the male's reproductive success, intelligence increases the reproductive success of both females and males. Intelligent females presumably gain an adaptive advantage in terms of greater ability in food acquisition and processing, better care of offspring, and perhaps social transmission of information to them, and so forth. Moreover, if our extraterrestrials were at all like baboons, females and lower-ranking males would use intelligence (in the form of social manipulation) to copulate despite the efforts of the dominant male.[36] It seems very unlikely that there could be intelligent males without intelligent females.

Could the extraterrestrials have intelligent *females* but unintelligent *males*? Suppose the males have specialized in a sexual competition feature such as size, so that

[f]Barton and Dunbar,[16] (pp. 257–258) dispute that ecological problems, including food strategies involving extraction, could have led to intelligence. They argue strongly, instead, for the importance of the processing of social information.

sexual selection favored very large bodies but not large brains. Brains being very costly, sexual selection might favor the males who sacrificed brain for body mass. Let us further assume that the females were selected for intelligence because their small size forced them to make tools and cooperate with one another in order to get food. The result would apparently be small but bright females and large-bodied but dull males. This scenario, too, is unlikely. If the females are more intelligent than the males, will they not find ways to copulate with the more intelligent even if not necessarily dominant males, as in the already-mentioned case of baboons? For our extraterrestrials, it seems most probable that, in the end, both sexes would be selecting one another for intelligence.

SOCIAL INTELLIGENCE AND THE SENSE OF JUSTICE

Will extraterrestrials share our ideas of fairness and justice? A sense of justice is an aspect of what, for our own species, has been called *social* intelligence. The nature of social intelligence, in turn, depends on the evolutionary bases of social cooperation of a species. We therefore must discuss social intelligence and cooperation before examining the sense of justice.

SOCIAL INTELLIGENCE

Rather than having been selected for intelligence because it enabled them to use tools or to be more effective at foraging or hunting, our ancestors may have been selected for intelligence because it led to their success in social competition. In recent years this approach (often associated with Humphrey[37,38]) has become part of a family of arguments linked to the notion of "Machiavellian" intelligence.[39] The term connotes deceit and manipulation, but has now become, in the words of Whiten and Byrne[40](p. 1), a "*banner*" for hypotheses that imply that "possession of the cognitive capability we call 'intelligence' is linked with social living and the problems of complexity" [italics in original].

Success in social competition may involve (among other abilities) skill in deceiving others and in detecting the attempts of others to deceive one. It is not, however, always in one's genetic interests to cheat or deceive: it depends in part on the evolutionary basis of social cooperation.

SOCIAL BASES OF COOPERATION: NEPOTISM

For many species, including our own, kinship is one of the bases for social cooperation. Essentially, cooperating with and aiding kin is a likely way to increase one's own genetic representation in the gene pool. Parental care, for example, involves the parent's investing in an organism that shares one half of its genes. We show similar care and altruism towards other relatives as well. As Richard Dawkins[41] has made clear, genes that lead their bearers to act in such a way that the duplicates of these genes in other carriers are favored will thereby increase in the gene pool. Nepotism and parental care, therefore, are readily understandable in evolutionary terms. Note, however, that for nepotistic behavior to evolve it must mirror the equations of population genetics: Aid should be given to others in proportion to the probability that they do indeed share one's genes. Moreover, the recipient's chances of reproducing (reproductive value) and/or aiding other relatives also needs to be taken into account, as well as the probability that the donor, in giving aid to others, is jeopardizing his/her own ability to reproduce successfully. Where nepotism is the sole basis of cooperation, therefore, there are only three types of deception that will benefit an individual: deception about degree of kinship to a potential aid donor, deception about the value of the aid for the recipient, and deception about the likely cost of the aid to the donor. Thus, if our extraterrestrials have evolved social intelligence on the basis of cooperation among kin, they may deceptively assure us that we and they are closely related; or they may expect us to make such a claim and may treat our denial of kinship as an indication that we do not desire to have a relationship with them. Note, however, that this kind of kin selection for cooperation and social intelligence does not appear to require the evolution of any sense of justice or fairness. (Selection for nepotism seems more likely to result in the evolution of mechanisms to determine degree of kinship, such as recognition of familial scents or distinctive family features.)

Suppose, however, that our extraterrestrials disperse at birth, or hatch like tadpoles with no contact with their parents and no means of detecting siblings: Under these conditions we cannot expect selection for social intelligence and cooperation based on nepotism. If intelligence and cooperation nevertheless do evolve in such a species, its basis most likely would be *reciprocal altruism.*

SOCIAL BASES OF COOPERATION: RECIPROCAL ALTRUISM

Reciprocal altruism[42] is one route to the evolution of cooperation among non-kin. Although non-kin by definition do not bear an above-average proportion of one's own genes, with reciprocal altruism aid donated is likely to be repaid so that aiding another is in effect aiding oneself. Even more than in the case of nepotism, however, proffering aid entails the risk of being cheated. The individual who accepts aid but fails to return it or returns scant measure will clearly have an adaptive advantage over the individual who never "cheats." In spite of this risk, reciprocal altruism is so advantageous that cheating leads not to selection against reciprocal altruism *per se,* but rather to the evolution of mechanisms that detect or otherwise discourage cheating. In human beings, these mechanisms apparently have to do with a sense of fairness, of justice and ethics and morality.[g]

[g]Trivers[42]; L. Cosmides. 1989. The logic of social exchange: has natural selection shaped how humans reason? Studies with the Wason selection task. Cognition **31:** 186–276; Irons, W. 1991. How did morality evolve? Zygon: J. Religion & Sci. **26:** 49–89; R. D. Masters & M. Gruter. 1992. The Sense of Justice: Biological Foundations of Law. Sage Publications. Newbury Park, CA; Nitecki, M.H. & D.V. Nitecki. 1993. Evolutionary Ethics. State University of New York. Albany, NY; Arnhart, L. 1995. The New Darwinian Naturalism. Am. Polit. Sci. Rev. **89:** 389–400; Corning, P.A. 1996. Evolution and ethics: an idea whose time has come? (Part I). J. Soc. Evol. Systems **19:** 277–285; Thiessen, D. 1996. Bittersweet Destiny: The Stormy Evolution of Human Behavior. Transaction Publishers. New Brunswick, NJ; De Waal.[16]

Anthropologist Donald E. Brown[43] (p. 139) includes reciprocity as a "key element" in all human moral systems. Underlying these systems is an emotion having to do with our judgments about fairness and justice. McGuire[44] speaks of *moralistic aggression*, defined as "anger and retaliatory thoughts in response to another's failure to reciprocate prior helping." Moralistic aggression is a capacity we share with the chimpanzee. de Waal[45] tells us that chimpanzees have a "sense of social regularity," which, he suggests, "may be a precursor of the sense of justice." This precursor is "a set of expectations about the way in which oneself (or others) should be treated and how resources should be divided, a deviation from which expectations to one's (or the other's) disadvantage evokes a negative reaction, most commonly protest in subordinate individuals and punishment in dominant individuals." For reciprocally altruistic species, selection for social intelligence and cooperation has meant selection for the mechanisms and emotions underlying systems of morality and ethics.

If the social cooperation of extraterrestrials is based at least in part on reciprocal altruism, then their social intelligence will necessarily include either ideas of justice and fairness or else their functional equivalent. Most likely, their notions of obligation and reciprocity will overlap with our own, and they will probably be capable of moralistic aggression. *Warning*: because the sense of justice is an evolved mechanism to minimize cheating, it follows that extraterrestrials that share our ideas of fairness will also share our tendencies towards both sharp practice and deception.

SOCIAL BASES OF COOPERATION: FEAR

Could there be a social intelligence originating neither in nepotism nor in reciprocity but in *fear*? Our working definition of intelligence presupposes the capacity to accumulate and transmit huge quantities of knowledge: fear tends to constrict information flow, as we will see, so that it is difficult to envisage social organization based on fear producing a high level of technology. Nevertheless, let us explore the consequences of social intelligence and cooperation based on fear.

Michael Chance[46, 47] has distinguished between hedonic and agonistic modes of attention and social organization in primates. Chimpanzees have social inequality, but the highest-ranking individuals are not the most aggressive but the most socially skilled, who thereby benefit from alliances/friendships and strategic sharing. Chimpanzee social organization is therefore largely hedonic. In contrast, macaques have agonistic social structures, social structures based largely on fear. Frans de Waal[16] (who has had long experience observing both macaques and chimpanzees) comes to a similar conclusion, one emphasizing the relative tolerance of high-rank chimpanzees compared to high-rank macaques.

These differences in attention structure have important implications for communication and for social intelligence. The social intelligence of a species with agonistic attention structure necessarily focuses on how to influence the behavior of others through threat and appeasement, thereby constricting communication and cooperation. A hedonic attention species, however, may be expected to have a much broader flow of information among individuals[48] and a wider basis for cooperation. In particular, hedonic attention structure species would presumably be far more likely than agonistic attention structure species to develop elaborate systems of cooperation based on reciprocal altruism.

Let us now return to our extraterrestrials. If their social intelligence and cooperation are largely agonistic in nature, then we should expect reciprocal altruism to be relatively underdeveloped. They therefore would lack our own sense of justice and quite likely would be unable to understand our concepts of ethics and fairness. The basis of our relationship with them would be one of mutual threats and intimidation. Fortunately, it seems unlikely that we would find such a species: Their narrow and agonistic social intelligence would probably not permit them to develop the complex forms of social cooperation and immense accumulation of technological knowledge needed for interstellar contact.

WILL THE EXTRATERRESTRIALS HAVE CULTURE?

As a social-cultural anthropologist, I find the question of whether extraterrestrials will have culture especially consequential. By "have culture," I mean whether they are heavily dependent on an accumulation of socially transmitted information. In this context, "a culture" is an information pool from which individuals select, enter, and edit items.[13] While psychologists have paid much attention to individual cognition, for the social-cultural anthropologist the most salient trait (other than language) that distinguishes human from nonhuman primates is that humans accumulate and socially transmit far larger stores of information (culture). Will our extraterrestrials be similar to us, in this regard?

The extent to which a species is selected for individual learning and intelligence, rather than reliance on socially transmitted information, is a matter of the rate of change of the local ecology. Boyd and Richerson[49,50] have discussed the circumstances under which social transmission of information, as opposed to individual learning, is favored. In a very slowly changing environment, selection favors neither type of learning but instead itself tracks change, adapting the organism's behavior to its environment. In contrast, an environment that changes too rapidly for natural selection to track selects for a capacity for individual learning. But suppose we have an environment whose rate of change falls between these poles—it is too fast for genetic adaptation, too slow to require continual individual learning: The result is a species that relies on *social* learning, particularly learning from parents, while retaining a capacity for at least some individual learning.

Let us take the example of what Paul Rozin[51] has termed "the omnivore's dilemma ... the great advantage of discovering a new source of nutrition, versus the danger of ingesting a toxin." In a stable (moderate change) environment, socially transmitted information is likely to be comprehensive and reliable; the omnivore is best off relying on social learning rather than on an individual learning process that risks the ingestion of toxins. In a more rapidly changing environment, however, old food sources may become scarce and new plants and animals may appear. In this situation, the omnivore is likely to be selected for greater reliance on individual learning, despite its risks. To generalize: When the environment is reasonably stable over long periods of time, then selection will favor the capacity to accumulate and transmit information from generation to generation; where it undergoes prolonged change at a rate too rapid for its tracking by natural selection (or when the species repeatedly changes habitats), it is independent learning that will be favored. (Rapid change would also favor horizontal or within-generation learning, as opposed to vertical or between-generation learning.)

If a rapidly changing environment leads to selection for individual learning and intelligence, could we not find extraterrestrials who, while capable of prodigious individual learning, do not rely heavily on accumulated, socially transmitted information? Could such a culture-free species contact us? Probably not. An extraterrestrial individual would have to independently invent in a single generation the full panoply of scientific and engineering information, as well as the industries required to fabricate the components needed for contact. Indeed, that individual would first have to conceive of the idea of life on other planets! Even given the existence of an extremely long-lived species of unimaginably vast intelligence, it seems unlikely that such an individual could or would devote itself to a SETI-like project. We are obliged to conclude that any intelligent extraterrestrial species would have a society in which, at a minimum, vast amounts of technical information can accumulate and be socially transmitted. Extraterrestrials will be culture-bearing.

Our own culture-bearing species has developed many distinct societies with overlapping but distinct information pools. We should therefore not be surprised to find that the extraterrestrials also have multiple cultures.

DISCUSSION

The EEA and Emergents

The modus operandi of this thought experiment has been to look at specific environments and selection pressures one at a time, despite the fact that the EEAs of a species vary both in time and in space. Evolution is always a sort of resultant-of-forces calculation—many selection pressures operate simultaneously, and their sequencing and interactions are liable to be very important. The result of this process has been, in our own species, an extraordinarily complex intelligence. As Gibson[52] puts it, "the fundamental foundations of modern human cognition rest, not upon one specific ability, such as language or symbolism, but rather upon a highly plastic, environmentally responsive 'biocultural' brain and a suite of interacting, mutually reinforcing neurological capacities each of which is present in rudimentary form in other animals, but greatly expanded in our own species." Intelligence does not evolve in terms of one trait and one selection pressure at a time. Worse, human intelligence—and perhaps self-awareness—could be emergents from multiple selection pressures acting in a particular sequence. There is no way to model such emergents in extraterrestrials, given how poorly understood they are for our own species.

Amplifiers

The co-predation, auto-predation, and sexual selection processes are important amplifiers in understanding the evolution of intelligence. They represent reciprocal positive feedback loops that can greatly expand intelligence. However, "intelligence" is not a black box, and we need to think about what specific abilities and psychological traits would be amplified by each of these processes. For our own species, it is quite likely that both autopredation and sexual selection were involved in the generation of our complex evolutionary psychology, and it would be useful to compare the traits that each of these processes would likely most affect.

It is perhaps worth noting that, if we are wrong about our extraterrestrials having sex, they would necessarily have developed intelligence through an amplifying process involving either auto-predation or co-predation. Thus, a single-sex intelligence would be either xenophobic or ethnocentric. Evolution is a slower process for a one-sex species than it is for a species with two sexes: the predation process would have required an extremely long time period to amplify cognitive abilities into intelligence, implying an exceedingly stable ecology.

Group Selection

Could it be that our extraterrestrials will have reached intelligence through a form of group selection in which the evolutionary unit is neither gene nor individual but the group? Cultural group selection, for example, may have been involved in human evolution.[13,50] Group selection continues to be discussed,[53,54] and it would be useful to explore group selection scenarios that could lead to extraterrestrial intelligence.

This thought experiment could readily be broadened. For example, we could well ask whether extraterrestrials and we will share a sense of esthetics. Orians and Heerwagen[55] apply habitat selection theory to landscape esthetics: Applying it to extraterrestrials might help us to determine whether they would have, for example, any desire to possess our planet (or even to be tourists on it). It would also be interesting to explore whether the extraterrestrials would have our type of self-awareness. Finally, this experiment has deliberately neglected the important topic of language. Extraterrestrials who rely on socially transmitted information must have a form of communication, whether acoustic, visual, tactile, electromagnetic or chemical (the last including taste, smell, and pheromone transmission).

CONCLUSIONS

The results of this thought experiment are obviously provisional: Different assumptions would yield different conclusions. Still, it does appear that if we are not quite in the Star Trek universe, where the differences among species seem mostly cosmetic and cultural, we are not too far away, either. Extraterrestrials are probably culture-bearing animals with two intelligent sexes. They could be xenophobic and dangerous or at best ethnocentric, but it seems likely that they and we may share a capacity for fairness and for moralistic aggression, and to at least be able to understand one another's ethics. Physically they may be very different from us, but we should have some common ground to understand one another. Some advice for SE TI: If the extraterrestrials do contact us, have some evolutionary anthropologists and psychologists standing by.

Finally, even after all this effort, some may still be thinking, "well, if there are all those intelligent extraterrestrials out there, why haven't we ever seen them or at least received their radio transmissions?" One possible answer to this question is rather worrisome: Richard Dawkins'[56] suggestion that "intelligent life may arise quite frequently, but typically only a short time elapses between the invention of radio and technological self-destruction." Given this possibility, it behooves us to think carefully not just about the evolutionary psychology of extraterrestrials, but also about our own.

ACKNOWLEDGMENTS

I am grateful to Walter and Dori LeCroy for their support for this colloquium series. My thanks, too, to Dr. LeCroy and Dr. P. Moller for having invited me to participate, and for their helpful editing.

REFERENCES

1. SHKLOVSKII, I. S. & C. SAGAN. 1967. Intelligent Life in the Universe. Dell. New York.
2. SAGAN, C. 1973. The Cosmic Connection: An Extraterrestrial Perspective. Doubleday. New York.
3. SAGAN, C. 1973. Communication with Extraterrestrial Intelligence. MIT Press. Cambridge, MA.
4. SAGAN, C. 1977. The Dragons of Eden: Speculations on the Evolution of Human Intelligence. Random House. New York.
5. MCDONOUGH, T. 1987. The Search for Extraterrestrial Intelligence. Wiley. New York.
6. DRAKE, F. & D. SOBEL. 1992. Is Anyone Out There? The Scientific Search for Extraterrestrial Intelligence. Delacorte. New York.
7. GOLDSMITH, D. 1997. Worlds Unnumbered. University Science Books. Sausalito, CA.
8. ACZEL, A.D. 1998. Probability I. Why There Must be Intelligent Life in the Universe. Harcourt Brace. New York.
9. 1999. Looking for a wink from ET [news item]. Science **283:** 629.
10. GOULD, S.J. 1989. Wonderful Life. Norton. New York.
11. MORRIS, S.C. 1998. The Crucible of Creation: The Burgess Shale and the Rise of Animals. Oxford University Press. New York.
12. BARKOW, J.H. 1994. Evolutionary psychological anthropology. *In* Handbook of Psychological Anthropology. P.K. Bock, Ed.: 121–138. Greenwood. Westport, CT.
13. BARKOW, J.H. 1989. Darwin, Sex, and Status: Biological Approaches to Mind and Culture. University of Toronto Press. Toronto, Canada.
14. BYRNE, R. 1995. The Thinking Ape: Evolutionary Origins of Intelligence. Oxford University Press. New York,
15. RUSSON, A.E., K.A. BARD & S.T. PARKER. 1996. Reaching Into Thought: The Minds of the Great Apes. Cambridge University Press. Cambridge, England.
16. DE WAAL, F. 1996. Good Natured: The Origins of Right and Wrong in Humans and Other Animals. Harvard University Press. Cambridge, MA.
17. BARTON, R.A. & R.I.M. DUNBAR. 1997. Evolution of the social brain. *In* Machiavellian Intelligence II: Extensions and Evaluations. A. Whiten & R. W. Byrne, Eds.: 240–263. Cambridge University Press. Cambridge.
18. CRAWFORD, C. 1998. Environments and adaptations: then and now. *In* Handbook of Evolutionary Psychology: Ideas, Issues, and Applications. C. Crawford & D.L. Krebs, Eds.: 275–302. Erlbaum Associates. Mahwah, NJ.
19. IRONS, W. 1998. Adaptively relevant environments versus the environment of evolutionary adaptedness. Evol. Anthropol. **6:** 194–204.
20. LALAND, K.N., J. ODLING-SMEE & M. FELDMAN. 1999. Niche construction, biological evolution and cultural change. Behav. Brain Sci. In press.
21. READ, C. 1917. On the differentiation of the human from the anthropoid mind. Philos. Library **8:** 395–422.
22. KEITH, A. 1949. A New Theory of Human Evolution. Philosophical Library, New York.
23. ALEXANDER, R.D. 1971. The search for an evolutionary philosophy of man. Proc. Roy. Soc. Victoria, Melbourne **84:** 99–120.

24. BIGELOW, R.S. 1973. The evolution of cooperation, aggression, and self-control. *In* Nebraska Symposium on Motivation 1972. J. K. Cole and D. D. Jensen, Eds. University of Nebraska Press. Lincoln, NE
25. ALEXANDER, R.D. 1974. The evolution of social behavior. Annu. Rev. Systematics **5:** 325–383.
26. ALEXANDER, R.D. 1975. The search for a general theory of behavior. Behav. Sci. **20:** 77–100.
27. HAMILTON, W.D. 1975. Innate social aptitudes of man: an approach from evolutionary genetics. *In* Biosocial Anthropology. R. Fox, Ed.: 133–155. Wiley. New York.
28. ALEXANDER, R.D. 1979. Darwinism and Human Affairs. University of Washington Press. Seattle, WA.
29. VAN DEN BERGHE, P. 1981. The Ethnic Phenomenon. Elsevier. New York.
30. WILLIAMS, G.C. 1975. Sex and Evolution. Princeton University Press. Princeton, NJ.
31. BARTON, N.H. & B. CHARLESWORTH. 1998. Why sex and recombination. Science **281:** 1986–1990.
32. GEARY, D.C. 1998. Male, Female: The Evolution of Human Sex Differences. American Psychological Association. Washington, DC.
33. TRIVERS, R.L. 1985. Social Evolution. Benjamin/Cummings, Menlo Park, CA.
34. BUSS, D.M. 1989. Sex differences in human preferences: evolutionary hypotheses tested in 37 cultures. Behav. Brain Sci. **12:** 1–49.
35. MILLER, G. 1998. How mate choice shaped human nature: a review of sexual selection and human evolution. *In* Handbook of Evolutionary Psychology: Ideas, Issues, and Applications. C. Crawford & D.L. Krebs, Eds.: 87–130. Erlbaum Associates. Mahwah, NJ.
36. STRUM, S., D. FORSTER & E. HUTCHINS. 1997. Why Machiavellian intelligence may not be Machiavellian. *In* Machiavellian Intelligence II: Extensions and Evaluations. A. Whiten & R.W. Byrne, Eds.: 50–85. Cambridge University Press. Cambridge, England.
37. HUMPHREY, N.K. 1976. The Social Function of Intellect. *In* Growing Points in Ethology. P.P.G. Bateson & R.A. Hinde, Eds.: 303–318. Cambridge University Press. Cambridge, England.
38. HUMPHREY, N.K. 1983. Consciousness Regained: Chapters in the Development of Mind. Oxford University Press. Oxford, England.
39. BYRNE, R. & A. WHITEN. 1988. Machiavellian Intelligence: Social Expertise and the Evolution of Intellect in Monkeys, Apes, and Humans. Oxford University Press. Oxford, England.
40. WHITEN, A. & R. BYRNE. 1997. Machiavellian Intelligence II: Extensions and Evaluations. Cambridge University Press. Cambridge, England.
41. DAWKINS, R. 1989. The Selfish Gene, 2nd ed. Oxford University Press. New York.
42. TRIVERS, R.L. 1971. The evolution of reciprocal altruism. Q. Rev. Biol. **46:** 35–37.
43. BROWN, D.E. 1991. Human Universals. McGraw-Hill. New York.
44. MCGUIRE, M.T. 1992. Moralistic aggression, processing mechanisms, and the brain: biological foundations of the sense of justice. *In* The Sense of Justice: Biological Foundations of Law. R.D. Masters & M. Gruter, Eds.: 67–92. Sage Publications. Newbury Park, CA.
45. DE WAAL, F.B.M. 1992. The chimpanzee's sense of social regularity and its relation to the human sense of justice. *In* The Sense of Justice: Biological Foundations of Law. R.D. Masters & M. Gruter, Eds.: 241–255. Sage Publications. Newbury Park, CA.
46. CHANCE, M.R.A. 1967. Attention structure as the basis of primate social rank. Man **2:** 503–518;
47. CHANCE, M.R.A. & R.R. LARSEN, Eds. 1976. The Social Structure of Attention. Wiley. London.
48. BARKOW, J.H. 1976. Attention structure and the evolution of human psychological characteristics. *In* The Social Structure of Attention. M. R. A. Chance & R. R. Larsen, Eds.: 203–220. Wiley. London.
49. BOYD, R. & P.J. RICHERSON. 1995. Why does culture increase human adaptability? Ethol. Sociobiol. **16:** 125–143.
50. BOYD, R. & P.J. RICHERSON. 1985. Culture and the Evolutionary Process. University of Chicago Press. Chicago, IL.

51. ROZIN, P. 1987. Psychobiological perspectives on food preferences and avoidances. *In* Food and Evolution: Toward a Theory of Human Food Habits. M. Harris & E. B. Ross, Eds.: 181-205. Temple University Press. Philadelphia, PA.
52. GIBSON, K.R. 1996. The biocultural human brain: seasonal migrations and the emergence of the Upper Palaeolithic. *In* Modelling the Early Human Mind. P. Mellars & K. R. Gibson, Eds.: 33–46. Cambridge University Press. Cambridge, England.
53. WILSON, D.S. & E. SOBER. 1994. Reintroducing group selection to the human behavioral sciences. Behav. Brain Sci. **17:** 585–654.
54. SOBER, E. & D.S. WILSON. 1998. Unto Others: The Evolution and Psychology of Unselfish Behavior. Harvard University Press. Cambridge, MA.
55. ORIANS, G.H. & J.H. HEERWAGEN. 1992. Evolved responses to landscapes. *In* The Adapted Mind: Evolutionary Psychology and the Generation of Culture. J.H.Barkow, L. Cosmides & J. Tooby, Eds.: 555–579. Oxford University Press. New York.
56. DAWKINS, R. 1996. Climbing Mount Improbable. :284. Norton. New York.

Freud: The First Evolutionary Psychologist?

DORI LECROY

Department of Psychology, Hunter College of CUNY, New York, New York 10021, USA

ABSTRACT: An evolutionary perspective on attachment theory and psychoanalytic theory brings these two fields together in interesting ways. Application of the evolutionary principle of parent-offspring conflict to attachment theory suggests that attachment styles represent context-sensitive, evolved (adaptive) behaviors. In addition, an emphasis on offspring counter-strategies to adult reproductive strategies leads to consideration of attachment styles as overt manifestations of psychodynamic mediating processes, including the defense mechanisms of repression and reaction formation.

INTRODUCTION

Evolutionary psychology posits the existence of species-typical psychological mechanisms in humans. So does psychoanalytic theory. This paper will argue that these two fields may, in part, be talking about the same constructs. Freud's concept of defense mechanisms, repression in particular, will be examined in the context of the evolutionary principle of parent-offspring conflict theory.[1] I will suggest that an evolutionary analysis of attachment theory, applying the concept of parent-offspring conflict, will link it to psychoanalytic theory.

Psychoanalytic theorists speak of *defense mechanisms*, and evolutionary psychologists refer to *evolved adaptive mechanisms*. That both use the word "mechanism" may be more than a semantic coincidence. When used in the Darwinian sense, it refers to *behavioral* tendencies, mediated by emotive and cognitive underpinnings, which were honed by natural selection to meet adaptive challenges during our evolutionary past. In the psychoanalytic sense, it refers to the organization of perceptions, thoughts, and feelings for the minimization of painful affect. It refers to *intrapsychic* processes.

The only causal process capable of producing complex physiological or psychological mechanisms is natural selection.[2] From this we conclude that something as complex as Freud's psychodynamic mechanisms could only have arisen by natural selection, and they could only have arisen if they served inclusive fitness as well as subjective comfort. This leads to the question: Are psychodynamic mechanisms actually evolved adaptive mechanisms?

Several authors suggest that they are. Leak and Christopher[3] argue that the id, ego, and superego are evolutionarily sound divisions of personality, as are the concepts of the unconscious and defense mechanisms. Nesse and Lloyd[4] come to similar conclusions as they examine repression, the defenses, and mental conflict. Badcock[5] also finds evolutionary value for psychoanalytic concepts. In addition, Slavin and Kriegman[6] connect evolutionary psychological concepts with Freud's legacy in contemporary psychoanalytic and related schools of thought. To argue that psychodynamic mechanisms, originally considered to be completely intrapsychic processes, are candidates for mechanisms in the Darwinian sense, it must be shown that they have overt manifestations that foster survival and reproduction.

DEFENSE MECHANISMS AS ADAPTATIONS

Freud posited an array of defense mechanisms, among them projection, denial, rationalization, regression, splitting, and reaction formation. All of these work by systematically distorting information so that one perception is held in consciousness while another is repressed and stored outside of awareness in a construct called the unconscious. Many theorists believe that all normal human functioning entails various degrees and combinations of such mechanisms with disorders representing sustained exaggerated versions. What this all means, of course, is that we all operate within one degree or another of self-deception as described by Robert Trivers.[7] Because his is an evolutionary account, he discusses the social advantages of distorted information-processing. Similarly, the following suggests that Freud's defense mechanisms are adaptive behavioral mechanisms in the Darwinian sense.

Projection

The classic example of projection is the case of the individual whose public contempt for homosexuality arises out of reaction to his own unconsciously perceived, and disapproved, homosexual feelings. By his projection of homosexuality outside himself he is self-deceiving and avoiding painful anxiety and shame. But the Darwinian view of self-deception is that it is in the service of deceiving others. Hence, projection, from an evolutionary perspective, is a socially beneficial advertisement of (false) "virtue" through public proclamations of another's guilt to divert attention from one's own.

Identification

In the psychoanalytic sense, identification describes processes where an individual integrates (introjects) aspects of another's personality. One variety of it is in "identification with the aggressor." This occurs when a victim of mistreatment mitigates the intensity of distress by identifying with the actions of the mistreating individual. This is a "kick the dog" scenario. You feel kicked around at work so you come home and kick the dog. This is considered a defense in that it lowers distress because there is comfort in knowing one can be the kicker as well as the "kicked." But from a Darwinian perspective, identification with the aggressor may be seen as a mechanism that encourages submission to others when it is strategically advantageous to be a follower rather than waste energy on futile clamoring for higher status.

Regression

Regression is a process in which one returns to a level of reduced autonomy and competence. Periods of minor regression from a psychoanalytic viewpoint are times of intrapsychic reorganization perhaps triggered by disappointed expectations. More extreme or pathologic degrees result from trauma or a pervasive sense of inadequacy or other feelings of helplessness and hopelessness. Regression in this view is a form of taking cover in a less anxiety-evoking level of functioning. It is, however, a social as well a personal act, and may be effective in soliciting goods and services. A recent analysis suggesting that the reduced functioning, symptomatic of postpartum depression, is an example of this.[8] Thus, a Darwinian view is that this may be the advantage that selected for regression rather than psychic relief.

Repression

The capacity to retain information but in a way unavailable to conscious consideration is termed repression. It is another defense mechanism, and it is considered to be operating as fundamental to the other defense mechanisms as well. This will be explored in some detail later.

The above are some examples of how the intrapsychic processes posited by psychoanalytic theory as anxiety-management mechanisms may be reinterpreted as mechanisms that mediate social functions. Freud emphasized psychic relief as the function of defense mechanisms rather than social advantage. An evolutionary view would be that varieties of psychic discomfort are both internal signals that circumstances are not serving one's fitness and motivators of adaptive behavior.

DEFENSE MECHANSMS AND PARENT-OFFSPRING CONFLICT THEORY

Freud saw the beginnings of psychodynamic processes in infancy. This assumption can be supported by the evolutionary theory of parent-offspring conflict by demonstrating that the defense mechanisms are psychological processes favored by natural selection because they mediate adaptive coping strategies starting in early life. It is easy for us to accept that natural selection favored maternal care of young. But we can also see that under conditions where resources must be carefully husbanded (as was likely the case for much of hominid evolutionary history) minimizing maternal investment in certain offspring might also be adaptive.[8] This would be the case for a sickly infant, or when a birth occurs too close to a previous one, the mother's health is poor, social support lacking, resources are particularly scarce, or any time when sacrificing one offspring to increase investment in its siblings serves parental inclusive fitness. There is considerable evidence for assuming that neglect, abandonment, and outright killing of offspring has a long history. From her studies of maternal psychology, Janet Mann[9] concludes that prevailing social and psychological circumstances have a powerful effect upon decisions about investment in particular offspring.

Offspring are a big investment for the human female: nine months of pregnancy, several years of breast-feeding (certainly for our hominid ancestors), and many more of nurture advance each conception into a viable descendant. Since under certain adverse conditions maternal commitment to some infants would constitute a net lifetime reproductive loss, natural selection should have favored individuals able to cut their losses. There are frequent news reports of babies killed by parents or found abandoned, alive or dead. In the majority of cases, the mothers of these children are single and without resources. Are they responding to an evolved mechanism activated by an assessment of unpromising reproductive circumstances and capable of overriding the mechanisms of maternal devotion? If they are, by the same rules, the demands of the inclusive fitness principle that fosters a mother's capacity to withhold investment in a particular offspring also demands equipping offspring with their own strategies to counter suboptimal parenting.

It may even be that prevalence of infanticide during hominid evolution served to foster an innate suspicion about parental intentions in young minds. At least one clinician believes that she routinely finds an unconscious fear of infanticide in her child patients. Dorothy Bloch[10] has concluded that children are universally predisposed to a fear of infanticide and any violence that they witness whether toward them or another activates this fear. Dr. Bloch remarks that, since fear of infanticide comes up so often in her work with children, she is left with a choice between believing that the children's parents actually do have infanticidal thoughts and occasionally show signs of them, or that children come equipped with this specific fear at the ready. She chooses the latter because it is more "palatable," but application of the principle of parent-offspring theory suggests the conclusion that both may be true.

However, whether infanticide is a possibility installed into the minds of children or not, maternal attention is variable and children are well known to play an active role in acquiring it. The infant cry is an example of a nurture-gaining tactic. Where maternal attention is hard-won, natural selection may well have supported more complicated offspring counter-strategies to parental reproductive strategies expressed as suboptimal parenting.

ATTACHMENT AND PARENT-OFFSPRING CONFLICT THEORY

Current versions of attachment theory that incorporate evolutionary principles, seem to be the most promising link between evolutionary thought and psychodynamic theory because they can connect the latter with the experimental disciplines in psychology. The emphasis needed to forge this link is a more emphatic application of parent-offspring conflict theory to the study of attachment. This would bring the counter-strategies of offspring into greater focus.

Aspects of offspring counter-strategies may be the varieties of behaviors that attachment theorists designate as secure and avoidant/insecure and resistant/insecure. These are behavior patterns that are systematically traceable to the quality of early parental care. Part of this categorization of infants is based on their reaction to separation from their mother. Secure infants may or may not be mildly distressed upon separation, and they show pleasure at reuniting with the parent. They have parents who readily respond to their needs. Infants with avoidant type insecurity show neither distress when separated from, or pleasure when reunited with, the mother. Their parents are consistently unresponsive to them. Insecure/resistant types of children are associated with unpredictable parents and are very upset upon separation and generally cling to their mothers.

Application of the evolutionary principle of parent-offspring conflict suggests that these patterns of behavior make sense as strategies for attaining resources. In particular, the avoidant/insecure attachment may represent low expectations of nurture from parents and reduction of wasted effort by continuing to make appeals in that direction, and the resistant/insecure type may be an adaptive parent-centered strategy.

Yet attachment theorists, even those with an evolutionary perspective, do not emphasize the varieties of attachment as coping strategies during childhood, but stress their adaptive value during later reproductive life. They point out that the style of attachment during early life is correlated with that of later life, particularly as it is manifested in the nature of male-female pair-bonds, short-term and exploitative, or enduring and mutualistic. For example, Jay Belsky[11] acknowledges that attachment in the generic sense would have evolved to emotionally connect mothers and infants, but fails to distinguish separate infant coping functions for the different types. He goes on to state that "...the attachment system evolved as an environmentally contingent mechanism for promoting reproductive fitness in adulthood...."[11] (p. 364) He does suggest that the varieties of insecurity may be specific to local conditions and that, for example, responses to "...inconsistently responsive parental care evolved as a means of fostering indirectly reproductive "helper at the nest" behavior."[11] (p. 373) But even here he is focused on parental interests and does not refer to offspring counter-strategies. In spite of this focus on the reproductive adult, the current evolutionary perspective on attachment is leading in interesting directions.

Evidence for an adaptive function for attachment styles is that they are intergenerationally transmitted, environmentally sensitive, adaptive cultural patterns. Cross-cultural studies indicate that secure and insecure attachment styles that influence the nature of the male-female pair-bond are correlated with the reliability of resources.[12] The first is represented by long-term and cooperative type male-female relationships and are commonly found where the efforts of both parents are needed to provide for young. The insecure attachment style is reflected in the more fleeting relationships that prevail in groups where resources are more accessible to mothers who can manage more or less without mate participation. With this range in the degree of paternal participation, degrees of father-absence or father-presence is a variable in young lives. An analysis of differences in cultures where fathers eat and sleep with mothers compared with where they do not revealed several correlates.

In father-absent societies one is apt to find local warfare and raiding in order to capture women, hostile or avoidant relations between men and women, and aggressive, competitive ones between men. In addition, women engage in sexual activity earlier, and with less discrimination, than they do in father-present cultures, and maternal interest tends to wane with weaning. Children are typically left in the care of older siblings, or fostered out when the mother takes a new mate. Things are generally more peaceable in father-present groups and both parents take a longer term interest in offspring. They engage in a quality-over-quantity strategy for parental investment.

A very interesting point is that the relationship between father-absence or -presence and reproductive style, along with attendant expressions of attitude and temperament, is not merely a cultural-level phenomenon, for it still holds true for individual cases where the condition is not normal for the culture. Hence the cues that bias one toward reproductive styles and attendant personality characteristics don't appear to rely on culture-wide features so much as more local intra-family cues.

There is speculation about what might be the mediating factors in the intergenerational transmission of attachment style. Since enduring pair-bonds are typified by father-involvement and short-term ones by his absence. Draper and Harpender[13] make the case that father-presence or -absence during childhood is not merely a correlate to reproductive style, but *the* influential stimulus that shunts individual development toward one or another style. However, this "black box" imprinting model again ignores a role for coping strategies in attachment style in childhood.

With a shift in emphasis, we can consider that attachment style may be adaptive in childhood for the same reasons that it is adaptive for the reproducing adult because it is formed during early life in response to the same challenges of concern to adults: that of attaining resources. This suggests a concordance between the availability of resources for the young and for the mature. I suggest that this concordance is due to the fact that reproductive strategies are linked to ecological conditions, and parental attitudes in terms of responsiveness to offspring are linked to reproductive strategies. Thus the emotional resources available to children reflect the ecological realities confronting their parents, and which they themselves will face when they reach reproductive age. Since ecological realities are reflected in the pair-bond status of mothers, they would be correlated with father-presence or -absence. But their influence may be the way they have an impact upon the emotional environment of the family, rather than as a cue, in the sense of an imprinting model.

In support of the point that it is not father-presence or -absence *per se* that acts as a stimulus for attachment style, but rather the emotional field around this figure, is the finding that the sexual behavior of daughters of widows is more like that found in father-present homes than is that of daughters of divorced women.[14] This may be explained by a tendency for widowed mothers to refer to the father often, and in positive terms, and divorced ones less often and in negative terms. In addition, even with father-absence, individuals with a high measured I.Q. seem biased toward an offspring-investment strategy, and so does perception of upward mobility, perhaps not unrelated effects. Social controls such as religious and secular influences also promote this shift in reproductive strategy.[15]

These exceptions lead to consideration of alternatives to the imprinting model for the causative factors for the various attachment styles, specifically to consider other details of the environment within the family, particularly the way the parent-offspring interactions that reflect attachment style influence emotional and cognitive structures.

INTRAPSYCHIC PROCESSES

Attachment theorists have designated the terms *secure* and *insecure* to identify the classes of behavior they observe. However these are attitudinal terms, not behavioral ones. And quite rightly so, for they refer to emotional and cognitive underpinnings to biases in perceiving and interpreting information that results in the ordering of behavior in children and adults. If these behaviors are adaptive, and were shaped by natural selection, then the mediating attitudes must have been as well, however indirectly. This presumes the existence of influences that set up attitudinal biases, during early life, rather than produce inclinations toward particular behaviors.

The choice of these terms, *secure* and *insecure*, indicates implicit acceptance by attachment theorists. However, in not emphasizing the adaptive nature of attachment style during early life, the attachment theorists do not emphasize identification of the circumstances that are concordant during youth and adulthood. An analysis with this in mind would identify factors whose existence has two effects: one that influences the development of secure or insecure attitudes that are adaptive during early life, and another that also makes these same attitudes adaptive in later life.

I suggest that application of the evolutionary principle of parent-offspring conflict theory will emphasize this concordance. Parental interest is in distributing resources so as to raise as many reproductively viable offspring as possible, and offspring interest is in exaggerating need and getting more than a parent willingly offers. This puts parents and offspring in a conflict, one that will intensify as resources become more limited. It was mentioned above that one of the insecure attachment styles acquired during infancy could lead to an eventual "helper at the nest" reproductive strategy. This is a term used most often for birds and refers to dispersal patterns. In rich habitats, the inclusive fitness of young birds might be served by remaining in the natal territory for a while and helping with siblings. In less promising habitats, they do better by leaving.[16] For humans it similarly refers to situations where, rather than pursuing one's own reproductive interest, an individual cares for siblings or otherwise assists the parent. Also, as with birds, and as described above, reproductive style is sensitive to features of the habitat (resource availability). However, human relationships, those between adults and those between parents and young, are mediated by complicated psychological processes, both secure and insecure ones, to use attachment theory terminology, and it is within these that the individual interests of both the young and mature are negotiated.

The details of these psychological processes, I argue, are the attitudes correlated with reproductive style, and also represent the action of defense mechanisms described by Freud. The example I will explore is the insecure-resistant attachment style, and the supposition that it can generate a helper-at-the-nest reproductive strategy.

PSYCHODYNAMICS AS ADAPTIVE MECHANISMS

Freud's idea of the function of infantile psychodynamic processes was mediation between the inborn drives (of the id) and social expectations. It is an intrapsychic conflict model, but a little retooling can fit it into the theory of parent-offspring conflict. If maternal reproductive strategies include decisions that can result in the neglect or elimination of ill-timed offspring, then natural selection would have encouraged offspring behavior which could tip the balance toward personal survival. This would comprise behavioral strategies emerging from the psychological organization of the variable experiences of satisfaction or frustration of needs and desires by caretakers (usually the mother). Fundamental to these strategies would be the Freudian concept of repression.

Displays of distress and anger are the usual ploys of frustrated children. They work to gain resources from parents. However, in the presence of a doubtfully committed parent these demanding tactics may prove maladaptive. But complete elimination of these responses would also prove maladaptive because in general social interactions they are useful in inhibiting exploitation in reciprocal exchanges or other kinds of mistreatment. Thus repression, in the psychoanalytic sense, may have been natural selection's "solution." Repression of certain emotional reactions to a parent's ambivalence, and even the perception of it, would promote strategically advantageous behavior otherwise impossible.

An evolutionary interpretation of repression suggests that it is an evolved mechanism of self-deception that promotes the deception of others[7]. He who believes his own lie is a more convincing liar. However, self-deception need not be limited to one's own motivation; one can equally well benefit from deceiving oneself about another's intentions.[4] Conscious awareness of another's treachery may not always be wise, for it might show. If the other is vitally needed, as a parent is for a child, repression of knowledge of another's true intentions may prove adaptive.

Children in need of continued nurture by unsatisfactory parents cannot afford to antagonize them and would benefit from behaving in a manner that solicits vital care instead. Psychological disconnection from grief and rage, or repression, permits the deployment of other behaviors that can better seduce parents into increased nurture. Attachment studies have found that instead of showing anger and resentment, the children of inconsistently responsive parents remain close to them and seek nurture by other means. These include, as has been suggested, a solicitous attitude that reduces their cost to parents. In this way, taking care of siblings or employing other helping behaviors results in acquisition of resources not otherwise forthcoming. This scenario would require repression of negative feelings about, and knowledge of, suboptimal parenting. Repression also explains why abused children tend to defend abusing parents and when removed from them cry to be returned.

That disturbing feelings become repressed is a basic assumption in psychoanalytic thought. As with all defense mechanisms their function is considered to be the reduction of psychological pain, fear, guilt, shame, and associated anxiety. But they might also adaptively structure behavior in social interactions, an important point not usually considered by psychoanalytic thinkers. In the face of suboptimal parenting, a child, instead of expressing disappointment, grief, resentment, or even suspicion concerning the mother's attitude, might adopt a less demanding and more solicitous role and thereby gain vital nurture. This tactic entails not only Freud's concept of repression, but another mechanism as well: reaction formation, defined as the display of behavior reflecting sentiments opposite to the repressed ones. Clinicians frequently discover such conflicts of sentiment about parents during psychotherapy.

In summary, the foregoing is an example of how the defense mechanisms, and all they imply in terms of the intrapsychic structures and processes of what has been metaphorically called the unconscious, can be reinterpreted as inclusive fitness strategies. It also shows how these mechanisms may function to deal with the vicissitudes of parenting encountered in early life. It does so by unifying aspects of attachment theory with the evolutionary principle of parent-offspring conflict theory and the integration of intrapsychic processes as described by psychoanalytic theory.

CONCLUSION

There is a huge body of psychoanalytic thought, albeit quite disparate, but with little communication between the different schools. However, each of their respective theories reflect decades of consideration. An evolutionary perspective, I believe, would unify the various drive, ego, self, and object threads of psychodynamic thinking and also link them to the experimental biosciences. Further, I believe we can expect to find that the storage and organization of information outside of awareness, or in what Freud called the unconscious, may operate by certain rules (defense mechanisms) that foster adaptive behavior.

In light of the current understanding that natural selection is the only cause that can bring about complex adaptive behaviors, it seems time for this kind of examination of psychoanalytic thinking. Such consideration of a Freudian approach would not only be an intellectually exciting project, but may prove widely useful, as some therapists are already finding with the integration of adaptationist thinking into their psychotherapeutic practices. An evolutionary view of the imperfect overlap of genetic interest between family members brings a whole new meaning to family strife. One of the participants in this colloquium, a happily married young father, spoke of the temptations that threaten the stability of family life, and he emphatically stated more than once, "I don't trust my genes for one minute!"

REFERENCES

1. Trivers, R. 1974. Parent-offspring conflict. Am. Zool. **14:** 249–264.
2. Buss, D.M. 1995. Evolutionary psychology: a new paradigm for psychological science. Psychol. Inquiry **6(1):** 1-30.
3. Leak, G.K. & S.B. Christopher. 1982. Freudian psychoanalysis and sociobiology: a synthesis. Am. Psychol. **37(3):** 313–322.
4. Nesse, R. & A.T. Lloyd. 1992. The Evolution of Psychodynamic Mechanisms. *In* The Adapted Mind. J.H. Barkow, L. Cosmides & J. Tooby, Eds. Oxford University Press. New York.
5. Badcock, C. 1998. PsychoDarwinism: the new synthesis of Darwin and Freud. *In* Handbook of Evolutionary Psychology. C. Crawford & D. Krebs, Eds. Erlbaum Associates. Mahwah, NJ.
6. Slavin, M.O. & D. Kriegman. 1992. The Adaptive Design of the Human Psyche: Psychoanalysis, Evolutionary Biology, and the Therapeutic Process. The Guilford Press. New York.
7. Trivers, R. 2000. The elements of a scientific theory of self-deception. Ann. N.Y. Acad. Sci. **907:** xxx [this volume].
8. Hagen, E.E. 1999. The functions of postpartum depression. Evol. Hum. Behav. **20(5):** 325–359.
9. Mann, J. 1992. Nurture or negligence: maternal psychology and behavioral preference among preterm twins. *In* The Adapted Mind. J.H. Barkow, L. Cosmides & J. Tooby, Eds. Oxford University Press. New York.
10. Bloch, D. 1978. So the Witch Won't Eat Me. Grove Press. New York.
11. Belsky, J. 1997. Attachment, mating and parenting: an evolutionary interpretation. Hum. Nature **8(4):** 361–381.
12. Goldberg, S. 1997. Attachment and childhood behavior problems in normal, at risk and clinical samples. *In* Attachment and Psychopathology. L. Atkinson & D.J. Zucker, Eds. Guilford Press, New York.
13. Draper, P. & H. Harpending. 1988. A sociobiological perspective on the development of human reproductive strategies. *In* Sociobiological Perspectives on Human Development. K. MacDonald, Ed. Springer-Verlag. New York, NY.
14. Blain, J. & J. Barkow. 1988. Father involvement, reproductive strategies and the sensitive period. *In* Sociobiological Perspectives on Human Development. K. MacDonald, Ed. Springer-Verlag. New York.
15. MacDonald, K. 1997. Life history theory and human reproductive behavior: environmental/contextual influences and heritable variation. Hum. Nature **8(4):** 327–359.
16. Alcock, J. 1998. Animal Behavior. An Evolutionary Approach, 6th ed. Sinauer. Sunderland, MA.

Female Reproductive Strategies as Social Organizers

DIANA PRASCHNIK-BUCHMAN[a]

Hunter College of CUNY, New York 10021, USA

ABSTRACT: When male philopatry is linked to patriarchy, it is often assumed that female reproductive strategies are secondary to male reproductive strategies. By comparing the social structures of chimpanzees (*Pan troglodytes*) and bonobos (*Pan paniscus*) with those of other non-human primates, I argue that female reproductive strategies can be viewed as primary principles of social organization, including the establishment of patriarchies through differential investment in offspring. Emphasis on the contributions of female reproductive strategies may lead to a different picture of the evolution of primate social organization.

It is often assumed that among group-living primates, male reproductive strategies constitute the chief group organizing principle, with female reproductive strategies considered as counter-strategies. However, it could be considered that primate social organization, even the most patriarchal variety, reflects female strategy at least as much as it does that of the male.

I suggest that females can be seen as primary organizing movers in primate social structures. Specifically, I will outline why social bonds may be seen as serving female strategies that optimize reproductive success by various means, including the setting up of patriarchies by differentially investing in male offspring. This argument will be supported by describing the social systems of Old World monkeys and those of our closest relatives the "common" chimpanzee and bonobo (*Pan troglodytes* and *Pan paniscus,* respectively) as reflections of female reproductive strategies.

Central to my argument for female influence on social systems is differential parental investment. Robert Trivers[1] defines parental investment as "any investment by the parent in an individual offspring that increases the offspring's chance of surviving" and hence the parent's reproductive success. Among primates, females are the higher-investing sex and show smaller variations in the number of offspring produced compared to males, who can produce a great many or none at all due to competition from other males. Based on this, it has been theorized that when resources are sufficient, a female will invest more in her male offspring than in her female offspring to guarantee the greatest number of grandchildren. The pay-off of this strategy is sufficient to offset the fact that males generally take a longer period of investment before reaching reproductive maturity.[2] When resources are insufficient, a female will differentially invest in female offspring.[3] These predictions have been tested and upheld in prosimian primates (*Galago crassicaudatus*),[4] red deer (*Cervus*

[a]Address for correspondence: 14 Butler Place #85, Brooklyn, New York 11238, USA.

elaphus),[5] red cockaded woodpeckers (*Picoides borealis*),[6] and the spotted hyena (*Crocuta crocuta*).[7]

However, the patterns of investment strategies in the preponderance of Old World monkeys are not entirely consistent with these predictions. Although dominance is always correlated with greater access to resources, studies have found correlations between maternal rank and differential investment in male offspring, between maternal rank and differential investment in female offspring, and also, no correlation between maternal rank and investment in offspring (reviewed in Ref. 8). What is nearly uniform about Old World monkeys is that their groups consist of related females who remain together from birth, with natal males transferring out, and breeding males coming in from other groups.[9]

Wrangham[10] suggests that female philopatry and female-bondedness evolved through competition for high-quality, patchy feeding sites that groups could better defend, and that forming these groups with related members would be favored because of kin selection. In addition, females will preferentially bond with other females because bands of females are sufficient for protection, whereas males, who are larger in body size, would increase feeding competition without adding benefit.[9] So for ecological reasons, female philopatry prevails and can be considered at least as much a female reproductive strategy as that of males, if not more so, even though males are dominant in individual interactions. Thus this strategy serving female interests can be considered a fundamental aspect of social organization. Further female reproductive strategies in Old World monkeys proceed within this constraint of female philopatry and feature differential investment in offspring.

Clark's[4] Local Resource Competition model states that mothers try to minimize competition between themselves and their mature and reproducing offspring for food and that this affects their investment strategy. If resources are limiting to a female, as is the case for lower-status individuals, she will preferentially invest in male offspring who will leave the group and whose reproductive success is not as closely linked to this limiting resource. This theory, along with Wrangham's philopatry theory, is used to explain the variability of investment strategies found among Old World monkeys.[11]

To summarize, philopatry and social bonds may be considered a direct result of female reproductive strategies, and thus female reproductive interests may be central in the evolution of social structures. This remains true even in male-philopatric species.

Although not as universal as once thought, male philopatry prevails in humans, chimps, and bonobos (*Homo sapiens, Pan troglodytes,* and *Pan paniscus,* respectively). Male philopatry is usually defined as "males forging alliances with locally available males (usually kin) to patrol access to females in a community, protecting these females and their offspring from males in neighboring communities."[11] In this definition, male philopatry is considered the result of male reproductive strategies. This, too, might be considered a reflection of female reproductive strategy, specifically as resulting from the preferential investment of mothers in male offspring.

The closest living relatives to humans, the "common" chimpanzee and bonobo (*Pan troglodytes* and *Pan paniscus,* respectively) are typically male-philopatric. Both these species "tend to associate in large communities containing anywhere from around 20 to over 100 individuals consisting of smaller temporary parties that last from a few minutes to several days and vary in size from 1 to 77."[12] Both groups are also characterized by sociable adult males who form temporary alliances to compete for status and resources. Despite these commonalities, their social systems differ dramatically when it comes to interactions between intra-group females. Chimpanzee females rarely interact with one another.[13] In contrast, bonobo females form non-kin associations among which are dominant matriarchs and newly entering females.[14] Another difference is that in chimpanzees all mature males are dominant to all females,[12] while the dominance hierarchy among bonobos is integrated with a female matriarch as most dominant animal and with her son's dominance rank closely associated with hers.[15,16]

As stated before, the evolution of male philopatry is usually attributed to strategies that primarily facilitate male reproduction. Wrangham[13] (p. 365) theorizes that male chimpanzees form alliances "in an attempt to defend access to females from extra-group males." He believes that for chimpanzees food patches are distributed in such a way that females must minimize feeding competition to maintain a high fertility rate, so female grouping is minimal. In bonobos, the less patchy nature of food sources permits females to aggregate and form social alliances, but Wrangham hypothesizes that they do so because a group of females is more effective in attracting groups of bonded males. Thus he considers female grouping in bonobos as a counter-strategy to male reproductive strategies.

But, here, too, the evolution of male philopatry, usually thought a primary social organizer resulting from male reproductive strategy, can be reformulated into a female reproductive strategy by application of the theory of differential investment in offspring. Preferential female investment in male offspring may be instrumental in leading males to remain in their natal group and female offspring to leave. Behavioral observations of chimpanzees and bonobos show that the most stable social relationships are between mothers and male offspring.[14,16,17] In chimpanzees "the only long-term party is a mother with her dependent offspring."[12] (p. 167) Even as adults, sons continue to travel with their mothers and have long grooming bouts.[9] Wrangham's ecological model[13] predicts that the closest associations should be between either maternally related males or males and sexually receptive females. In actuality, males and unrelated females (whether sexually receptive or not) were found to have the least amount of associations of all dyad types both for bonobos and chimpanzees.[14,16] Male–male alliances in chimpanzees, which are key in determining dominance and access to resources such as estrous females, are, in contrast to mother–son relationships, opportunistic and transitory.[16]

It has been hypothesized that in bonobos, females form bonds to reduce the cost of transfer from the natal territory and reduce inter-birth intervals, two key factors limiting reproductive success in females.[18] The key argument against this hypothesis is that "it relies on the evolution of cooperation through mutualism or reciprocal altruism," and "inclusive fitness is a more stable and reliable (evolutionary strategy)."[18] (pp. 87–99) When male philopatry is viewed as a form of maternal investment, this phenomenon can be explained in terms of inclusive fitness. Since the environment allows for female aggregation, mothers would benefit from these relationships with unrelated females if these females mate with their sons and produce their grandchildren. This has been supported by behavioral observations.[19] Hence the female–female relationship that is characteristic of the bonobos and distinguishes bonobo society from chimpanzees may be seen as a secondary reproductive strategy to differential investment in offspring, where matriarchal mothers try to maximize reproductive success through inclusive fitness.

While feeding competition in chimpanzees tends to prevent females from aggregating, some daughters do remain and breed in their natal communities. In territories that are resource-rich "mothers and daughters traveled together frequently and supported each other in interactions with others."[13] (p. 358) These philopatric females breed at an earlier age, produce offspring after shorter intervals, and produce offspring with higher survival rates,[20] supporting Parish's hypothesis. It might be asked why matriarchal daughters transfer when bonobo ecology permits females to aggregate. The ultimate causation may be attributed to inbreeding avoidance; however, a proximate mechanisms could be due to social interactions between mother and daughter. This speculation might be addressed in further research.

Hrdy [this volume, p. 75] reviews ideas about the social organization of our early hominid ancestors and the diversity of social systems found in human culture. In the eagerness of researchers to link male philopatry to patriarchy, there is an assumption that female reproductive strategies are counter-strategies to purportedly primary male reproductive strategies. However, when the emphasis is reversed, a different picture of evolutionary history can emerge. Patriarchal social systems evolving over the course of primate evolution. as Hrdy[21] suggests. might have their origins in female reproductive strategies.

REFERENCES

1. Trivers, R.L. 1972. Parental investment and sexual selection. *In* Sexual Selection and the Descent of Man. B. Campbell, Ed.: 136–179. Aldine. Chicago, IL.
2. Clutton-Brock, T. 1991 The Evolution of Parental Care. Princeton University Press. Princeton, NJ.
3. Trivers, R.L. & Willard, D. 1973. Natural selection of parent ability to vary the sex ratio of offspring. Science **179:** 90–92.
4. Clark, A. 1978. Sex ratio and local resource competition in a prosimian primate. Science **201:** 163–165.
5. Clutton-Brock, T., S.D. Albon & F.E. Guinness. 1984. Maternal dominance, breeding success, and birth sex ratios in red deer. Nature **308:** 358–360
6. Gowaty, P.A. 1993. Differential dispersal, local resource competition, and sex ratio variation in birds. Am. Naturalist **126:** 347–353.
7. Holekamp, K.E. & L. Smale. 1995. Rapid change in offspring sex ratios after clan fission in the spotted hyena. Am. Naturalist **145:** 261–278.
8. Van Schaik, C. & S.B. Hrdy. 1991. Intensity of local resource competition shapes the relationship between maternal rank and sex ratios at birth in cercopithecine primates. Am. Naturalist **138:** 1555–1562.
9. Pusey, A.E. & C. Packer. 1987. Dispersal and Philopatry. *In* Primate Societies. B.B. Smuts, D.L. Cheney, R.M. Seyfarth, R.W. Wrangham & T.T. Struhsaker, Eds.: 250–266. University of Chicago Press. Chicago, IL.
10. Wrangham, R.W. 1980. An ecological model of female-bonded primate groups. Behavior **75:** 262–300.
11. Silk, J. 1983. Local resource competition and facultative adjustment of sex ratios in relation to competitive abilities. Am. Naturalist **121:** 56–66.
12. Nishida, T. & M. Hiraiwa-Hasegawa. 1987. Chimpanzees and bonobos: cooperative relationships among males. *In* Primate Societies. B.B. Smuts, D.L. Cheney, R.M. Seyfarth, R.W. Wrangham & T.T. Struhsaker. Eds.: 165–177. University of Chicago Press, Chicago, IL.
13. Wrangham, R.W. 1986. Ecology and Social Relationships in Two Species of Chimpanzee. *In* Ecology and Social Evolution: Birds and Mammals. D.I. Rubenstein & R.W. Wrangham, Eds.: 353–378. Princeton University Press. Princeton, NJ.

14. FURUICHI, T. 1989. Social interactions and the life history of female *Pan paniscus* in Wamba. Int. J. Primatol. **10:** 173–197.
15. HOBE, H. 1992. Male-male relationships among wild bonobos (*Pan paniscus*) at Wamba, Repblic of Zaire. Primates **33(2):** 163–179.
16. FURUICHI, T. & H. IHOBE. 1994. Variation in male relationships in bonobos and chimpanzees. Behaviour **130 (3-4):** 211–228.
17. GOODALL, J. 1968. The behavior of free-living chimpanzees in the Gombe Stream Reserve. Anim. Behav. Monog. **1:** 161–311.
18. PARISH, A.R. 1996. Female relationships in bonobos (*Pan paniscus*): evidence for bonding, cooperation, and female dominance in a male-philopatric species. Hum. Nature **7(1):** 61–96.
19. NISHIDA, T., H. TAKASAKI & Y. TAKAHATA. 1990. Demography and reproductive profiles. *In* The Chimpanzees of the Mahale Mountains: Sexual and Life History Strategies. T. Hishida, Ed.: 63–97. University of Tokyo Press. Tokyo, Japan.
20. PUSEY, A., J. WILLIAMS & J. GOODALL. 1997. The influence of dominance rank on the reproductive success of female chimpanzees. Science **277:** 828–831.
21. HRDY, S.B. 1997. Raising Darwin's consciousness: female sexuality and the prehominid origins of patriarchy. Hum. Nature **8(1):** 1–49.

Sex, Sex Differences, and Social Behavior

VITA CARULLI RABINOWITZ AND VIRGINIA VALIAN

Department of Psychology, Hunter College of CUNY, New York, New York 10021, USA
The Graduate Center of the City University of New York, New York, New York 10016, USA

ABSTRACT: Sex differences in social behavior are center stage in recent formulations of evolutionary psychology. Evolutionary psychology, with its emphasis on the long-term consequences of early adaptations, offers itself as an alternative meta-theory to mainstream social psychology, which emphasizes the importance of social structures in determining the existence and extent of social and cognitive sex differences. Using a range of examples, we argue that evolutionary psychology is open to criticism on several fronts: It does not (*a*) include a role for mediating and moderating variables or test predictions rigorously; (*b*) appreciate the importance of the difference between first- and second-order effects; (*c*) offer a truly interactionist theory; or (*d*) seriously consider the social implications of sex-based inequities. We also argue that social psychology has, in its turn, failed to appreciate the nonintuitive richness of some evolutionary hypotheses or that there is a role for evolutionary psychology in a genuinely interactionist theory This paper restates the need for that perspective, and suggests how it may be achieved.

Evolutionary psychology has set its sights on the mind, challenging classical psychological explanations of everything from mate selection to cognition. The "new" theoretical perspective offers evolutionarily sophisticated adaptationist alternatives to current situational, sociocultural, and developmental explanations. Some of the affected subfields seem not to know what has hit them, while other subfields have easily absorbed and reconstructed models of evolution that best suit their subject matter, and still others have warily resisted the most seemingly relevant aspects of evolutionary psychology.

Perhaps nowhere is the resistance more evident than in social psychology, the broad subfield of psychology most explicitly dedicated to understanding social behavior and social differences. The stakes are high in this clash of perspectives, because what hangs in the balance are prospects for reinventing phenomena as diverse as developmental trajectories, personalities, interpersonal relationships, and social policies and institutions. If ancient adaptations are the foundations of contemporary personal dispositions and societal structures, then the likelihood of significantly changing the fortunes of social groups appears diminished. If, on the other hand, contextual and cultural conditions are the crucial causal forces, then efforts at reform seem more likely to succeed.

Our own position, as sketched in this commentary, is that evolutionary psychology and social psychology make separate and distinct contributions to the understanding of the complexities of social interaction. Each has something to offer and each leaves some ground uncovered. Evolutionary explanations of behavior are not inherently incompatible with sociocultural ones even though they have often been cast and read that way. Social and evolutionary approaches would profit from engaging some of the other's theoretical, empirical, and societal concerns.

An important recent (1999) paper by Eagly and Wood[1] exemplifies some of the issues in the current debate. These authors reanalyzed the data of David Buss's 1989 study[2] in 37 cultures of the characteristics people desire in mates. Buss had found strong support for near-universal sex differences in the desire for physically attractive mates, for mates with high earning potential, and for age preferences. The major differences were in the direction predicted by the evolutionary theory of sexual selection, and were used to support the notion of sex-specific evolved psychological mechanisms (see Buss, this volume, p. 39).

Eagly and Wood confirmed Buss's basic findings, but also analyzed previously unreported data on the value placed on domestic work and correlated them with measures of gender equality in order to demonstrate the importance of social roles. They found that women's desire for older mates with high earning capacity and men's desire for younger mates (with good domestic skills) are moderately to strongly correlated with indices of gender equality in a society. Males' preference for physical attractiveness in mates, however, was unrelated to gender equality. While granting that their findings are not inconsistent with evolutionary psychology's program, Eagly and Wood argue that they are best explained by social-role theory, which states that the division of labor by sex within a society drives mate preferences. For example, in more equal societies, women don't need rich, older men to take care of them. Thus, some aspects of mate preference seem best explained by reference to social factors.

Via a comparative or between-groups approach, collapsing *across* cultures, Buss's 1989 data provided strong support for the evolutionary perspective; via a correlational approach that looked at relationships among variables *within* cultures, the same data set yielded strong support for a social-role perspective. There is indeed something here for everyone, which allows for endless debate. Only by examining a wide range of variables and measures will we be able to understand exactly *what* there is for everyone.

We opened with this example in part because it is the latest salvo in the gender difference wars, and in part because it reveals the general shape of debates about how to explain social behavior. Evolutionary theories look to the causal role of biological sex, whereas social theories look either to variables such as learning and cognitive processes that intervene between sex and behavior, or to the effects of other variables—new independent variables that may interact with sex. In doing so, the theories highlight different parts of a larger explanatory model and explain somewhat different phenomena.

Consider, for example, research on sex differences in jealousy. There are replicable sex differences in the triggers of sexual jealousy: women are more likely than men to report distress at emotional infidelity; men are more likely than women to be upset about sexual infidelity.[3] That difference follows from certain assumptions in evolutionary psychology. Finer-grained analyses, however, have measured the influence of other variables, especially the perception that one kind of infidelity implies the existence of the other (the "double shot" hypothesis of DeSteno and Salovey[4]). Sex covaries with the extent to which one kind of infidelity implies the other: for men more than women, a partner's sexual infidelity implies emotional commitment, whereas for women more than men, a partner's emotional infidelity means that sex is in the air. Most people choose as most distressing the type of infidelity that more implies the existence of the other. Thus, inference patterns that vary with sex appear to influence infidelity choice.[4,5] And, counter to what we might expect from the theory of parental investment and sexual selection, men are no more likely to be upset by sexual than emotional infidelity; instead, both are highly distressing to men.

The two types of explanations highlight different causal paths, and in so doing, illuminate different phenomena. One theory predicts sex differences in attitudes toward infidelity as a result of sexual selection pressures. Another theory predicts sex differences in the meaning attached to infidelity as a result of current sociocultural mores. What the two perspectives on sex differences in jealousy show us is just how much more there is to learn about it than either perspective alone would suggest.

In this paper, we offer an integrative explanatory model of sex differences that takes evolutionary and social factors into account and suggests how to conceptualize and study the many confounding variables that have plagued research in these programs. For illustrative purposes, we focus on the site regarded as evolutionary psychology's greatest success story,[6] and the one in which evolutionary theory has hit social perspectives with most force: the theory of parental investment and sexual selection as an explanation of sex differences in social behavior.[7,a] We first discuss the theoretical and methodological problems to be addressed by this model, arguing that lack of clarity on these issues has needlessly divided social and evolutionary perspectives, and frustrated evolutionary psychology's attempts to broaden and deepen its impact on the field. We then note the implications of the model for the distinction between historical and current causes, and for a truly interactionist perspective. Finally, we discuss the social policy implications of evolutionary and social explanations.

TOWARD AN EXPLANATORY MODEL OF SEX DIFFERENCES

The presence of myriad uncontrolled variables in the programs of evolutionary and social psychology has deeply compromised causal inference. A time-honored way of probing more deeply into the nature of biological and social processes and integrating seemingly irreconcilable theoretical positions is to classify those variables as *mediators* or *moderators*.[8] A mediator variable is an intervening process that accounts for or explains a relationship between an independent variable like sex and a dependent variable like jealousy. The path diagram in FIGURE 1 illustrates a three-variable system with three causal paths, *a*, *b*, and *c*, in which the independent variable operates directly (path *c*) and indirectly (paths *b* and *c*). Mediators explain how or why events occur, for example, how or why biological sex predicts reactions to infidelity (through different inferences men and women make about infidelity types).

[a]It is important to note, however, that evolutionary psychologists in this area as in many others are hardly monolithic in their views. Whereas most researchers probing the theory of sexual selection focus on sexual dimorphisms—sex differences in courtship—some, like Miller,[6] point out that sexual dimorphism is a common but not necessary outcome of sexual selection, and that important factors like the mutuality of mate choice and genetic linkage between the sexes constrain the nature and extent of sexual dimorphism. Thus, we are not discussing all evolutionary theories, but characterizing some representative views.

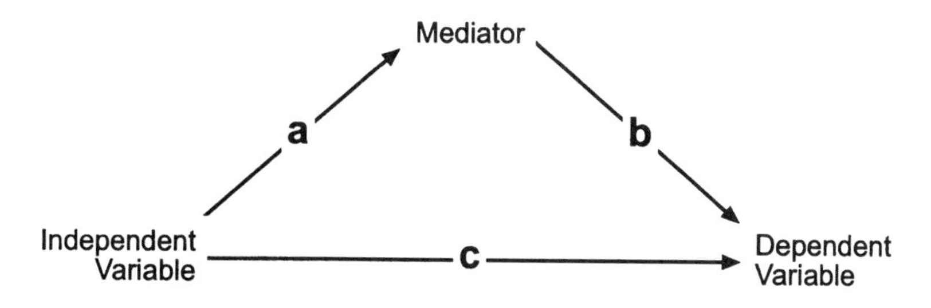

FIGURE 1. Mediational model. (Adapted from Baron and Kenney.[8])

In some cases, the only effect of an independent variable is through the mediator variable. Many cognitive, learned, or biological processes can mediate a given effect.

A moderator variable is an independent variable that affects the direction and/or strength of the relationship between a focal independent variable and a dependent variable.[8] The path diagram in FIGURE 2 has three causal paths, a, b, and c. In analysis of variance terms, a moderator interacts with the focal independent variable to specify the appropriate conditions for its operation and the generality of its effects. In the Eagly and Wood study, gender equality suggested limits to the relationship between biological sex and mate preferences: At high levels of gender equality, preferences for age differences in partners diminished.

One key difference we see between social and evolutionary psychology is in the treatment of mediators and moderators. Social psychology focuses almost completely on such variables, but often without recognizing the important differences between the two types. For its part, evolutionary psychology leapfrogs from sex to social behavior, paying lip service to the role of situational and cultural moderators, and expressing interest in only one mediator—the underspecified hypothetical "evolved dispositions." Only by explicitly attending to the models illustrated in FIGURES 1 and 2 will we have a genuinely explanatory theory of social behavior.

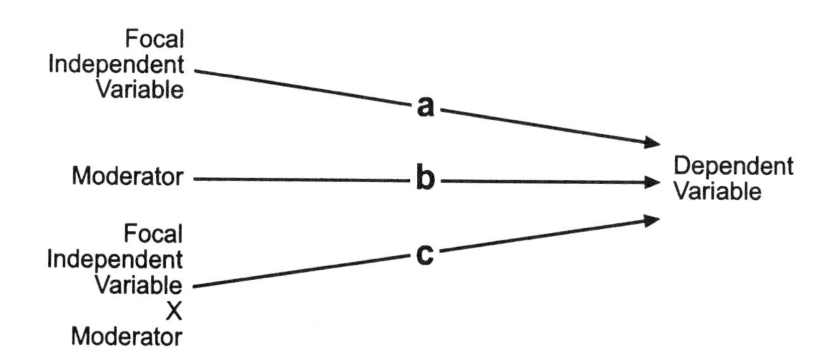

FIGURE 2. Moderator model. (Adapted from Baron and Kenney.[8])

Despite its narrow focus, evolutionary psychology has launched or invigorated many research programs in social psychology. The theory of parental investment and sexual selection alone has spawned numerous testable, nonobvious, original hypotheses about the qualities that males and females find appealing in both short- and long-term relationships, and about the ways that people try to attract and retain mates, among other phenomena. In many cases, social-role, schema, and learning theories cannot make these predictions in advance, and, as in lines of research that suggest that women's preferences for men's smells or facial features change across the menstrual cycle,[9] can barely explain the findings after the fact.

Evolutionary psychology has been multi-method in its research program, using experimental or quasi-experimental survey methods along with naturalistic observation and content analysis of archival data. But we question (*a*) the extent to which experimental laboratory and survey data collected on humans in the present can shed light on adaptations that developed in the past,[10] (*b*) the validity of programs in which the data collectors are not blind to the hypotheses,[11] (*c*) the sheer number of assumptions and inferential leaps that characterize certain aspects of the program, and (*d*) the practices of comparing nonequivalent groups and making causal inferences from correlational and quasi-experimental studies.

We focus here only on the last point. Even in the most experimental parts of the program, where investigators manipulate variables under controlled laboratory conditions, there is a crucial variable that cannot be manipulated: the sex of research participants. Since men and women are never equivalent, group differences between men and women in key areas cannot be attributed to evolutionary factors without evidence about the causal agent or strict control of the myriad factors that are known to vary with biological sex. If, for example, women on average are poorer than men, that difference in economic status might be the causal factor in an experiment. Were economic status controlled or built into mediator and moderator models, sex differences might disappear.

Evolutionary theorists have argued that the cognitive and social variables that correlate with biological sex—which may also explain some of the variance in a given response—are just further evidence for the power of biological sex rather than causal variables in and of themselves. Perhaps, but no evidence backs up the claim. Because of the power and prestige of evolutionary theory in biology and biopsychology, evolved dispositions are given an unearned priority in explaining human behavior. In the evolutionary psychology project, "the tie goes to biology." But as we have noted, the notion of evolved dispositions, variously called mechanisms and adaptations, is a mysterious and vague construct that straddles psychology and biology with no clear definition in either field.

Evolutionary psychology will remain less persuasive than it might be as long as simple group comparisons are made with potentially important covariates unmeasured and uncontrolled. In the case of jealousy research, for example, biological sex did not predict which kind of jealousy is more distressing as well as did individuals' beliefs concerning the covariation between sexual and emotional infidelity. At the same time, biological sex is correlated with type of belief and, evolutionary psychologists might add, it is important to understand why that is so. We agree. But, as the mediational model suggests, there is a difference between claiming that sex differences in jealousy are a first-order consequence of our evolutionary heritage and claiming they are a second-order consequence, derived from cognitive sex differences.

Another innovative and promising line of research in the evolutionary psychology program, fluctuating asymmetry, is similarly plagued by multicollinearity problems. Gangestad, Thornhill, and their colleagues have studied how fluctuating asymmetry—asymmetry in bilateral traits due to random errors in the development of the two sides—indicates underlying genetic fitness and may affect male success in having sex (at least in casual relationships). According to Gangestad,[12] symmetrical men—those with same size ears, elbows, wrists, ankles, feet, and fingers—are far more likely to have had sex at an early age, to have more sex partners, and to engage in more extra-pair copulations than males who are asymmetrical, even though asymmetry is presumed to be undetectable in normal social interaction. There is the suggestion, along with some evidence, that women can "smell" it.[9] Some research even suggests that symmetrical men are more attractive to women when women are particularly fertile, and are more likely to bring women to orgasm. Fascinating if true.

But at least to this date, the program has left unanswered the question of whether it is asymmetry (and the underlying developmental imprecision representing the "bad genes") or the host of other unmeasured variables correlated with symmetry—like masculinity, overall handsomeness, social competence, self-confidence, intelligence, and warmth, to name a few—that drives the effect. Some of these variables are measured (and statistically controlled for) and some are not. Sometimes some of them correlate at least moderately with fluctuating asymmetry and sometimes they do not. There are many issues raised by this intriguing program, not the least of which has to do with the meaning of asymmetry and its relationship to developmental imprecision and "good genes," and the utilitarian role of male physical attractiveness. But the problem of multicollinearity—the intercorrelation of variables— must be addressed if the preference for symmetry is to retain any real meaning beyond the observation that good looking guys get around more.

Given the problems involved in comparing nonequivalent groups, we question whether univariate analyses and null hypothesis testing can continue to serve as a major analytic tool for evolutionary psychology. For one thing, some sex differences are so small as to be of little theoretical and practical significance; many fluctuate in size across cultures. Throughout the past decade, mainstream social psychology has increasingly moved in the direction of measuring the size as well as the existence of effects, and of summarizing areas of research quantitatively via meta-analysis. Using effect sizes in sex-difference research, several investigators have found that, where they exist, most sex differences are small to moderate by social science standards, though a few are quite large, notably permissive attitudes toward casual sex and incidence of masturbation.[13] Sex differences are not static, with some sex differences, like those in verbal and mathematical ability, for example, changing—and diminishing—over time, and others not.[14, 15]

In any case, evolutionary psychology has clearly provided a coherent theoretical statement with which to guide empirical work on sex differences, and sex will obviously remain a key variable in this project. But a variable that bears this burden demands more thoughtful study. Men and women differ on numerous biological, psychological, and social variables, any and all of which may be operating in a given study. If sex differences are to be at the heart of any theory-building, they must be more carefully examined using effect sizes, meta-analyses, and more sophisticated multivariate analysis strategies guided by explanatory models that build in mediational and moderational processes.[b]

RETHINKING "HISTORICAL" VS. "CURRENT" CAUSES

Evolutionary psychology has opened up new areas of discourse concerning the relationship of social psychology to other branches of knowledge, particularly the natural sciences. It achieves this with its focus on the origins and adaptive significance of social behaviors, including those that differ in males and females. Traditionally, social psychology has focused on more proximate (situational) causes of behavior, including gendered behavior. Social psychology has also looked to more distal causes, but these have been located more often in structural (e.g., division of labor based on sex) and cultural (e.g., patriarchy) than biological domains, and non-specialized cognitive and learning mechanisms are seen as the means by which roles and hierarchy had their effects. Social psychology has been successful in identifying such factors, and using them to explain important sex differences.

As Eagly and Wood note, the distinction between the search for historic and current causes is not really what separates evolutionary and social perspectives. Evolutionary causes are not necessarily historic; indeed, evolved mechanisms are presumed to operate in the present, and social causes are not necessarily current, with many deeply embedded in culture and institutions. Neither theory has a hold on historic or current causes, and neither type of cause is inherently more important.

The importance of current causes can be seen in a clever set of experiments by Hoffman and Hurst.[16] They showed how stereotypes can arise in direct response to the way that categories of individuals are distributed into social roles. They argue that common gender stereotypes or schemas are an attempt to justify a pre-existing sexual division of labor, and propose that even if sex segregation into social roles were completely fortuitous, it requires rationalization once it exists. Specifically, we attribute to each sex those qualities deemed necessary for the performance of a particular function, for instance, bearing and feeding infants, a role so distinctive, salient, and critical that it swamps the field.[17]

Interestingly, Hoffman and Hurst also found that stronger stereotypes were formed when groups were presented as differing biologically. If people differ biologically, we expect those differences to be revealed in traits and behaviors. Conversely, external differences lead us to postulate internal, biological differences. We call this the biologization of difference. Evolutionary psychology has taken this route by querying the nature of the fit between the organism and the environment, including why the division of labor by sex so often takes the form that it does, and why some learning histories and perspectives are more characteristic of one sex than the other. But, as work like Hoffman and Hurst's shows, social psychology is finding answers to similar questions.

[b]At a more conceptual level, recent formulations of sex and gender in psychology describe these constructs as dynamic ones that draw and impinge upon processes at the individual, interactional, group, institutional, and cultural levels. Deaux and LaFrance,[29] for example, argue for enlarging rather than shrinking the frame of analysis to take into account political systems and cultural traditions as well as smaller contextual factors. They note that ignoring context and focusing on group differences is bound to produce opposites rather than overlap, to emphasize the person rather than the setting, to identify stable dispositions rather than fluctuating patterns, and to highlight biology or socialization rather than assignment of people into different and unequal social positions. Such biases need to be addressed theoretically and methodologically.

IN SEARCH OF INTERACTIONISM

In psychology generally, the *Zeitgeist* is to speak of interactions among nature and nurture and the need for multiple levels of analysis of all complex behaviors—not just human social behavior but the behavior of lower organisms as well. For instance, chimps appear to transmit culture,[18,19] and even male rats need certain kinds of stimulation to develop normal sexuality.[20]

Both evolutionary and social psychological approaches to sex differences claim to avoid the simplistic old nature/nurture impasses that have dogged the discipline in the past. Instead, each at least nominally considers a range of variables from the biological to the sociocultural.[1,21] But it is also clear from even the most recent and reasoned statements of their theories that each camp pushes hard for one type of causal explanation in a way that recreates the dichotomy all claim to disavow.

On the social side, consideration of biological variables often begins and ends with a mention of a few gross physical differences between men and women—almost always men's greater physical size and upper body strength and women's capacity to bear and nurse children. This moves quickly to speculation about how such characteristics shunt men and women into different social roles, and arrives at the conclusion that observed psychological differences between men and women are the results of social roles and structures. Theorists do not linger long on how we move from physical attributes to social roles, or on how reasonable it is to assume that major physical differences are irrelevant to psychological ones.

Indeed, there is clear reluctance to grant a major role to complex biological and developmental factors—brain structure and function or hormones, for example. Findings that are inconvenient for a social role analysis, such as the fact that desire for physical attractiveness in a mate is unrelated to gender equality, are somewhat weakly explained by an appeal to the notion that men value physical attractiveness because it is a marker for social competence or sexual warmth, attributes with which physical attractiveness may be correlated.

On their side, evolutionary psychologists rail against reductionism, claim to consider a broader range of variables in their analyses, and strive to be inclusive. But their embrace of interactionism is undermined by the research questions, variables, and designs that characterize many of their research programs. The place of environmental and contextual factors is regularly acknowledged in a general way, but, as Eagly and Wood note,[1] the few that are actually studied in the evolutionary psychology program are cues believed to trigger the hypothetical evolved mechanisms. As such, they are closely tied to the narrow and specific conditions of interest to middle-range evolutionary theories, for example, whether mating is long- or short-term, and are rarely the broader social and contextual factors that have long occupied psychologists who study complex processes like stereotyping.

Cultural variations in sex-linked behaviors and traits are recognized, though minimized, because the goal of much of the program on the theory of sexual selection is to find universal sex differences on behaviors relating to mate selection. Culture is a "nuisance variable" to be generalized across rather than a rich set of moderator and mediator variables in a broader explanatory model. Individual differences within gender are similarly ignored, even when there is great within-group variability, as in the case of the triggers of jealousy in men.

At least until now, what is social in the evolutionary psychology project is mostly on the dependent variable side, and the major causal factors are dispositional. In contrast, social psychologists are interested in using social factors to explain social effects, and know well that complex behavior is multiply determined, with no single set of factors accounting for the lion's share of variability in social responses. In that light, calls for evolutionary psychology as "the new paradigm for psychological science"[22] (p. 1), the grand metatheory that will integrate and unify a fractured discipline, are premature. There is widespread skepticism about a project that siphons the social out of social psychology. The nuanced interactionist perspective that is needed and promised on both sides has not, in our view, been realized in the research programs or discourse of either framework, and adherents continue to talk past each other.

Interestingly, it is in the study of primates that a truly interactionist model is more common.[19,23] De Waal has shown, for example, that young rhesus monkeys reared together with a group of stump-tailed macaques learned to behave more like macaques: They became more cooperative, social, and egalitarian. The rhesus monkeys became so adept at reconciliation that when they were returned to their own kind, they continued to use their new skills to make peace among their despotic peers. Such flexibility among our primate cousins is good evidence that, even among animals that have clear "hard-wired" behavioral predispositions, current cultural conditions influence behavior. Indeed, in their comprehensive synthesis of sixty-five chimpanzee behaviors, Whiten *et al.*[18] found thirty-nine that fit their definition of cultural variation. If chimpanzees are so susceptible to culture, then surely humans cannot be far behind.

PSYCHOLOGY AND SOCIAL PROGRESS

It is hard to write about the place of evolutionary psychology in social psychology and related subfields without noting its "extra-science" or sociopolitical aspects. Mainstream social psychology seems to have tried to ignore or dismiss evolutionary psychology for as long as possible and contain it when it could no longer dismiss it. Today, major chapters on evolutionary psychology appear in the most influential handbooks, but its principles and heuristics have not permeated the field. Frustrated to see its inevitability denied, evolutionary psychology has kicked back hard, with some of its proponents clearly exasperated by what they see as ignorance about biology and evolution, and prejudice against their program, a prejudice rooted in insecurity about the value of social explanation and political correctness.[24,25]

Evolutionary psychologists resist characterizations of evolved psychological mechanisms as built-in, hard-wired, and unchangeable, of the theory of evolution as easily falsifiable, and of their politics as reactionary. They are impatient with social psychology's reluctance to appreciate the nature and scope of evolutionary theory and resistance to considering evolved dispositions in any serious way. But at the same time, evolutionary psychology has attempted to integrate the field around a set of highly specific concerns and evolved psychological mechanisms, some of which may differ by sex, whose "engineering characteristics"[26] (p. 435) are completely unknown. In effect, social psychology is being asked to buy a theory that has yet to demonstrate why what "must" be the case must be the case. The biological arguments and evolutionary theories that have widest acceptance and greatest respect, like the overarching theory of natural selection, illuminate what it is to be human. But historically, such arguments and theories, no matter how nuanced or "interactionist," have run into trouble when they are used to explain group differences, especially differences among people who differ in power, goods, and other resources that we value. Differences between more and less powerful groups—whether the marker of power is race, ethnicity, or sex—are, as we have seen countless times in the past, interpreted as deficiencies in the disadvantaged groups.

Evolutionary psychology is replete with references to the advantages males have over females and the instability of modern movements to secure equal rights for women. Evolutionary psychologists often note that they do not view sex differences in selected social behaviors as good, morally correct, or the way things ought to be. Indeed, they frequently caution feminist social psychologists, among others, not to see a determinism that is not intended. And it is true that evolutionary explanations of inequality need not justify or reproduce the status quo. For example, strong evidence of evolved mechanisms that put one group at a social disadvantage could presumably lead to calls for the most stable and resolute policies to reduce inequities.

But there is a worrying inconsistency in evolutionary psychology. Determinism may not be intended, but the program's goals are to explain key elements of social inequalities as due to evolved mechanisms and essential sex differences. That looks a lot like determinism, especially since evolutionary pressures and essences cannot be changed. The resolution of the inconsistency would be an acknowledgment that sex-specific evolved mechanisms can be preempted by developmental and ecological conditions and, in consequence, vary greatly within and among individuals and cultures. Indeed, with the current rapid rate of cultural evolution, evolved dispositions may be expected to explain less and less of the variance in human behavior. But even when evolutionary psychologists have noted cultural effects, it is with reservations. Buss,[27] for example, has noted that different cultures invoke different mating strategies. Yet, he has also rejected the idea that cultural explanations of behaviors are alternatives to evolutionary explanations.

As recent research by Regan[28] suggests, in modern industrialized societies, where men and women have considerable—and considerably more equal—powers of selection in the form of increased access to potential mates, better economic opportunities, and decreased sanctions against divorce and premarital sex, they are becoming more similar in what they look for in prospective mates (and, for short-term mates, that may well be physical attractiveness). There is evidence that social psychological models that stress the proximal (i.e., situational, contextual) determinants of gender differences in behavior over distal (i.e., early experiences, social roles, evolved dispositions) ones may be more predictive of behavior.[13,29] Our point is that first causes and present causes are neither redundant nor mutually exclusive.

Obviously, social policies are best based on the richest understanding of the processes underlying them, including evolved mechanisms. Just as clearly, the social implications of a program designed to study social behavior cannot be ignored, no matter how "basic" the research. The place of biological and evolutionary arguments in discourse about group differences in social behavior and outcomes may always be contested, and should be approached with an immense sense of responsibility. A challenge we offer to evolutionary psychologists is to propose an outline of an evolutionarily informed remedy for sex-based inequities. Such an outline would have the theoretical value of placing evolved mechanisms in a context of other influences and would have the social value of demonstrating that evolutionary psychology is compatible with social progress. To date, no such outline exists. A recent evolutionary theory of rape,[30] for example, offers an educational program that owes no insights to evolutionary psychology (and spends three paragraphs on "educating" men and ten on "educating" women).

Social explanations have not been in any sense outflanked. Instead, both social and biological levels of explanation need to be enriched, with more attention paid to how they co-develop and interact. No one theoretical perspective captures the dynamics of complex social, sexual, and cultural phenomena, and evolutionary psychology will flourish as a key level of analysis in social psychology, informing but not transforming the field.

REFERENCES

1. Eagly, A.H. & W. Wood. 1999. The origins of sex differences in human behavior: Evolved dispositions versus social roles. Am. Psychol. **54:** 408–423.
2. Buss, D.M. 1989. Sex differences in human mate preferences: evolutionary hypotheses tested in 37 cultures. Behav. Brain Sci. **12:** 1–14.
3. Buunk, B.P., A. Angleitner, V. Oubaid & D.M. Buss. 1996. Sex differences in jealousy in evolutionary and cultural perspective: tests from the Netherlands, Germany, and the United States. Psychol. Sci. **7:** 359–363.
4. DeSteno, D.A. & P. Salovey. 1996. Evolutionary origins of sex differences in jealousy? Questioning the "fitness" of the model. Psychol. Sci. **7:** 367–372.
5. Harris, C.R. & N. Christenfeld. 1996. Gender, jealousy, and reason. Psychol. Sci. **7:** 364–366.
6. Miller, G.F. 1998. How mate choice shaped human nature: a review of sexual selection and human evolution. *In* Handbook of Evolutionary Psychology: Ideas, Issues, and Applications. C. Crawford and D. Krebs, Eds.: 87–130. Erlbaum Associates. Englewood Cliffs, NJ.
7. Trivers, R.L. 1972. Parental investment and sexual selection. *In* Sexual Selection and the Descent of Man. 1871–1971. B. Campbell, Ed.: 136–179. Aldine. Chicago, IL.
8. Baron, R.M. & D.A. Kenny. 1986. The moderator-mediator variable distinction in social psychological research: Conceptual, strategic, and statistical considerations. J. Pers. Soc. Psychol. **51:** 1173–1182.
9. Gangestad, S.W. & R. Thornhill. 1998. Menstrual cycle variation in women's preference for the scent of symmetrical men. Proc. Roy. Soc. London, B **265:** 927–933.
10. Fausto-Sterling, A. 1997. Beyond difference: a biologist's perspective. J. Soc. Issues **53:** 233–258.
11. Thornhill, R., & S.W. Gangestad. 1994. Human fluctuating asymmetry and sexual behavior. Psychol. Sci. **5:** 297–302.
12. Gangestad, S.W. 2000. Sexual selection, good genes, and human mating. *In* Anthology of Evolution and Human Behavior. H. Holcomb, Ed. In press.
13. Oliver, M.B. & J.S. Hyde. 1993. Gender differences in sexuality: a meta-analysis. Psychol. Bull. **114:** 29–51.
14. Eagly, A.H. 1995. The science and politics of comparing women and men. Am. Psychol. **50:** 45–158.
15. Hyde, J.S. & E.A. Plant. 1995. Magnitude of psychological gender differences: another side to the story. Am. Psychol. **50:** 159–161.
16. Hoffman, C. & N. Hurst. 1990. Gender stereotypes: perception or rationalization. J. Pers. Soc. Psychol. 58: 359–363.
17. Valian, V. 1998. Why so Slow? The Advancement of Women. MIT Press. Cambridge, MA.

18. Whiten, A., J. Goodall, W.C. McGrew, T. Nishida, V. Reynolds, Y. Sugiyama, C.E.G. Tutin, R.W. Wrangham & C. Boesch, C. 1999. Cultures in chimpanzees. Nature **399:** 682–685.
19. de Waal, F.B. 1989. Peacemaking among Primates. Harvard University Press. Cambridge, MA.
20. Moore, C. L. 1985. Another psychobiological view of sexual differentiation. Devel. Rev. **5:** 18–55.
21. Buss, D.M., M.G. Haselton, T.K. Shackelford, A.L. Bleske & J.C. Wakefield. 1999. Interactionism, flexibility, and inferences about the past. Am. Psychol. **54:** 443–445.
22. Buss, D. M. 1995. Evolutionary psychology: a new paradigm for psychological science. Psychol. Inquiry **6:** 1–30.
23. Hrdy, S. B. 1997. Raising Darwin's consciousness: female sexuality and the prehominid origins of patriarchy. Human Nature **8:** 1–49.
24. Kendrick, D. T. 1995. Evolutionary theory versus the confederacy of dunces. Psychol. Inquiry **6:** 56–62.
25. Buss, D. M. 1995. The future of evolutionary psychology. Psychol. Inquiry **6:** 81–87.
26. Roney, J. R. 1999. Distinguishing adaptations from by-products. Am. Psychol. **54:** 425–426.
27. Buss, D.M. 1996. The evolutionary psychology of human social strategies. *In* Social Psychology: A Handbook of Basic Principles. E.T. Higgins & A.W. Kruglanski, Eds. Guilford Press.New York.
28. Regan, P.C. 1998. What if you can't get what you want? Willingness to compromise ideal mate selection standards as a function of sex, mate value, and relationship context. Pers. Soc. Psychol. Bull. **24:** 1294–1303.
29. Deaux, K. & M. LaFrance. 1998) Gender. *In* The Hadnbook of Social Psychology, Vol. 1. D.T. Gilbert, S.T. Fiske & G. Lindzey, Eds. :788–827. McGraw-Hill. New York.
30. Thornhill, R. & C.T. Palmer. 2000. A Natural History of Rape: Biological Bases of Sexual Coercion. MIT Press. Cambridge, MA.

Mood as Mechanism

CYNTHIA SCHUPAK

Department of Psychology and Ph.D. Subprogram in Biopsychology, Hunter College of CUNY, New York, New York 10021, USA

... it was the form
of the thing, if a thing is what it was,
and not the merest wisp of a part of
a process—this unraveling inkling
of the envisioned, of states of being

past alteration, of all that we've
never quite imagined except by way of
the body ...
–AMY CLAMPITT, "MAN FEEDING PIGEONS"

An *evolved psychological mechanism* is a set of processes inside an organism that: (1) Exists in the form it does because it (or other mechanisms that reliably produce it) solved a specific problem of individual survival or reproduction recurrently over human evolutionary history. (2) Takes only certain classes of information, or input (*a*) can be either external or internal, (*b*) can be actively extracted from the environment, and (*c*) specifies to the organism the particular adaptive problem it is facing. (3) Transforms that information into output through a procedure (e.g., decision rule) in which output (*a*) regulates physiological activity, provides information to other psychological mechanisms, or produces manifest action and (*b*) solves a particular adaptive problem. Species have evolved psychologies to the degree that they possess mechanisms of this sort.

—DAVID M. BUSS[1]

This paper was written in response to David Buss's reply to my comment that the bulk of his evidence was correlational: he said, "Yes, but we're starting to get some really interesting hard stuff from imaging studies."

INTRODUCTION

To biologists and animal behaviorists, a behavioral mechanism immediately implies an integration of known neurological, sensory and muscular structures that are accountable for the enactment of the behavior in question. Together with associated environmental releasers, these behavioral mechanisms have become familiar as modal action patterns[2] or similarly designated heritable mediators of adaptivity.

Such behavioral mechanisms have been studied for decades as palpable proponents of proximate causation, and comparative studies have described their functional adaptedness or ultimate causation (the "how" and "why" explanations, respectively).[3,4] Thus it shouldn't be surprising that the nebulous notion of a psychological mechanism is not easily accommodated by those accustomed to the biological application of the term. To many, it seems that the "black box" concept has crafted a conspicuous comeback in evolutionary psychology. As Robert Wright[5] states:

> ...This is partly because the biochemical links among genes, brain, and behavior are largely unfathomed. It is also because the elegant logic of evolutionary analysis oftenlets us figure out the roles of genes without worrying about the nuts and bolts of theirinfluence. But, of course, there always *are* nuts and bolts. Whenever we talk about theinfluence of genes (or environment) on behavior, thought, or emotion, we are talking about a biochemical chain of influence.

It follows, then, that somewhere in this biochemical chain the influx of environmental impetus and efflux of behavioral responsiveness should meet, in some locatable body structure. Indeed, for some time brain research has implicated a locality involved in both mood and attention that seems to be a reasonable candidate for an evolved psychological mechanism.

A PROPOSED MECHANISM: CONSTRUCTION AND RATIONALE

This "candidate mechanism" is a fairly discrete assembly of specialized, highly integrated nuclei regulating both mood and attention. Located intermediate to the midbrain and the neocortex, this region incorporates the dienephalon, portions of the basal ganglia, and the limbic forebrain system. In rats, monkeys, and other mammals these associatively plastic yet structurally conserved nuclei have been extensively studied with regard to their individual and mutual control of affect and orientation, including fear, aggression, approach, avoidance, and various aspects of copulatory behavior.

In humans, research comparing individuals with and without mood or attentional disorders has offered the bulk of recent experimental evidence in this area. Imaging studies have identified locations—prominently including that described above—in which brain activity appears abnormal in depressed patients. Additionally, the effectiveness of a host of new antidepressant medications known to target specific neurotransmitter systems (SSRIs, like Prozac) have been used as pharmacological probes, illuminating neurochemical machinations within these structures. The influence of mood on choices in social and reproductive behavior can be applied to most of evolutionary psychology's propositions—status, reciprocity, deception, and mate selection. The mediation of these choices within a largely conserved, plastic and primitive system of emotionality is particularly resonant of the ancestral condition of our species.

IMAGING AND PHYSIOLOGICAL EVIDENCE

Orienting and focus are vital to evolutionary psychology, as attention to salient cues from potential allies, enemies and mates all underlie the engagement of psychological mechanisms necessary for recognizing socially and reproductively advantageous interactions. It's not surprising that the specific brain structures that monitor focus and attentional responses overlap with those that determine emotionality. Thus, this region can be viewed as a motivation center governing interest, as well as preference or elusion. Imaging technologies including PET and functional MRI have isolated loci within this candidate mechanism that receive and modulate sensory information (diencephalon), attach emotional significance by labeling it positive or negative (amygdala), before relaying it to the left prefrontal cortex, where judgments are made regarding the social implication of behavioral responses.

The left prefrontal cortex along with its connections to important areas of the limbic system have been found to be especially active during attention tasks concerned with making selections among competing, complex contingencies.[6] Utilizing input from noradrenergic neural tracts, the left prefrontal cortex is notorious for its primary function of monitoring intentional behavior. PET scans of the brains of depressive patients reveal striking increases in blood flow to the left prefrontal cortex, implicating this region in the emotional state of depression.[7] Alterations in blood flow to this region in depressives suggests a variation in the type of focus or attentiveness engendered here. This change in focus may range from extreme vigilance to external environmental stimuli (as evidenced by such depression-related symptoms as hypersensitivity, social anxiety and phobic avoidance) to heightened attention to internally generated information (such as that held in long-term memory). The latter focus would be consistent with symptoms of intrusive negative thoughts and ruminations common in depression.[8]

Another prominent region in which brain activity in depressives differs from that of controls is the amygdala, a cluster of limbic nuclei located in the anterior temporal lobe. This structure is responsible for assigning emotional meaning to visual, auditory and olfactory events which have biological significance, including those that signal the presence of food, water, pain, potential mates or rivals, and infants requiring maternal care.[9] This is clearly the integrating station for the attribution of affective responsiveness to relevant external stimuli.

The amygdala receives regulatory input from dopaminergic cells originating in the midbrain and ascending rostrally through the medial forebrain bundle (MFB), which is well-studied with respect to its capability as a behavioral reinforcer. Noradrenergic tracts which project through the MFB to similar limbic forebrain areas[10] have the primary effect of increasing arousal and vigilance. Serotonin inputs from other midbrain nuclei also ascend through the MFB and release serotonin diffusely throughout these locations. In this area of the brain, serotonin serves as a neuromodulator of both dopaminergic and adrenergic tone. Hence the notable effects of serotonin reuptake inhibitors, which increase the bioavailability of serotonin and thereby control neural receptivity and modulate activity in circuits regulated by dopamine (the pleasure neurotransmitter) and by norepinephrine (the manager of arousal and attentiveness). The SSRIs have been used successfully in treating anxiety and obsessive-compulsive disorder, as well as a group of behavioral disturbances that appear to be quite the opposite of depression, includingimpulsivity, aggression, and rage. In fact, psychopharmacologists who treat affective aswell as attentional disorders have noted that the same basic areas of the brain discussed above seem to "light up" in brain images of these patients, irrespective of the particulars of pathology. Taken together, this evidence strongly suggests that moodiness of all types can be located in these same neurochemical circuits.

Thus, a mechanism has been introduced—one that describes the biological correlates of the psychological notion of: *I see/hear/smell it* (sensory cue), *I want it* (emotional response), *I'll go for it* (strategy chosen). Gradations in affect can easily be construed as tractable agents for the selection of preferential attention, and consequent determinations regarding attraction or repulsion, avoidance or desire. The apparatus that generates these gradations is biological in substance, but psychological in its level of analysis. And perhaps the black box becomes less opaque.

REFERENCES

1. Buss, D.M. 1995. Evolutionary psychology: a new paradigm for psychological science. Psychol. Inquiry 5–6.
2. Barlow, G.W. 1968. Ethological units of behavior. *In* The Central Nervous System and Fish Behavior. D. Ingle, Ed. University of Chicago Press. Chicago, IL.
3. Tinbergen, N. 1963. On aims and methods of ethology. Z. Tierpsychol. **20:** 410–433.
4. Alcock, J. 1998. Animal Behavior: An Evolutionary Approach, 6th ed. Sinauer. Sunderland, MA.
5. Wright, R. 1994. The Moral Animal. Random House. New York.
6. Posner, M.I. & M.E. Raichle. 1994. Images of Mind. Scientific American Library. New York.
7. Drevets, W. C., T. O. Videen, J. L. Price, S. H. Preskorn, S. T. Carmichael & M. E. Raichle. 1992. A functional anatomy of unipolar depression. J. Neurosci. **12:** 3628–3642.
8. DSM-IV. 1994. Diagnostic and Statistical Manual of Mental Disorders, 4th ed. American Psychiatric Association. Washington, DC.
9. Carlson, N. R. 1998. Physiology of Behavior, 6th ed. Allyn and Bacon. Boston, MA.
10. Kandel, E. R., J. H. Schwartz & T. M. Jessell. 1991. Principles of Neural Science, 3nd ed. Appleton & Lange. Norwalk, CT.

Resisting Biology

The Unpopularity of a Gene's-Eye View

THOMAS A. TERLEPH

Department of Psychology and Ph.D. Subprogram in Biopsychology, Hunter College of CUNY, New York, New York 10021, USA

ABSTRACT: David Haig's intragenomic conflict theory concerning the possible evolutionary origins of genomic imprinting is discussed. It is suggested that a useful way in which one might represent Haig's theory to a popular audience would be by emphasizing a gene's eye viewpoint. In doing so, an author may help to dispel common misconceptions about evolution and natural selection, misconceptions which arise in part from an overemphasis on the individual, rather than the gene, when discussing natural selection. Although it is possible to view either the gene or the individual as a unit of natural selection, our own proclivity towards overemphasizing the role of individuals in evolution is seen as a common impediment to a more complete understanding of both natural selection, as well as the philosophical implications arising from a gene's eye view of evolutionary theory.

Misconceptions by both scientists and lay people about how evolution and natural selection work are, unfortunately, quite common. Typical examples include dichotomous thinking about "nature versus nurture"; confusions about the proximate and ultimate (the *how* and *why*) factors involved when explaining traits; assuming that a genetic basis to a trait means that the trait is developmentally fixed; presuming that evolutionists actually believe that organisms (and even genes) consciously attempt to maximize their fitness; believing that some human behaviors are actually being advocated by evolutionists simply because the theorists think that such traits might have been adaptive in our past; and teleological views about the "progress" of evolution. Fortunately, the most common errors often stem from misunderstandings about the factors that contribute to the evolutionary process, and thus these errors travel down predictable paths.

These issues have been argued over for decades in academic circles, so antidotes to many misconceptions are often available. Nonetheless, misconceptions seem doomed to repeat themselves again and again, as is evidenced by some of the latest waves of controversy swirling around evolutionary psychology (for recent responses to some of evolutionary psychology's critics, see Refs. 1 and 2). In order to dispel many myths and misconceptions, what is needed is a clear understanding of the roles played by both the phenotype and the genotype in selection. But such understanding is elusive, and misunderstanding seems to be the path of least resistance.

Such misunderstanding finds its way into the following example. It has been discovered in recent years that some genes are differentially expressed, or genomically imprinted, depending on whether they are inherited via an egg or sperm (for reviews, see Refs. 3, 4, and 5). Somehow, these genes are capable of retaining information about their parental origin. A theory recently put forth as an explanation for the ultimate origins of genomic imprinting is Haig's idea of intragenomic conflict. This theory has sparked interest in the popular press,[6–8] in part because it involves conflict in one of the most intuitively unlikely of places (within the genome).

Haig has elaborated Robert Trivers'[9] parent-offspring conflict theory to include instances of predicted *intra*-genomic conflict.[3] In the case of species where mothers often have offspring with more than one father (such as humans), a current fetus's paternally derived genes are less likely to be present in the mother's future children than are the maternally derived genes. As a result, paternally derived genes are expected to maximize their own fitness by transferring more resources to the current child (such as nutrients supplied in the mother's blood) than maternally derived genes *in that same child* are selected to take. Maternally derived genes in the embryo are expected to maximize their fitness by taking fewer resources from the mother, as she may be capable of producing future offspring. By referring to the expression of a conflict within rather than between individuals, Haig helps to highlight the ultimate players in selection: the genes.

Genomic imprinting, which is hypothesized to have arisen as a result of such gene conflict, was first found in mice. *Igf2* (insulin-like growth factor 2) is a gene contributing to fetal growth, and is expressed in mouse fetuses when paternally derived, but not when maternally derived. Another gene, *Igf2r* (insulin-like growth factor 2 receptor), has the opposite pattern of expression. It is expressed when maternally derived and silent when paternally derived. This maternally expressed gene inhibits growth by degrading the product of *Igf2*.[5,10] The phenotypic expression of this conflict in the fetal offspring is the maternally expressed degradation of a paternally expressed growth-promoting substance.

Haig's evolutionary explanation for genomic imprinting requires a modification of Hamilton's theory of inclusive fitness.[4] Inclusive fitness theory assumes that gene expression is not affected by parental origin. In the cases of genomically imprinted genes, however, parental origin does affect expression. Thus in some cases, natural selection will act differently on gene expression depending on whether the gene is maternally or paternally derived.

Haig's theory of intragenomic conflict is based upon the concept developed in Trivers'[11] parent-offspring conflict theory, an extension of Hamilton's[12] 1964 theory of inclusive fitness. These theories take a gene-level view of selection. Yet Haig's views have been misrepresented, with reviews overemphasizing the individual rather than the genes as the unit of selection.

Although intragenomic conflict and traditional parent-offspring conflict are both derived from similar lines of thinking, intragenomic conflict is different. In parent-offspring conflict the phenotypic expression of conflict is seen between individuals, whereas intragenomic conflict is phenotypically expressed within an individual. In both cases, however, the conflict itself is thought to have arisen from a disagreement between genes. Intragenomic conflict can be thought of as resulting from an evolutionary "arms race" expressed within offspring, and due to a conflict between alleles of maternal and paternal origin.

A view of the intragenomic conflict as a conflict between individuals rather than between the genes within those individuals is what has been implied in the popular press.[6,8] There seems to be a resistance to a clear explication of the notion that it is the genes that are at odds, genes possessed by both sexes, and passed on to offspring of either sex.

One example of an article that overemphasizes the role of the individual rather than the genes in Haig's theory is a recent (12/1/98) *New York Times* story[6] by Gina Kolata entitled "Mouse Study Fails to Verify an Evolutionary Theory." The author characterizes Haig's theory as one "involving a kind of molecular arms race between the sexes." She goes on to say "Males will develop genes that make their offspring grow quickly. And females will develop genes to counteract those male genes." This statement makes it sound as if Haig is truly describing a battle between individuals of both sexes. It is not as simple as it sounds, however, as both types of genes are found within any given individual, regardless of that individual's sex. There is indeed an arms race. But its phenotypic expression is within offspring, not between individuals.

The notion of a "battle of the sexes" is misleading for yet another reason. Consider the example of a polygamous female who has given birth to a female offspring. It will be in the interests of the (male) father's genes that the mother invest more resources in the offspring (a female) than she is expected to be willing to invest. Incidentally, daughters actually share more genes with their fathers (due to the X chromosome) than sons do. The point here is that the putative origins of this arms race are thought to have arisen from commonly occurring genetic asymmetries characteristic of the different kin relationships seen in a species, and those asymmetries do not necessarily fall neatly into battle lines between the sexes.

If one wants to make the analogy to a battle, the combatants might be seen as battling for their own representation in the next generation. If the combatants find themselves in one type of body (like a mother, father, son or daughter), the adaptive course of action would be to change battle strategies, such as adopting a particular pattern of genomic imprinting. Even when Haig discusses the evolution of social interactions *between* individuals (such as species-typical behavioral differences discussed in this volume [p. 149]) the interactions are again predicted to result from asymmetries of genetic relatedness between kin types. The behaviors themselves are simply the proximate expression of an underlying genetic conflict.

Authors in the popular press, however, often present the chicken as if it is the egg, or at the very least they muddy the waters between the proximate and ultimate. When Kolata[6] states that "Males will develop genes that make their offspring grow quickly. And females will develop genes to counteract those male genes" she does not clarify for the layperson what the putative *source of conflict* is. It is *gene conflict,* over the course of evolutionary time, which the author should be emphasizing. Her description emphasizes the proximate phenotypic result of a predicted ultimate genetic conflict, but she does not make a clear distinction between the phenotypic *outcome* of the conflict, and the genetic conflict itself.

Authors of such popular accounts are in fact probably quite aware of how genomic imprinting, as well as evolution, work. It seems, however, that in simplifying the issue for popular consumption, one often overemphasizes the idea of competition between males and females, rather than a more enlightening description of how the differential pattern of allele activation within individuals might have arisen.

I believe that taking the time to adequately describe the basic principles behind Haig's arguments would be a more worthwhile endeavor than misleading simplifications, such as the following one from Kolata's *New York Times* article: "Each male will want to be sure his progeny survive, even at the expense of the other offspring and the mother. And so … it will be in a male's interests to carry genes that make his fetuses grow very big, very quickly." Of course she is speaking metaphorically about "interests," and does not imply conscious intent. Nonetheless, this shorthand way of speaking about "interests" raises the specter of male-female conflict. Note also that instead of using the terms *mother* and *father* here, she chooses to use "mother" and "male." An adequate level of emphasis on the different elements involved in Haig's theory would make clear that while "male interests" (the interests of alleles of paternal origin) are being served, this is carried out at the genetic level, where intent is nonexistent. Not emphasizing the gene's-eye view in both the ultimate origins and the proximate outcomes is an opportunity missed.

People are traditionally uncomfortable with ideas referring to selection at the genetic level. S. J. Gould, for example, sees gene-selectionist views as stemming from a "Western" attitude characterized by "atomism, reductionism, and determinism… that all events and objects have definite, predictable, determined causes."[13] This popular view sees reductionism as a dirty word. Given the great successes of assuming a predictable world, however, and assuming that the components of a system can inform "higher" levels, I believe that throwing the baby out with the bath water should not be our first course of action.

It thus seems likely that this kind of critical interpretation of Haig's theory stems in part from the fact that it has leveled its focus upon the gene. If one wants to insinuate that Haig's theory is politically inflammatory, a good way to confuse the issue is by characterizing it as a "battle of the sexes" involving those nasty genes. The public already presupposes that genetic inheritance equals developmental fixity. All one has to do is present an inadequate description of Haig's argument, and it will fit the evolutionary biology-is-sexist stereotype. If Haig's theory (or for that matter evolutionary theory and its sociobiologic evolutionary psychology offspring) is sexist, it does not appear to be very kind to either sex. And even if it is unkind, evolutionary theory cannot be expected to describe the world as we might want it to be (the moralistic fallacy; see Crawford [this volume, p. 21]). Similarly, any attempt to accurately describe an aspect of the world does not necessarily mean that one condones that aspect (the naturalistic fallacy; see Crawford [this volume, p. 22]). Suggesting that Haig is an advocate for some kind of a sexist agenda requires one to overemphasize the role of individuals in his theory, rather than the role of genes. Of course no one has made such a statement; but insinuations can also be effective.

Whatever the underlying reasons (maybe because Haig attacks the sacred mother-infant bond or the sanctity of monogamy?), Kolata's account of Haig's theory is unfairly simplistic. The author's main purpose is to emphasize the results of a single experiment that failed to support Haig's theory, devoting little space to adequately explaining the theory and even less space to additional evidence supporting the theory.

Such popular biased reporting returns us to the question of why it is that the gene's-eye selectionist viewpoint has so often met with resistance. Like most scientific ideas that have removed the narcissistic individual from the spotlight, gene-selectionist views do not find ready acceptance. People do not like perceiving themselves as what is described in *The Selfish Gene* by Dawkins[14] (and later much maligned by his critics) as "lumbering robots," whose ultimate job is merely to pass on the replicators. We similarly dislike views that splinter our sense of self. We feel like individuals, not the end product of a committee comprised of members that do not always agree, as Haig's theory of intragenomic conflict suggests. Modern evolutionary theory seems to have taken away not only our individual purpose, but our sense of individuality.

It would be nice if reality conformed to the hope that some ultimate purpose exists in our lives beyond the passage of replicators. But reality seems to dictate that as far as biological (not cultural) evolution is concerned, only DNA is passed on. It is therefore instructive to emphasize the role of gene selection when discussing evolution, no matter how tempting it is to concentrate on a description that puts individuals in the spotlight.

The concept of kin selection, using the same gene-selectionist logic that informs Haig's theory, is an illustrative example. Gould,[13] in arguing against a gene-selectionist view, claims that "kin selection is a form of Darwinian individual selection." But one's kin do not share his or her phenotype; they only share a part of the genotype. If (as is common in eusocial species), one foregoes reproduction in order to assist a relative in reproducing, it is difficult to conceive of that altruistic individual as being selected for. The genes influencing that individual's behavioral tendencies, however, have the potential to be propagated through kin. Note, interestingly, that genes for both foregoing reproduction and for reproducing are being passed on in the reproductive individual. Rather than calling this a form of individual selection, it is intuitively reasonable to call this the selection of genes, as these genes underlie two different behavioral adaptations generally seen active only in different individuals.

Such cases inevitably weaken our biased view of the primary importance of the individual. It is of course possible to assert that it is adaptive for the eusocial reproductive individual to possess nonreproductive genes. These genes are not merely "hitchhiking" since they will prove useful to the individual when she or he reproduces. The individuals are linked to each other by their shared genes, so why not view these cooperating genes as the unit of selection? Alternatively, one can view a nonreproductive as an extended phenotype of the reproductive's genes. Either way, the lines of individuality are blurred. Although an individual usually behaves in ways that promote his or her phenotypic survival, from a gene-selectionist viewpoint this is merely an indirect consequence of the adaptations that ultimately arose to propagate the genes within that individual. The bodies that carry these committees of genes are but transitory players in the process.

Gould demeans gene-selectionism as being "reductionism." Ironically, one may in fact argue that viewing the individual rather than the gene as the unit of selection is in fact the more reductionistic view. After all, by concentrating on the selection of an individual, one is essentially looking at a snapshot in time. Changing allele frequencies, not individual frequencies, are what matter over evolutionary history. The selection of individuals is only a piece of the puzzle. The selection of the alleles that they carry, over the course of evolutionary time, is the big picture.

Unfortunately, new insights are not always spiritually satisfying. In the last century, people did not want to accept that they were just another species of ape. Most educated people, now, accept this fact. Now we are asked to accept that the reason we have come to exist is for the propagation of genes. This meets resistance because it is often misconstrued as a challenge to the myriad of proximal purposes that give meaning to human lives. Resistance to such a view is also due to the fact that it is seen as an affront to our sense of individual identity.

Haig's "reductionist" ideas have a great deal more to say than simply being an explanation for some anecdotes about human pregnancy, species-typical kin social interactions, and mouse gene expression. Like Darwin and many evolutionary biologists since, Haig has helped to craft a view of the big picture through an exploration of its particulars. Surely in this century, physics has already told us that the universe is not put together in a way that allows for a comforting and easily intuited human understanding of nature. Why should we now expect a comforting and easily intuited understanding of human nature?

REFERENCES

1. Crawford, C. 1998. The theory of evolution in the study of human behavior: an introduction and overview. *In* Handbook of Evolutionary Psychology: Ideas, Issues, and Applications. C. Crawford & D. Krebs, Eds.: 3–39. Erlbaum Associates. Mahwah, NJ.
2. Cosmides, L & J. Tooby. 1997. Evolutionary Psychology: A Primer [online]. http://www.psych.ucsb.edu/research/cep/primer.htm.
3. Haig, D. 1993. Genetic Conflicts in Human Pregnancy. Q. Rev. Biol. **68(4):** 495–532.
4. Haig, D. 1997. Parental Antagonism, Related Asymmetries, and Genomic Imprinting. Proc. Roy. Soc. Lond. B. **264:** 1657–1662.
5. Haig, D. & C. Graham. 1991. Genomic imprinting and the strange case of the insulin-like growth factor II receptor. Cell **64:** 1045–1046.
6. Kolata, G. 1998. Mouse Study Fails to Verify an Evolutionary Theory. The New York Times (December 1) :F2.
7. Mestel, R. 1998. The genetic battle of the sexes. Natural History **107(1):** 44–49.
8. Sapolsky, R. 1999. The war between men and women. Discover (May): 56–61.
9. Trivers, R.L. 1985. Social Evolution. Benjamin/Cummings. Menlo Park, CA.
10. de Chiara, T.M., E.J. Robertson & A. Efstratiadis. 1991. Parental Imprinting of the Mouse Insulin-like Growth Factor II Gene. Cell. **64:** 849–859.
11. Trivers, R.L. 1974. Parent-offspring conflict. Am. Zool. **14:** 249–264.
12. Hamilton, W.D. 1964. The genetical evolution of social behavior. J. Theoret. Biol. **7:** 1–52.
13. Gould, S.J. 1980. Caring groups and selfish genes. *In* The Panda's Thumb.: 85–92. W.W. Norton. New York.
14. Dawkins, R. 1976. The Selfish Gene, revised edition [1989]. Oxford University Press. Oxford, England.

On the Evolution of Misunderstandings about Evolutionary Psychology

JASON YOUNG[a] AND ROGER PERSELL[b]

Departments of [a]Psychology and [b]Biology, Hunter College of CUNY, New York, New York 10021, USA

ABSTRACT: Some of the controversy surrounding evolutionary explanations of human behavior may be due to cognitive information-processing patterns that are themselves the result of evolutionary processes. Two such patterns are (1) the tendency to oversimplify information so as to reduce demand on cognitive resources and (2) our strong desire to generate predictability and stability from perceptions of the external world. For example, research on social stereotyping has found that people tend to focus automatically on simplified social-categorical information, to use such information when deciding how to behave, and to rely on such information even in the face of contradictory evidence. Similarly, an undying debate over nature vs. nurture is shaped by various data-reduction strategies that frequently oversimplify, and thus distort, the intent of the supporting arguments. This debate is also often marked by an assumption that either the nature *or* the nurture domain may be justifiably excluded at an explanatory level because one domain appears to operate in a sufficiently stable and predictable way for a particular argument. As a result, critiques inveighed against evolutionary explanations of behavior often incorporate simplified—and erroneous—assumptions about either the mechanics of how evolution operates or the inevitable implications of evolution for understanding human behavior. The influences of these tendencies are applied to a discussion of the heritability of behavioral characteristics. It is suggested that the common view that Mendelian genetics can explain the heritability of complex behaviors, with a one-gene–one-trait process, is misguided. Complex behaviors are undoubtedly a product of a more complex interaction between genes and environment, ensuring that both nature and nurture must be accommodated in a yet-to-be-developed post-Mendelian model of genetic influence. As a result, current public perceptions of evolutionary explanations of behavior are handicapped by the lack of clear articulation of the relationship between inherited genes and manifest behavior.

As a social psychologist and a biologist, we are acutely aware of the differences in emphases given to "nature vs. nurture" explanations for behavior. Nowhere is this distinction more crucial and controversial than in the recent increase in attention on evolutionary influences on social behavior.

Repeatedly throughout the proceedings of this colloquium, the speakers revealed that a large part of the controversy surrounding evolutionary explanations of behavior may come from our own cognitive reasoning styles, which themselves are likely to have an evolutionary basis. That is, we humans seem particularly adept at relying upon thinking strategies that serve to convince us in our day-to-day lives that we hold correct assumptions about the world. One of the dominant 20th century assumptions, for example, has been that the inheritance of traits follows a simple Mendelian pattern: a gene determines a defined trait. Ironically, such uncritical reliance on explanatory strategies, including Mendelian genetics, reflects a tendency that itself has probable evolutionary origins.

For instance, research in the social, cognitive, and clinical areas of psychology has repeatedly found that some cognitive belief systems persist, despite a recent active desire to change them. The study of social stereotyping in recent years has frequently focused on cognitive mechanisms that serve to perpetuate beliefs, even in the face of contradictory evidence (e.g., Ref. 1). Most often highlighted are the means by which we tend to oversimplify social knowledge so as to not "overtax" our limited memory and processing capacity. Stereotypes result, then, when we indiscriminately lump people into pre-existing, self-defined categories, often leaving little opportunity for any given individual to demonstrate his or her uniqueness and distinction from his/her assigned category. Some researchers suggest that what is necessary here is to encourage the potential "stereotyper" to engage in "individuated processing"—that is, to avoid making a snap judgment and lumping someone into a category—and, instead, to focus on the individual characteristics of a target person (cf. Ref. 2). Such individuating strategies, when they can be activated, have been found to be effective in reducing stereotypical thinking. However, the challenge—and the evolutionary perspective on this—is that the default setting in processing social and other forms of global information is to engage in some form of data-reduction strategy so as to make the information more "manageable" within the limits prescribed by our personal cognitive processing mechanisms. The implication is that alternative processing strategies, such as using individuating information, will usually be possible, but they will always be more effortful than the default data-reducing mode. As presenters at this colloquium, such as Barkow, Buss, and Krebs, have repeatedly asserted in this volume, such cognitive limitations suggest that our current "thinking architecture" likely reflects a form that served our ancestors well enough for survival purposes, (though perhaps this architecture is adapting to current demands, albeit at a glacial pace).

Humans (and, likely, other higher primates as well) have always been at the mercy of the limited processing ability of their minds. It is only in the past few centuries, and the one we are now just completing in particular, that these limitations have become so pronounced. The bulk of our cognitive capacity developed during an earlier environment with less-complex information input. Hence, even though today there is higher demand for processing capacity, our genetics has not yet had time to "catch up" to a capacity that might more optimally match what recent technology demands from us. Thus, for the moment, we are mentally stuck with a 386 processor in a world that demands a Pentium level of computation.

This gap between current environmental demands (such as remembering many different phone numbers, or even recalling the intricate knowledge on evolution and behavior presented in the present volume), and our limited capacity to cognitively process this information, highlights our indelible reliance upon cognitive strategies and heuristics that serve to (1) reduce the demand on our cognitive resources (what we call "data-reduction strategies") and (2) render an all-important sense of predictability and stability to our world-view, even when such a conclusion is tenuous at best (what we refer to as a "desire for parsimony" heuristic) (see also Ref. 3 for a further discussion of the role of evolutionary pressures on social biases).

The example of stereotyping above is especially germane here since this default data-reduction strategy applies equally whether we are judging a social group *or* a scientific theory. It is often easier to combine all evolutionary explanations in one pot or another (e.g., nature *or* nurture) rather than to focus on the nuances of what is truly applicable when dealing with the disparate research findings presented in the field. Rather than focus, for instance, on whether sex differences follow from a primarily genetic or environmental source, it may be wiser to acknowledge the historical politicized views of sex differences and then make a cautious, though systematic, review of the whole picture of sex differences—whether in the form of cross-cultural similarities,[4] current situational pressures,[5] or evolutionarily developed adaptive strategies females and males used to cope with the social environment.[6]

There is a tremendous temptation to reduce our options to an either/or dichotomy that, upon further examination, may be supportable by neither the extant data nor by the theoretical claims used to analyze them. For example, the traditional distinction between "nature" and "nurture" is fast becoming a red herring, though still widely cited, as very few conditions are recognized as being solely biologically or environmentally determined. Indeed, it is now most frequently acknowledged that most behaviors result from interactions between nature and nurture, neither of which individually ever occur in a vacuum. Such a debate hardly well informs the public as to the ultimate goal of evolution-guided investigations of social behavior, which seek out past influences—from whatever sources—that helped to shape current social behavior. Yet the desire for a simple, parsimonious explanation too often yields an attempt to determine which source (nature? nurture?) is more influential and often sacrifices the detailed explanations that inevitably provide the most coherent representation of the world around us. For example, with stereotyping, it was once easiest to simply label people as good vs. bad or as prejudiced and non-prejudiced. More recent research points out that prejudice has many contributing factors, no one of which has been found to be the linchpin toward undoing antisocial thought. In addition, there is a temptation to view evolutionary explanations of behavior as a means of furthering other (often political) agendas, thus leading, for example, to a reluctance to acknowledge that men and women *do* differ in some respects, and that there need not necessarily be any value judgment attached to those differences. Discussants of evolution and its social implications must be mindful of committing the naturalistic fallacy. For example, describing what behavior differences between men and women existed in early environments is *not* prescriptive of what men and women ought to do. Remember, the environment itself affords some of the influence for determining what division of labor, if any, exists between the sexes. Hence, most evolutionary researchers examining sex differences indicate that, rather than attempting to justify the evolutionary "status quo," (and prescribing it as an "ought" for the future), they are interested in what combination of factors have produced whatever recurrent sex differences have been observed.

In higher primates, particularly humans, a relatively stable source of influence is considered to come from our biological heritage, as genetic change in humans occurs at a very slow rate, particularly compared with the potential rate of change of the environment. Consider: we humans have likely been bipedal and had relatively little body hair for thousands of years, despite the fact that at various points in the past, then-environmental demands might have made it more advantageous for us to have heavy coats of hair (such as during the series of ice ages) and perhaps even flippers (such as when the world-wide water level rose following each of the ice ages). Contrary to popular belief, our biology is hardly our destiny, but rather is always going to be reined in by the parameters set by the environment, whether that comes in the form of social pressures, geographic changes, or weather patterns—any of which can change on a whim, relatively speaking.

Thus, while recent reports of genetic engineering seem to indicate that humans will be able to overcome any problem in the future with some form of "gene splicing," such conclusions naively overlook the often unseen and unpredictable control that the environment takes on. We may be able to genetically alter our predisposition to catch the common cold, only to find that, perhaps, contracting colds actually warded off a more serious illness that may become even more opportunistic as a result. No genetic influence can overcome the interactive effects of the environment—and it is the environment that changes far more rapidly than any genetic root. We have absolutely no assurance of future environmental stability; hence, it is likely that whatever results from a gene–environment interaction today will only modestly resemble the results of such interactions in the future.

In this regard, the most crucial confusion that stems from a reliance on oversimplistic data reduction lies at the heart of our research paradigms into evolution and behavior: the extent to which behavioral traits are, in fact, influenced by genes. At least as early as Francis Galton, in the 1880s, questions have been asked about the heritability of behavioral characteristics. With the rise of Mendelian genetics in the early part of this century, geneticists themselves were lured into searching for individual genes that might "cause" musical ability, an extroverted personality, or intelligence.[7] The profound clarity of Mendel has dominated 20th century genetics research, and it still very much dominates science education. It is a beautiful, linear logic that leads us to still emphasize the "dogma" of modern molecular genetics in our discourse, from undergraduate science courses to the popular press. An individual gene, a coding sequence of DNA nucleotides, is transcribed to mRNA, which, in turn, is translated to a protein. The presence or absence of this protein should correlate neatly with the presence or absence of the trait. Impressive progress has been made in the understanding of the inheritance and cause of genetic diseases, such as sickle cell anemia, as a result of the clean model of simple Mendelian genetics.

Behavioral traits, of course, do not always follow the paradigm of simple Mendelian genetics. Does this mean that behavioral traits—aggression, social bonding, even sex-specific behaviors—have no genetic underpinning? They do, but scientists have not yet developed a model to describe the genetic influence on behavior that has anything like the compelling logic of Mendelian genetics. As a result, controversy and confusion will inevitably accompany any discussion of the relationship between genetics and behavior.

Seymour Benzer, the pioneer geneticist at the California Institute of Technology, has dissected an apparently simple trait in fruit flies—the tendency to move toward light—into hundreds of genes and components ranging from the characteristics of the fly's retina to areas deep within its brain. Yet, in an important way, our understanding of some complex behavior will move forward as we learn how each of these hundreds of components interact. In other words, some complex behaviors may begin to be understood as emerging from the sum total of many individual steps, each of which fits into a Mendelian model.

Even at the simplest level of Mendelian genetics, *epigenesis* may be evident. Biologists usually refer to this as the regulation of gene expression by environmental factors, but it is more appropriate to think of epigenesis as the interaction between DNA and environmental influences. The underlying genetics of behavior is almost always responsive to environmental cues. While simple Mendelian traits show convincing stability over a wide range of environments, traits that do not follow simple Mendelian patterns fluctuate with environment to such an extent that a nature-nurture dichotomy remains alive and well. Studies of the genetics of behavior, and therefore its heritability and its evolutionary origins, face the daunting task of unraveling the influence of multiple genes as well as how the expression of those genes reflects environmental cues. Without a convincing paradigm for how genes and environment interact, it is no wonder that in the face of such complexity we fall back on reductionist thinking and visualize a simple Mendelian design when talking about behavioral genetics.

A more challenging problem arises when the behavioral trait itself is only beginning to be described in measurable terms. The presence or absence of the mutant transporter responsible for cystic fibrosis is quantifiable, and the correlation between the protein and its Mendelian heritability is an incontrovertible argument for the power of the Mendelian paradigm. Behavioral traits, however, are not measurable to the same extent as protein function, and are frequently assessed using the most parsimonious measures available. At extreme examples, the definitions of deception (discussed by Robert Trivers, this volume, p. 114), the behavior of fetus and mother (discussed by David Haig, this volume, p. 149), or mate selection (discussed by Steven Gangestad, this volume, p. 50), are still matters of controversial discussion. Measurements of behaviors this complex are merely suggestive and still evolving. With so much discussion around what might constitute, say, deception—is it a form of self-deception?—questions about its evolution and, therefore, its genetic underpinning are that much more difficult to investigate.

As a result, public discussion of behavioral genetics, and its related field of evolutionary psychology, are handicapped by the lack of clear articulation of the relationship between inheritable genes and manifest behavior. Yet we are all firmly grounded in the Mendelian paradigm and continue, therefore, to hear references to "gay genes" or "novelty genes" or "happiness genes." No wonder reports about a genetic influence on some human behavior is greeted with roars of criticism. Without insight into the molecular links between genes and behavior, dismissive criticisms of behavioral genetics and evolutionary psychology can be expected.

Behavioral geneticists have, of course, turned to animals other than humans for their studies. Still, the absence of a clear relationship between a complex behavior and its underlying genetics makes lower-animal studies easy to dismiss as points of extrapolation for understanding human behavior. Richard Lewontin, a knowledgeable geneticist, is quick to use the nature-nurture argument against behavioral geneticists: "In terms of *Drosophila,* in terms of the evolution of its courtship, the work is interesting. But it's like saying that someone has understood why I eat what I'm eating because of smell perception in fruit flies. I'm eating what I'm eating because of my social position...."[8] Lewontin implies that his social behavior is divorced from genetic influences; and since there is no parallel between simple Mendelian traits and social behavior, his dismissive argument appeals strongly to the ingrained notion that social influence, or "nurture," is an independent agent in behavior, separate from the clear logic of Mendelian "nature." Of course, behavioral geneticists are beginning to demonstrate that social behavior is itself influenced by genetics. Yet, without a paradigm as compelling as Mendelian genetics, an argument like Lewontin's will continue to carry weight.

If specific behaviors evolved, our best understanding is that they must, therefore, have some inheritable genetic influence. Our task is not only to continue research into specific areas of human behavior, as evolutionary psychologists, but also to acknowledge the public context in which this research is presented and discussed. As we maintain, that context is invariably saddled with major simplistic ideas about genetics, especially those that carry the deterministic stamp of one-gene, one-trait Mendelian genetics. While biology faculty may bemoan the lack of understanding of Mendelian genetics, the public at large—and the discourse of behavioral scientists of all stripes as well—initially and incorrectly assumes a one-gene, one-trait relationship when faced with research on the evolution of human behavior.

REFERENCES

1. DEVINE, P.G. 1989. Stereotypes and prejudice: their automatic and controlled components. J. Pers. Soc. Psychol. **56:** 5–18.
2. FISKE, S.T. & S.L. NEUBERG. 1990. A continuum of impression formation, from category-based to individuating processes: influences of information and motivation on attention and interpretation. *In* Advances in Experimental Social Psychology, Vol. 23. M. P. Zanna, Ed.: 1–74. Academic Press. New York.
3. KREBS, D.L. & K. DENTON. 1997. Social illusion and self-deception: the evolution of biases in person perception. *In* Evolutionary Social Psychology. J.A. Simpson & D.T. Kenrick, Eds.: 21–47. Erlbaum Associates. Mahwah, NJ.
4. BUSS, D.M. 1989. Sex differences in human mate preferences: evolutionary hypotheses tested in 37 cultures. Behav. Brain Sci. **12:** 1–49.
5. EAGLY, A.H. & W. WOOD. 1999. The origins of sex differences in human behavior: evolved dispositions versus social roles. Am. Psychol. **54:** 408–423.
6. HRDY, S.B. 1997. Raising Darwin's consciousness: female sexuality and the prehominid origins of patriarchy. Hum. Nature **8:** 1–49.
7. GREENSPAN, R.J. 1995. Understanding the genetic construction of behavior. Sci. Am. 72–77.
8. WEINER, J. 1999. Lord of the flies. The New Yorker (April 5): 50.

Index of Contributors

Subject Index